Motor Learning and Human Performance

Motor Learning and Human Performance:

An Application to Physical Education Skills

Robert N. Singer
Michigan State University

The Macmillan Company
Collier-Macmillan Limited, London

Third Printing, 1970

Library of Congress catalog card number: 68-11853

THE MACMILLAN COMPANY
866 THIRD AVENUE, NEW YORK, NEW YORK 10022
COLLIER-MACMILLAN CANADA, LTD., TORONTO, ONTARIO

Printed in the United States of America

To Maita and Richie

Preface

For many years physical educators have realized that there is a strong relationship among the behavioral sciences, the applied sciences, and the field of physical education. Unfortunately, such recognition has not led to actual incorporation of these sciences into physical education curricula to the extent warranted.

Contributions of knowledge from related areas such as physiology, psychology, anthropology, chemistry, physics, and sociology to physical education are obvious and necessary. The physical educator should be aware of at least some of the more important relationships between his and these other fields. This attitude occurs when concerned faculty members deliberately present information selected from these sciences and apply it directly to the physical education domain. This procedure has been successfully enacted in applied physiology and physiology of exercise courses.

As in the case of physiology voluminous material on the topic of motor learning is currently accumulating. Psychological journals have presented many studies about a wide range of methods and materials utilized in this area of learning. Increasingly, investigations on this subject are appearing in physical education literature. There appears to be a need to condense, interpret, and apply this information for the teacher and learner of motor skills.

The purpose of this book is to encompass many aspects of learning and performance for the individual concerned with motor skills. The book attempts not only to present the information but also to make the necessary applications in order that the material may be more comprehensible and meaningful to the physical educator. Current literature is reviewed and many sources for further reference are presented.

The book may serve several purposes. Primarily it is designed as the textbook for a course in motor learning. However, it may well be utilized as a reference source for a methods course, a foundations course, a principles course, coaching courses, and the individual's own needs in teaching and learning various athletic skills.

The book has been organized in the following manner: A presentation of basic terminology and general information in the area of learning in general is followed by an analysis of the nervous system and the neural mechanisms involved in the learning process. Individual variables and the nature of the learner himself are then considered. This topic leads to a discussion of the effect of external conditions and manipulations (e.g., teaching methods, learning techniques) upon the acquisition of skill.

Theoretical developments in learning from the beginning of this century until the present time are analyzed, especially as they apply to motor skill learning. The final section of the book is concerned with the sociopsychological aspects of physical activity. Personality, attitudes, and values resulting from and contributing to participation and success in various motor skills are discussed.

There is a deliberate attempt on the part of the author to review research primarily concerned with motor learning and to apply these results to the conclusions formed in this book. Investigations dealing with human verbal learning and animal discrimination learning are referred to only in special situations. Another aim of the author is to concentrate on the more recently published experiments. This approach is not particularly difficult since most research concerning motor learning is of relatively recent vintage.

The focus of the book is on the psychological aspects of learning—experimental, growth and developmental, and social. The physical, physiological, and kinesiological aspects of learning and performance, although superficially treated here, have been left for experts in those areas. The author feels that the abundance of psychologically oriented material encourages the dedication of the present book to the treatment of this phase of learning. A branching out to include all contributing factors would jeopardize the potential contribution of this book on motor learning by encouraging only a generalized approach to the topic.

The author wishes to express his sincere appreciation to the individuals who contributed to this undertaking. Dr. Lawrence Locke of Columbia Teachers College provided many excellent, constructive suggestions in the preparation of the entire manuscript. Advice on the neurophysiological material of the book from Dr. Antoinette Gentile of Columbia Teachers College and Dr. Edna Wooten of the University of Oregon was warmly welcomed. Various individuals at Illinois State University were most helpful in providing services that hastened the organization and writing of the material. Encouragement from University officials was a definitely instrumental factor in this project. Faculty members and students alike were solicited for their reactions to various portions of the manuscript and readily offered their time. Among the many students to whom gratitude should be extended are Mr. Milt Neuman and Mr. Steven Weiss. Mr. Abraham Singer edited the writing, a contribution for which I am most grateful. Finally, to Miss Gail Haack who spent almost as many painful hours as I in the formulation of the book and who typed, corresponded, organized and edited it—one big "thanks."

R. N. S.

Contents

1
Introduction

The term *learning* is common to everyone's vocabulary. It is a frequently used term, and one that may apply to numerous situations. During our lifetimes we learn many things, including observable acts, as required in motor and verbal performances, and nonobservable acts, which include values, emotions, and attitudes. Habits, bad as well as good are learned. Learning does not even have to be intentional. It is demonstrated under such diverse conditions as performing athletic skills, remembering past situations, disliking opponents in a game, and believing in the team.

Interestingly enough, as one penetrates deeper into the concepts related to the study of learning, he finds that more and more questions are raised than are answered. How can one tell if learning has taken place? Is there actually more than one type of learning? What is the difference between learning and performance, if any?

These questions are but few of many raised by persons bewildered with the learning situation. Learning is the concern of almost every individual regardless of profession. Yet, the fact remains that educators in general and psychologists in particular are the ones most concerned in investigating and advancing knowledge in this area. Educational research undertaken directly in the classroom in order to work with the materials actually taught, has been criticized as being too broadly defined and lacking in necessary research controls to be meaningful. Difficulty in controlling classroom investigations in the same manner as laboratory research, however, certainly does not negate the worth of educational research. Experimental psychologists have primarily used animal subjects such as rats, dogs, chimpanzees, and chickens in their research. They have also been concerned with human learning, but in highly artificial situations and with such unusual learning material as nonsense syllables, mazes, pursuit rotors, and novel fine motor skills, in order to provide a more scientific control. Applications from such studies have been advanced to help explain and predict aspects of human learning.

These psychologists have been able effectively to control many extraneous variables in their research; however, the application of their findings to typically human learning situations leads to still further questions. Are nonsense syllables learned in a controlled situation mastered in a manner similar to prose studied by children in the classroom? Are the conditions prevailing in pursuit rotor tasks (maintaining a stylus on a moving target) comparable to those found related to other motor tasks? Can evidence from these studies be safely applied to the learning of educational materials, of physical education skills?

Although there are objections to both educational and psychological techniques, nevertheless from them both have emerged an adequate amount of scientifically verifiable information.

Because of the accumulation of research on a wide range of learning matter employing assorted conditions and procedures, an attempt must be made to relate the findings to a major concern of the physical educator: the learning of motor skills. Besides learning how to teach, educators must understand how learners learn. Physical educators have, in recent years, demonstrated an increasing interest in this area, as evidenced by the number of investigations and writings in physical education literature. Fortunately, the combined efforts of all the researchers interested in the area of learning and its facilitation, from the experimental psychologist to the industrial psychologist, from the physical educator to the engineer, from the educator to the neurophysiologist, have produced a substantial body of scientifically verified statements which together form the known aspects of learning. This book will present that information, with necessary qualifications, as it applies to physical education, and specifically to the learning of motor skills.

Before presenting concepts and facts relevant to the concern of this book, it is necessary to discuss and define some of the more characteristic and reappearing terms. As the reader will observe, there is no universal acceptance of the definition of any of these terms.

Learning

Learning has been defined in many ways, but an entirely satisfactory definition has yet to be proposed. Part of the difficulty lies in the confusion and failure to differentiate between the terms *learning* and *performance*. After discussing the problems connected with defining learning, McGeoch and Irion (1961) offer the rather general statement, "Learning...is a change in performance which occurs under the conditions of practice."

Other psychologists such as Wickens and Meyer (1961) would add to this definition that learning is also relatively permanent. According to one viewpoint, variable factors such as fatigue, influence of drugs, boredom, and the like would affect performance, not learning. Growth and development factors are also variables considered to influence performance rather than to be true indices of learning. All the variables mentioned reflect temporary states in the organism and as such are not associated with learning per se.

Still other psychologists insist that reinforcement, in the form of reward or approval as a necessary condition for practice, is likely to have a positive effect on learning. For the purpose of this book, *learning is defined as the relatively permanent change in performance or behavioral potential resulting from practice or past experience in the situation.*

Learning and Performance. The role of reinforcement in the learning process has been extremely controversial in psychology, and the reader will obtain a better understanding of this issue when he understands the potential differences between learning and performance.

The distinction between learning and performance is sharpened when considering the factor of reinforcement, for there appears to be much evidence that the amount of reinforcement affects performance rather than learning. Some theorists indicate the necessity of reinforcement for learning whereas others minimize or even omit it. Reinforcement by definition is an event that increases the probability of the occurrence of certain behavior.

Tolman (1930) through his research and writings contributed much to the differentiation between learning and performance. His concept of latent learning indicates that learning may be taking place all the time during practice trials but is not demonstrated until reinforcement brings it out. Latent learning has been verified in many experiments in which rats were employed as subjects. A representative study is one completed by Blodgett, and his data are illustrated in the form of learning and performance curves in Figure 1–1. Rats were timed in their speed to traverse a maze, and three groups of these animals were tested under different conditions: Group I was rewarded with food each day of the investigation; Group II was not rewarded until the seventh day; and Group III experienced reward on the fourth day.

It was observed that differences in performance between the groups disappeared as reward was introduced. The nonreward rats were developing a latent learning of the maze; meaning they were learning the maze but this was not evident until reward was offered. At present, there is much conflict of evidence on the theoretical and practical implications of latent learning, even as there is in the distinction between learning and performance. Nevertheless, although the reward form of reinforcement may have little to do with the learning process, it certainly will account for differences in performance. *Performance may be thought of as a temporary occurrence, fluctuating from time to time because of many potentially operating variables,* whereas learning is relatively more permanent.

Obviously though, in order to determine what learning has taken place, some measure is needed. *We usually use performance as representing the amount of learning that has occurred, for the process of learning must be*

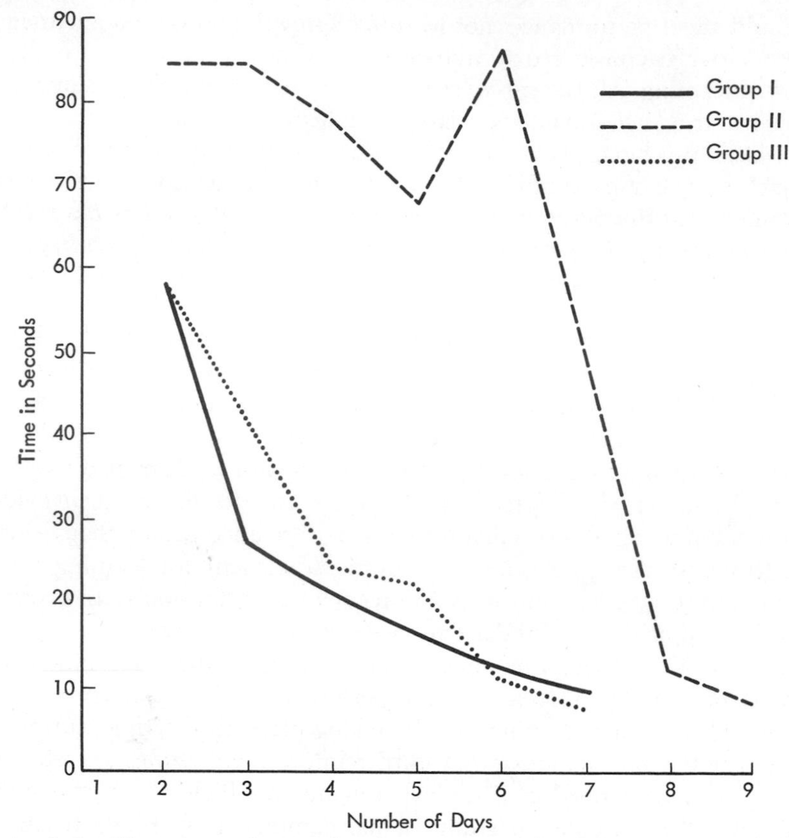

Figure 1–1. Time curves for rats learning a maze under different reward conditions. (From Blodgett, Hugh C. The Effect of the Introduction of Reward Upon the Maze Performance of Rats, *U. of Calif. Publ. Psychol.*, 4:113–134, 1929.)

inferred on the basis of observations of change in performance. We can measure what a person does directly, but what he learns is subject to only indirect estimates. The limited value of this practice is reflected by the results of such studies as the one reported by Blodgett. Nevertheless, a truer measure of learning has yet to be devised, and performance scores reflect the best means available at the present time.

Skill

The term *skill,* like the word *learning,* defies measurement and interpretation. It may imply various connotations, depending on what is to be defined and who is defining it. The Winston dictionary states that "skill is knowledge of any art together with expert ability to put that knowledge to use."

Skill can refer to a particular act performed or to the manner in which it is executed. All physical education activities may be considered as skills or as being comprised of skills, and the degree of proficiency attained by the individual reflects his *skill level.*

Skill is a relative quality, not to be defined in absolute terms. Performance displayed by an individual may be so outstanding as to warrant his being considered skilled, by comparison with a group of his peers on the neighborhood football field. The same person when placed with members of the varsity team may appear relatively unskilled. Skill as demonstrated by performance is an indication of that which has been learned. Skill and performance can be greatly influenced by a host of factors that may have psychological or emotional origins. However, it is usually thought that the highly skilled individual will be able to perform fairly consistently regardless of the factors present which might cause the "average" person's performance to fluctuate.

Requirements of various activities necessitate a complex development of both perceptual and motor facilities, with degree of emphasis dependent on the situation. In sports, physical processes must be developed before skill can be demonstrated. For example, gymnasts, wrestlers, and soccer players find their performances hindered if they have not shown concern for such underlying physical elements as strength, endurance, and flexibility.

Whereas the diver or gymnast primarily can concentrate on the act itself and display skill through a consistent performance, the team sport player must have mastered not only the basic skills but also an ability to react to changing, less predictable situations. Many people can shoot a basketball with a high degree of accuracy when called on to play 21, Horse, or other games not influenced by defensive players or players on the same team in a competitive situation. Their skills are limited to the given circumstance. Success may not be nearly as pronounced when these people have to demonstrate their skill in a game, a game that requires a mastery of techniques, response flexibility, perception, and emotional stability.

High degrees of skill coincide with high degrees of spatial precision and timing. Bartlett (1943), who has written extensively on the subject of human skill, states that timing is extremely important in skilled performance. If certain actions are performed at the wrong time they can be disruptive. During skilled performance responses to stimuli are set in an appropriate sequential order. Another aspect of skill is that the act is executed within a certain time limitation. The tennis player must stroke the ball at the proper moment and in a productive manner. He does not have time to meditate and ponder the situation; his response must be appropriate and quick. Generally, in a given situation a person who is skilled anticipates quickly and has more time to react.

The highly skilled individual demonstrates less variability in performance because he does not respond to every potential cue in the environment. He receives maximum information from a minimum number of identified cues. Skill is developed through constantly well-guided and informative practice, the result of which is selective perception and reactions to appropriate stimuli.

It appears that in order for skill to be present, for most motor acts at least four variables must be considered. These aspects of skill must be developed to a sufficient degree if the performer is to be called skilled. Johnson (1961) relates a colorful tale involving woodchoppers in a contest involving skill. Through the story, he describes how each of the following factors plays a role in determining skill:

$$\text{Skill} = \text{Speed} \times \text{Accuracy} \times \text{Form} \times \text{Adaptability}$$

Most skills have to be performed within a time limitation, hence the importance of speed. Accuracy is also involved in acts of skill for accurate movements will determine how successful these acts are evaluated. Form refers to economy of effort, and certainly, skilled acts should be executed with a minimal amount of energy expenditure. Finally, a skilled individual is adaptive; he can perform proficiently under varying and even unpredictable conditions.

Therefore, it can be seen that the development of skill is a highly complex involvement. Consistency in excellent performance infers the activation and formation of good habits. But habits if they are bad can weaken skill. Perhaps an acceptable interpretation of *skill* as referred to in these pages is *the degree of success in achieving an objective with efficiency and effectiveness.* The ease with which an act is performed is also part of the skill of the act. The object in a baseball game for the outfielder is to catch a fly ball. Certainly there would be a great deal of difference in the method employed by Mickey Mantle to achieve this goal as compared with the writer of this book, even though both might succeed (the former with ease and grace, the latter with reckless abandon and a prayer).

Motor Skill. The word "*skill*" by itself might imply an art in writing, memorizing, acting, painting, talking, or playing. To delineate the confusion *muscular movement or motion of the body required for the successful execution of a desired act is termed motor skill.* It is difficult to completely isolate skills as being perceptual, motor, or verbal, but primarily the emphasis of each process on the skill will decide its nature.

Motor does imply movement. Physical education activities and sports are motor by nature, and perhaps even psychomotor, as Klausmeier (1961) indicates. Various processes interact, e.g., cognitive, perceptual, and motor, in order that the act may be integrated, meaningful, and successful. Although it is important to realize that the presence of these factors is necessary to almost any skilled performance, in this book, for convenience sake, reference will be made to the various physical activities as motor skills. Motor skills are often categorized as being fine or gross, and a distinction should be made between the two.

Fine Motor Skill. The word *fine* denotes a delicate or sensitive quality.

Certain segments of the body move within a limited area in order to yield an accurate response. The neuromuscular coordinations involved in fine motor skills are usually precision oriented and often refer to eye-hand coordination. Typing, tracking with pursuit rotors, and piano playing have been described as fine motor skills by psychologists in their investigations.

Gross Motor Skill. The term *gross* refers to a quality opposed to fine: large, whole, entire, or obvious. Seashore (1942) offers the definition "... neuromuscular coordinations which involve vigorous contractions of large muscles and usually movement of the whole body." Sport skills of all kinds may be considered as gross motor skills, and though reference is usually made to these skills without the term *gross*, it is implied.

From a theoretical point of view, one might successfully argue that there are certain fine elements to every sport skill. Acts must be placed on a continuum, for nothing is purely black and white, and certainly sport skills would be concentrated toward the gross motor skill end. Such factors as strength, precision, and timing underlie gross and fine motor skills, with extreme emphasis on any of these factors distinguishing gross from fine skills.

Learning Curves and Skill Acquisition

One leading method of depicting skill acquisition is through the use of the learning curve. The curve is a graphic illustration of practice trials versus performance and an indicator what one or more individuals accomplish from trial to trial. Many factors, such as method of practice, administration of practice sessions, method of measurement, and nature and age of the subjects, will result in different curves for the same practiced skill. These curves reflect factors facilitating or hindering performance, and as such, are not truly representative learning curves.

Although it is extremely difficult to obtain a true learning curve, psychologists generally agree that four distinct types exist. It should be emphasized here that typical examples of learning curves which are found in real life examples have been smoothed out in order to make it easier to follow any apparent trends in skill acquisition. Actually, great irregularities usually exist from trial to trial and performer to performer.

Figure 1–2 presents four typical smoothed curves for a limited practice session. Curve A has been termed a *negatively accelerated curve*. Greatest gains are made in the early practice trials, with decreasing improvements in later trials. A leveling–off point appears to be reached, but positive gains, ever so small, still are occurring. This type of curve usually denotes the learning of a skill that is relatively easy and where insight into the skill is quick, as exemplified by the satisfactory performance on the early trials. As upper levels of skill are reached quickly, improvement diminishes, for little is left to be mastered.

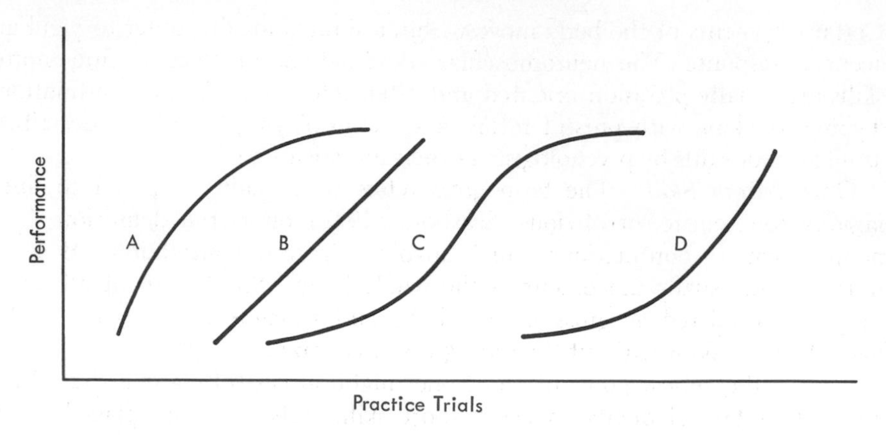

Figure 1–2. Typical learning curves.

Curve D is an example of a *positively accelerated curve* in which performance is poor in the early trials but increases from trial to trial. Although it appears to have no upper limit, this curve would ultimately level off with practice. The example offered in Figure 1–2 represents relatively few practice trials, so the curve appears to be accelerating indefinitely. Curve B, *the linear curve,* is essentially a straight line. This curve has been obtained in a few cases where proportional increments are noted from trial to trial. It too, would asymptote with increasing trials. Curve C, which is an *S-shaped curve,* indicates positive acceleration, approaching linearity, and finally negative acceleration. It contains many of the qualities of the other three curves.

It is important to note that no single curve of learning exists, that the nature of the skill or the learner will be reflected in the manner in which he acquires skill. Some psychologists, Thurstone (1930) and Estes (1950), for example, have attempted to form mathematical equations in order to predict and fit learning curves. Varying degrees of success have been achieved in this endeavor. Certain data might very well be described by one of the equations whereas this same operation would not be appropriate for other data. However, Culler (1928) and Culler and Girden (1951) present evidence which seems to indicate that complete learning curves are ogive (S-shaped) by nature. They employed a mathematical equation that is proportional to the product of the amount already learned and the amount remaining to be learned before the limit of learning is reached. As of the present time, there is no equation that would fit all types of data. Therefore one concludes that the nature of the learning task (e.g., motor skill, nonsense syllables, prose, or puzzle), and its degree of difficulty, as well as the nature of the learner, determine the method in which the task is learned.

The method of measurement will often determine the smoothness or irregularity of a curve. Although a typical learning curve is obtained from

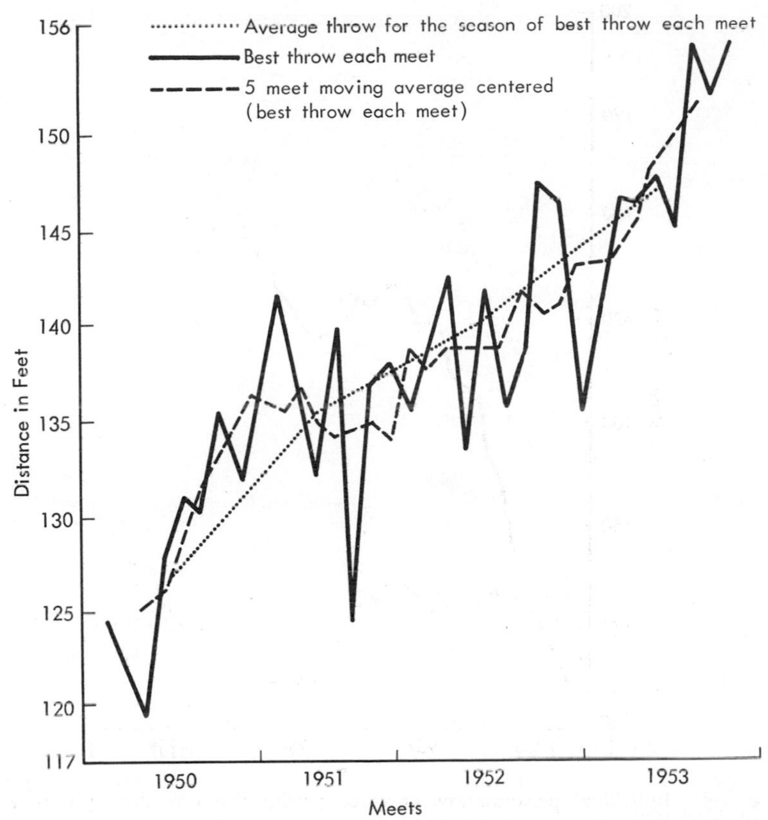

Figure 1–3. Three methods of analyzing performance. Representative of one discus thrower's record for four years.

practice trials completed in one or a few meetings, Figure 1–3 presents data collected on one discus thrower in competition during his four years at college. No doubt growth and development factors influence the curve, but it is presented for two reasons: (1) the similarity between this curve and a typical learning curve and, more important, (2) a comparison of three methods of measuring performance and each one's effect on the curve. Coach Carl Heldt of the Illinois State University track and field team has collected typical data such as these on all his performers during his many years as a coach.

It can be observed that when more scores are averaged together, the lines become smoother. The most irregular line represents the best throw each meet, a smoother line is obtained by averaging five throws per meet, and the smoothest curve is derived from the average throw each season. The athlete's record indicates fairly consistent improvement from meet to meet and year to year, although irregularities in performance are clearly apparent.

Because it would be erroneous to believe that every athlete's record would

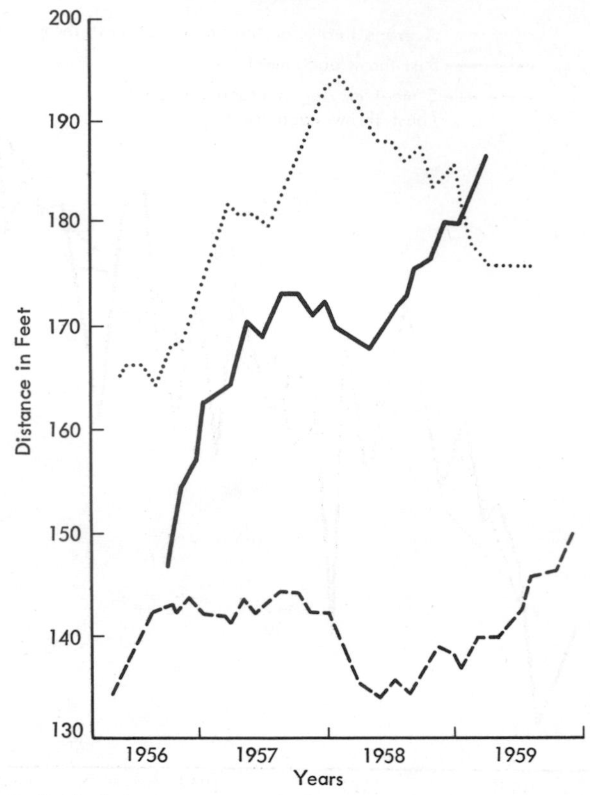

Figure 1–4. Individual performances of three javelin throwers during four years of competition.

be comparable as in the preceding case and improve so consistently, three other athletes, all javelin throwers, have their performances recorded by the five-throw-per-meet-average method for comparison in Figure 1–4. Note the differences in the curves, many of which may be actually explained by such factors as a student getting married, loss or gain in motivation, proper or improper understanding of mechanics, poorer or better health, and, in general, a whole host of psychological and physiological variables.

If these curves were smoothed by such a method as averaging the throws per season, they would more nearly approach those curves found in Figure 1–2. Poorer records, caused by backache, marriage, or lack of interest are really factors in performance and not truly indicative of learning as such. True curves of learning should reflect positive increments, even if they are so slight as to be outwardly unobservable. The plotting of individual trials results in more noticeable trial increments and decrements and can serve a definite purpose. Without any major detrimental factors operating, averaged practice trials should yield positive learning performances.

Figure 1–5 illustrates learning curves for two different groups of subjects

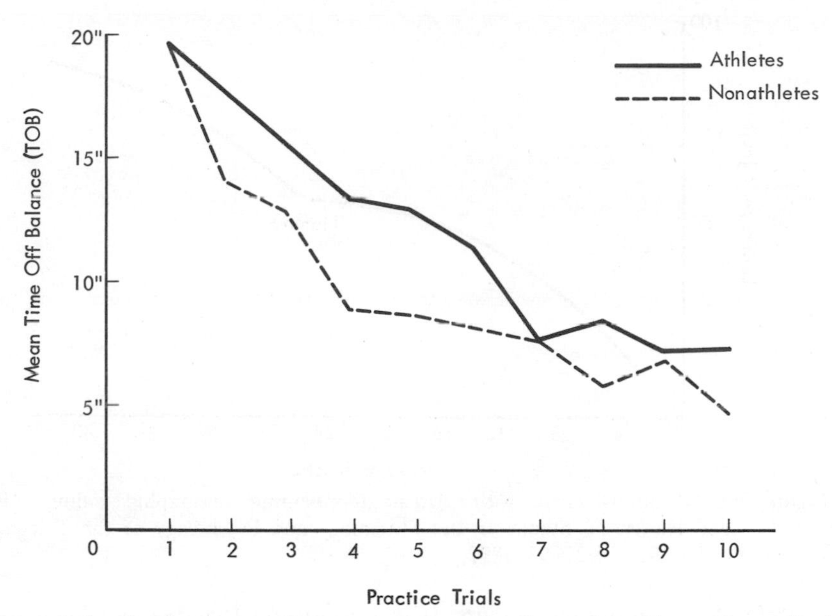

Figure 1–5. Stabilometer performance as a result of practice. (From Singer, R. N. Effects of Spectators on Athletes and Nonathletes Performing a Gross Motor Task, *Res. Quart.*, 36:473–482, 1965.)

receiving ten practice trials each in the same time period on the stabilometer (an apparatus used to measure balance ability). The time in each trial in which the board was not ideally balanced is recorded, and the curve decreases since performance was plotted against time off balance. If it were plotted against time on balance, the curve would go upward instead of downward, and it should be observable in either case that there is improvement in performance, hence learning, within the trials allocated for the experiment. If the curves are smoothed further, they would approach the typical negatively accelerated curve.

Plateaus

Almost everyone in a lifetime experiences a frustrating point of no apparent improvement in performance though the task to be learned is practiced over and over—maybe the golf game, which consistently stays in the low 90's, or perhaps the bowling average, which always remains about 145. Specific skill acquisition or general sport performance appear to level off and may remain there seemingly forever or for a short period of time before an acceleration occurs in performance.

This phenomenon has been termed a *plateau in the learning curve. A plateau represents stationary performance preceded and sometimes followed*

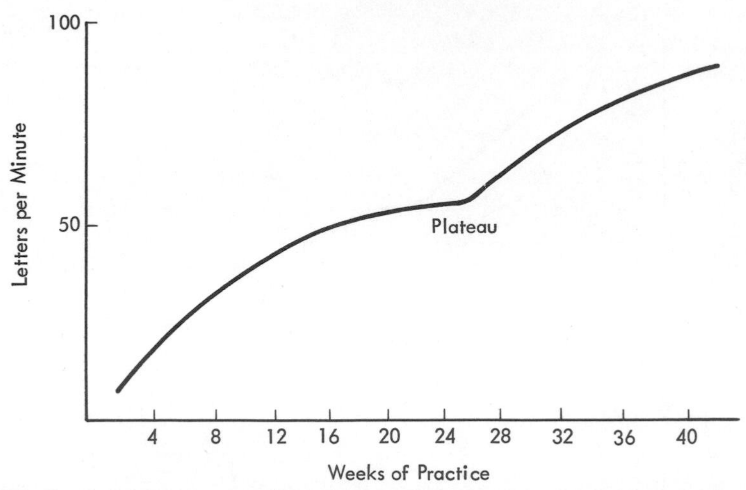

Figure 1–6. Learning curve with plateau representing telegraphic coding. (From Bryan, W., and Harter, N. Studies in the Physiology and Psychology of the Telegraphic Language, *Psychol. Rev.*, 4:27–53, 1897.)

by accelerated learning increments. It is a condition that has not been found to occur in many experimental learning tasks, but the classic example of a plateau in the learning curve is the one obtained by Bryan and Harter (1897). The graphic illustration taken from their data and presented in Figure 1–6 refers to one's ability to learn to receive telegraphic signals in the American Morse Code.

A hypothesis set forth to explain the plateau in learning is that there is a hierarchy of habits to be mastered by the individual when he attempts to learn a complex task. After succeeding in the first order, he might be fixated at a level for some time before becoming able to integrate the patterns needed in the second order habits. Information is consolidated and re-organized. An example of this situation is found in tennis. First order habits might be the acquisition of basic strokes and skills underlying the sport, such as learning to stroke the ball when in a stationary position. Second order habits could include hitting the ball while on the move, and a third order category might include the integration of effective movement patterns in the game situation. Theoretically, depending on the manner in which the sport is taught and the performer involved, a plateau could occur at any one of these transitional periods.

After a period of time in which one attempts to transcend from one hierarchy of habits to another, insight manifests itself in the form of an integration of past learned responses and new ones to be utilized. The curve accelerates sharply until the next plateau. Since actual plateaus are rare in experimental evidence, possibly due to the difficulty in setting up investigations that might demonstrate this phenomenon, we must draw more from theoretical implications and every-day experience. The latter evidence appears to indicate the reality of such an effect in the acquisition of skill, at last in some of the more complex sports.

Two questions naturally arise concerning the plateau in the learning curve and its theoretical explanation. (1) Will the manner in which the skill is taught affect the learning function? In other words, a skill may be treated as a whole and learning directed toward gaining insight into the entire movement pattern. Will this method of approach lessen the possibility of a plateau occurring during skill acquisition more than if the skill is broken down and the basic elements taught separately? (2), Is there *really* such a thing as the plateau in the learning curve? Taylor (1943) presents evidence to question the plateaus obtained by Bryan and Harter and plateaus in general. According to Swift (1918), the real reason for the leveling of performance is loss of motivation. If the learner was continually motivated, a plateau would not be observable.

Concerning the factor of motivation, Book (1925) indicates that disappointment and discouragement when not improving in performance make it even more difficult to advance the learning cause. Perhaps all these factors—task complexity, hierarchy of habits, interest, and frustration—contribute to the plateau, if indeed it does exist. Many other questions remain unanswered. No definite conclusions may be reached at this time until further experimental evidence is examined.

The Importance of Studying Learning

Although E. B. Newman is quoted by Kimble (1961) as stating that for many practical skills such as those required in batting a home run, fencing, and boxing, "a rabbit's foot is worth as much as the psychologist's sage advice," experimental psychologists have contributed most of the present knowledge found on the learning function. Physical educators have an obligation to examine, understand, and apply the learning concepts where feasible and apparently appropriate. Involvement in learning research should not end here. Physical educators, as teachers, are concerned with the most effective teaching techniques as applied to motor-skill learning. Since the abundance of psychological research has been done on everything but sport skills or skills resembling them, the danger in applying principles from one learning task to another must be realized and considered. The generalizations must be made with caution rather than with recklessness until further evidence on motor skills upholds or refutes these principles.

Investigations by physical educators in the area of motor learning have helped to lessen the gap between psychological learning laws and those governing motor-skill learning. With this greater interest by physical educators in psychological learning research as well as in their own field, greatest advancements in knowledge in the motor-skill area are expected during the coming years.

Following chapters contain the leading available findings on results of selected research studies that touch upon the factors governing skill learning. Those studies, concepts, and principles that appear to have the most direct implications for physical educators are emphasized. Physical, mental, and emotional factors underlying skill acquisition, growth and development considerations, environmental manipulations, personality factors, and theoretical developments related to skill learning are presented and discussed. These aspects of the learning situation should be of much interest to the teacher and the coach of physical activities. It would be most beneficial to these skill leaders if they would apply this knowledge, along with physiological and kinesiological information, to their respective situations and form a strong scientific basis for the promotion of skill attainment.

References

BARTLETT, F. C. Fatigue Following Highly Skilled Work, *Proceedings Royal Society,* 131:247–257, 1943.

BOOK, W. F. *Learning to Typewrite,* New York: Gregg, 1925.

CULLER, E. Nature of the Learning Curve, *Psychol. Bull.,* 34:742–743, 1928.

CULLER, E., and GIRDEN, E. The Learning Curve in Relation to Other Psychometric Functions, *Amer. J. Psychol.,* 64:327–349, 1951.

ESTES, W. K. Toward a Statistical Theory of Learning, *Psychol. Rev.,* 57:94–107, 1950.

JOHNSON, HARRY W. Skill = Speed × Accuracy × Form × Adaptability, *Percept. Mot. Skills,* 13:163–170, 1961.

KIMBLE, G. (ed.); HILGARD, E. R.; and MARQUIS, D. M. *Conditioning and Learning,* New York: Appleton-Century-Crofts, Inc., 1961.

KLAUSMEIER, H. J. *Learning and Human Abilities: Educational Psychology,* New York: Harper & Brothers, 1961.

MCGEOCH, J. A., and IRION, A. L. *The Psychology of Human Learning,* New York: David McKay Co., Inc., 1961.

SEASHORE, H. G. Some Relationships of Fine and Gross Motor Abilities, *Res. Quart.,* 13:259–274, 1942.

SWIFT, E. J. *Psychology and the Day's Work: A Study in the Application of Psychology to Daily Life,* New York: Scribners, 1918.

TAYLOR, D. W. Learning Telegraphic Code, *Psychol. Bull.,* 40:461–487, 1943.

THURSTONE, L. L. The Learning Function, *J. Gen. Psychol.,* 3:469–493, 1930.

TOLMAN, E. C., and HONZIK, C. H. "Insight" in Rats, *Univ. Calif. Publ. Psychol.,* 4:215–232, 1930.

WICKENS, D. D., and MEYER, D. R. *Psychology,* New York: Holt, Rinehart, and Winston, Inc., 1961.

2

The Nervous System: Coordination of Movement

Many psychologists, with the exception of physiological psychologists, have attempted to explain learning phenomena without regard for the physiological involvement in the learning process. Although they do not deny that changes must take place in the neurological structures during learning and performance, these psychologists feel that learning can be acceptably described in behavioral terms. Much is still not known about the nervous system. This fact, however, should not entitle the student of learning to a total disregard of the neural substrates involved in the learning process.

Psychologists primarily are concerned with the cognitive and perceptual aspects of learning or the learning of fine motor skills, whereas the physical educator is surrounded by situations in which gross body movement is taking place. Although one may state that learning is learning whether the material consists of a passage in a Shakespearean play or the golf swing, a certain amount of overlap probably exists between the neural processes affecting the learning of words and those involved in action, although the manner in which various neural structures interact may be determined by the nature of the material to be learned. Observable behavioral changes and internal neurological reactions are part of each act. This chapter will attempt to familiarize the reader with the neural structures and processes apparently involved in the learning and performing of motor acts.

The nervous system is extremely difficult to study and yet its importance cannot be denied. The ability to distinguish sensations and respond requires neurological organization. The behavioral functions of the nervous system are represented by such acts as perceiving and interpreting environmental changes (sensory); reacting to these stimuli in an appropriate manner (motor); memorization of past experiences, reasoning, and thinking (cognitive); and controlling the body so that certain functions may transpire as if automatic (autonomic).

As one can imagine, the appropriate approach to describing neural activity for this type of a book is difficult to determine. The traditional manner of anatomically and physiologically structuring the entire system (and in the process requiring the reader to memorize countless names, terms, subsystems, and processes), appears to be out of place here. This extensive treatment is beyond the scope of this book. What is called for in this text is an understanding of how learning and performance are controlled by the nervous system, a somewhat difficult objective in view of the lack of scientific evidence and agreement by those researchers interested in this topic. Perhaps an analogy, that of the nervous system to a computer, will best serve the intentions of this chapter.

Human Performance—Computer Performance

Computers. Computers are quite elaborately designed today and can serve many purposes. These man-made machines can be programmed to problem-solve, sort and classify, handle mathematical problems, and even play checkers. Their potential appears to be limited only by man's conceptual framework. All that is required for the computer to function in desired form, stated rather simply, are an accurate blueprint, a large amount of money for its construction, and its own *machine language* or code.

The computer performs in a prescribed manner and yields appropriate data, the output of which depends on the input. It generates voltage patterns that result in a series of operations, which appear complex but nevertheless can be broken down into relatively simple steps. In essence, the typical computer contains an input system, a transmission system, a central data processor with a permanent and temporary storage system, and an output system. With this brief description in mind, let us now examine the operational and mechanism similarities between the computer and the human nervous system.

The Analogy. It has become quite fashionable today to compare the nervous system to an electronic digital computer. For example, see Wooldridge, 1963. Both systems at a very general level obtain results by similar means. With a little stretch of the imagination, it is not too difficult to envision the similar operations each performs in order to produce desired outcomes.

Let us think of the computer as consisting of an orderly arrangement of wires that permits data to be processed accurately. The cabling organization is such as to interconnect certain wires with other wires and in turn certain mechanisms with other mechanisms. With the input of instructions or *coded words,* electronic operations begin, and appropriate wires and mechanisms are activated in order that the response, or output, be consistent with the input.

If the output is not consistent with the input, there then exists a state of incongruity. The machine is re-programmed, the organism continues to respond until the desired response occurs. A theory has been proposed by Miller, Galanter, and Pribram (1960) that accounts for homeostatic mechanisms that operate via a feedback loop. Instead of dealing with reflex arcs, these authors have formulated a feedback loop, which they call TOTE (test-operate-text-exit), in order to describe all of human behavior.

Input-output comparisons are dependent upon energy, information, and control in the TOTE unit. Energy is represented by neural impulses, information related to that which is transmitted from one place to another, and control gives order to the way an act is executed. The notion of a feedback helps to explain the relation between what is received and the resulting action.

All forms of life contain wiring arrangements of neural circuits with structures that permit particular behaviors to occur. The forms of behavior to be displayed by living organisms will depend on many factors, not the least of which will be the complexity of the arrangement of the neural pathways and associated structures. The computer accepts coded words and transforms them to electrical currents for processing; in the same way, the organism receives various types of environmental stimuli and may respond by immediately transforming them to electrical impulses, which will travel in the transmission system or neural network. In organisms, however, not all inputs are automatically transformed to impulses. The modulation of generator potential is affected by the nature of the input, in many cases not leading to an action potential.

The potential capabilities of the central data processor, or brain, will determine the resultant action. Specific and generalized areas of the nervous system are involved in every act, and without the necessary structures or at least structures becoming activated, outputs or responses to given stimuli will not be appropriate. At the same time, the input must not exceed the amount of data to be processed at any one time. A live creature can sample and respond to just so many surrounding stimuli, a situation which has advantages and disadvantages, as will be seen.

From this introductory analogy, the reader may now be aware of the direction taken in this chapter. It becomes necessary to handle the nervous system of man in a more elaborate manner, to pay respect to the intricate mechanisms and processes that are apparently involved in human learning and movement. Let us now analyze in greater depth how coordinated activity occurs from input to central control to output.

Input. An organism must have a means of receiving and transmitting a stimulus, hence, allowing it to respond in a meaningful manner to this stimulus. Actually, the entire nervous system, which permits this activity, is built up of independent units called *neurons*. These structures, though independent, are organized in how they function. The idea that the nervous system is composed of nerve cells was originated in the late 1800's, and the nerve cell was given the name neuron by Waldeyer in 1891. Neurons, or *nerve cells,* number over ten billion in the typical individual, and there are basically only three types according to function. Before examining these cells by their specific roles, a note or two on the general structure and function of all neurons is in order. Besides a cell body, the typical neuron has extensions, or projections, termed *axons* and *dendrites.* The dendrites usually consist of a number of short fibers that always conduct the nerve impulses to the cell body. Axons, on the other hand, always transmit the impulses away from the cell body (although in certain cases, e.g., in excised nerve, may conduct in either direction) and are usually much longer than dendrites, sometimes measuring three feet in length and up to twenty microns in diameter. Only one axon projection may be noted with a given neuron. Axons may make functional connections (*synapses*) with other cell dendrites or bodies, or terminate in effector organs, such as muscles.

Axons, referred to also as *nerve fibers* or in a broader sense *tracts,* are usually surrounded by one or two protective sheaths; dendrites are not. The *myelin sheath* contains fatty substances which give these fibers a white appearance. *Nodes of Ranvier* are gaps between segments of this sheath, and it is believed that these permeable indentations allow ions to pass in and out of the axon much easier than through the sheath. The impulse goes from node to node, and a branching of nerve fibers may occur at these nodes. Myelinated nerves transmit impulses more rapidly than nonmyelinated nerves and therefore demonstrate improved signaling efficiency. Skeletal muscles, which respond quickly, are innervated by myelinated fibers whereas the viscera abdominal slow-moving muscles are activated by nonmyelinated fibers. The *neurilemma sheath* surrounds the myelin sheath, and is a membrane responsible for transmitting electrical potentials as well as regenerating nerve fibers. It covers the fibers directly at the Nodes of Ranvier, where the myelin sheath is interrupted. The structures may be observed in Figure 2–1.

Although all nerve cells are structurally similar, certain ones are responsible for the input of information, others function in the output, and yet others act as *connectors* between two nerve cells. *Sensory* or *receptor* neurons play the role of transducers; that is, they convert the information input into electrical signals capable of being transmitted to other parts of the nervous system. The amazing quality of these transducers is their ability to change a specific kind of stimulus; e.g., visual, tactile, or auditory, to the same common transmission: the impulse. Each receptor is specific to one stimulus form only.

The nervous system is so wired that when fibers from the neurons are in close proximity, they are grouped together to form a *nerve.* Imagine the wire hook-up, with certain nerves designated to go to and come from specific structures in the nervous system. Information is transmitted from the sense receptors through the spinal cord and brought to the higher levels of the nervous system. In turn, instructions will be transmitted to the muscles and

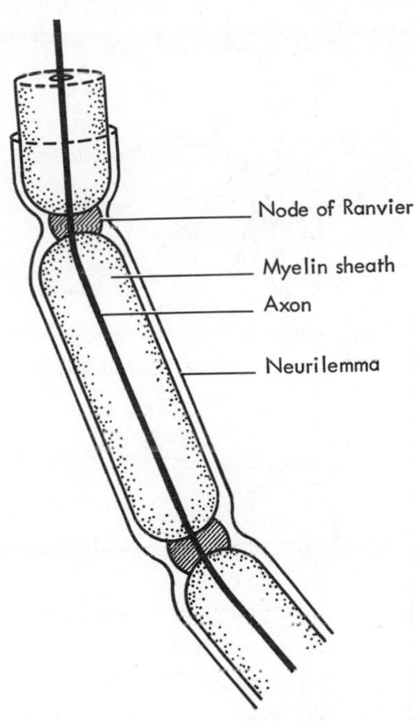

Figure 2–1. The axon and surrounding structures. (From Anthony, Catherine. *Anatomy and Physiology,* St. Louis: C. V. Mosby Co., 1963.)

glands. The spinal cord is not a passive carrier of impulses, but, as we shall see shortly, it can handle simple kinds of reflex actions.

Output. It is probable that specific receptor neurons are wired to specific terminals in the central nervous system, and it is equally probable that particular terminals are wired to particular effectors. *Motor* or *effector* neurons (see Figure 2–2) are responsible for the output of the system. Organs in which efferent nerve fibers terminate are called effectors. Of the different types of effectors, we are interested primarily in skeletal muscles and their role in following the orders of the nervous system.

The *myoneural junction* is the location where motor neuron axons supply muscle fibers with impulses. Each branch of the axon ends on one muscle fiber, and the axons themselves come directly from the spinal cord. Transmission of the impulse at the junction occurs in a manner similar to the synapse between two neurons. A *motor unit* refers to a motor neuron and the muscle fibers it activates. All muscle fibers responsible to a particular neuron are innervated when an impulse is transmitted through this neuron. With reference to muscle fibers, it is interesting to observe that skeletal muscle is the only type of effector in the body totally under the influence of the central nervous system for normal activity.

The cabling arrangement, the specificity of the nervous system intercon-

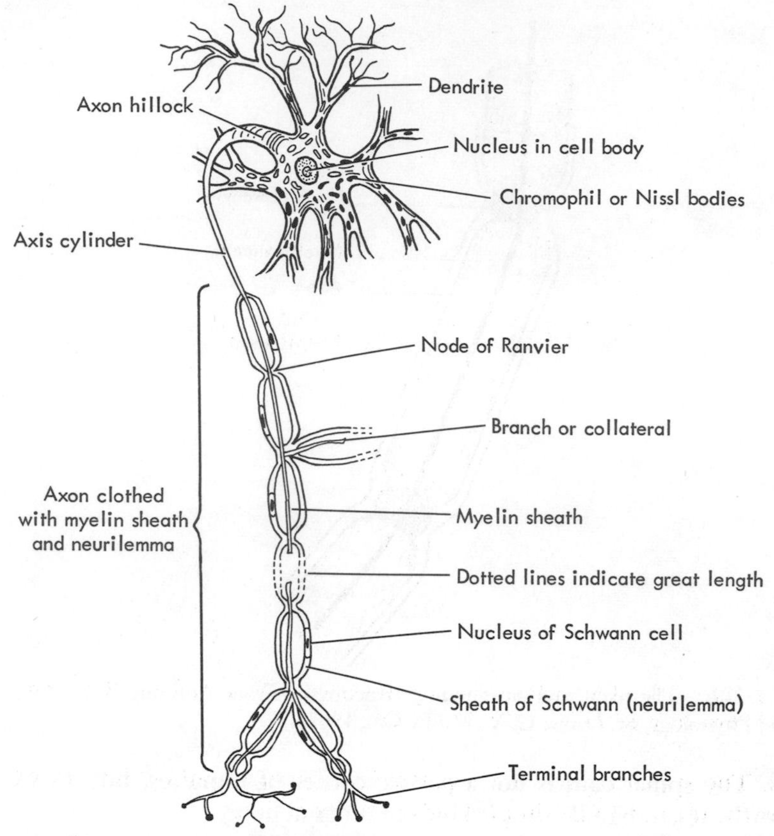

Figure 2–2. Diagram of a motor neuron from the ventral gray area of the spinal cord. (From Kimber, Diana Clifford, and others. *Anatomy and Physiology,* 15th ed., New York: The Macmillan Co., 1966.)

nections, it not yet adequately explained. Not only are sensory and motor neurons designated to and from certain points in the central points in the nervous system, but *internuncial* or *association* neurons are wired in the necessary places to send impulses from one neuron to another. Interestingly enough, of the billions of nerve cells in the organism, most of them are internuncial in nature.

Thus far, the input and output processes have been discussed without regard for how information is transmitted throughout the neural network. What causes the stimulus to go from the periphery to the central nervous system? What kind of activity is involved? The nature of neural transmission, of the nerve impulse, provides the basis for our next discussion.

Impulse Transmission. The modern concept of the nerve impulse began with the work of the great physiologist von Helmholtz, in 1850. Important strides have been made since that date in advancing knowledge related to the nature of the impulse and how it transmits information to and from the central transmitter, otherwise known as the brain. It appears that all *nerve impulses* are alike, regardless of their point of origin and termination. Although the impulse itself does not vary in its physiochemical nature, differences in sensations and responses can usually be attributed to the nature of the receptors and effectors stimulated. In a specific nerve fiber, impulses are of the same magnitude but travel at different rates of speed, depending on the strength of the stimulus. A variation in the stimulus will not affect the magnitude or the rate of the impulse but rather its frequency of discharge. The number of impulses a nerve fiber can potentially send in a second is influenced by the *refractory period* and the *size* of the fiber. For instance, the largest nerve fiber of 20 microns can transmit about 2500 impulses per second, while a small fiber of 0.5 microns allows 250 impulses to pass through it.

During the resting stage, positively charged (*cation*) ions and negatively charged (*anion*) ions are found both inside and outside the neuron. However, there is a difference in relative concentrations of each, i.e., the outside of the cell is positively charged as compared with the inside. This relationship of positively and negatively charged ions of electrical equilibrium is called *polarization*. Sodium (Na^+) ions are concentrated outside the neuron membrane while potassium (K^+) ions are abundantly found in the interior. When a fiber is stimulated, a portion of it undergoes reversal; that is, the ions exchange, thus giving rise to what can be recorded electrically as an impulse. Sodium ions diffuse in and potassium ions diffuse out of the permeable point. This *depolarization* occurs throughout the fiber, and once the impulse has gone through a section of the fiber, that area becomes polarized once again. The recently charged area is unable to conduct another impulse for approximately 0.001 to 0.005 second, and during this *refractory period* polarization is reestablished. The refractory period may be broken down to absolute and relative refractory periods. No stimulus regardless of its strength, can excite the impulse during the *absolute refractory period*. A *relative refractory period* follows the absolute refractory period in which a greater stimulus than usual is needed for an effective stimulus. The absolute refractory period lasts from 0.5 to 3 milliseconds, whereas the relative refractory period extends up to 10 milliseconds. Figure 2–3 illustrates the passage of an impulse through an axon.

The speed with which an impulse is conducted depends upon the size of the nerve fiber; i.e., fibers with large diameters will have a greater rate of conduction than smaller fibers. In fact, Tasaki (1959) reports a correlation of .92 between fiber diameter and conduction velocity. Impulses in the largest nerve fibers may travel at a rate of over 300 feet per second, whereas impulses in the smaller ones may conduct at a speed of three feet per second.

Each nerve fiber reacts under the *all-or-none principle* in a manner similar to that of muscle cells. If a stimulus is powerful enough to influence neural activity, and every neuron has a specific threshold, the neuron will conduct. For the stimulus to excite nerve-fiber conduction of an impulse, two prop-

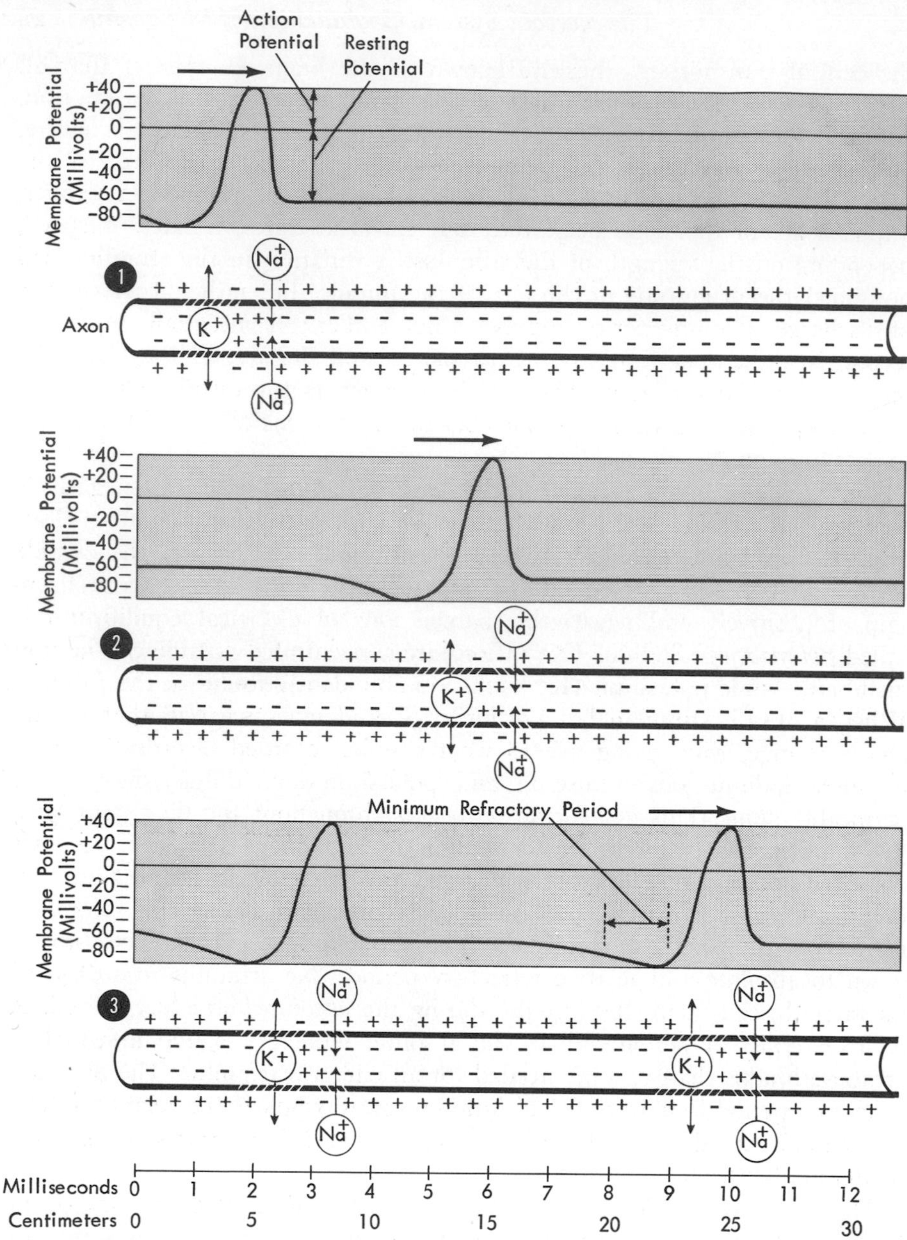

Figure 2–3. Propagation of nerve impulse coincides with changes in the permeability of the axon membrane. Normally the axon interior is rich in potassium ions and poor in sodium ions; the fluid outside has a reverse composition. When a nerve impulse arises, having been triggered in some fashion, a "gate" opens and lets sodium ions pour into the axon in advance of the impulse, making the axon interior locally positive. In the wake of the impulse the sodium gate closes and a potassium gate opens, allowing potassium ions to flow out, restoring the normal negative potential. As the nerve impulse moves along the axon (1 and 2) it leaves the axon in a refractory state briefly, after which a second impulse can follow (3). The impulse propagation speed is that of a squid axon. (From Katz, Bernard. How Cells Communicate, *Scientific American,* 205:209–220, 1961.)

erties must be present: (1) *strength* of sufficient magnitude, and (2) ample *duration* of stimulus application.

Electrical activity of nerve impulses has been recorded with the use of a cathode-ray oscilloscope (see Figure 2–4). When nerve activity is studied, a phenomenon referred to as *action potential* is revealed. The nerve impulse involves electrochemical events, including depolarization and repolarization, and action potential is the accompanying voltage change. The different portions of action potential are illustrated in Figure 2–5. The *spike* takes up the shortest amount of time of the action potential and represents the actual passage of the impulse. The *negative after-potential* and *positive after-poten-*

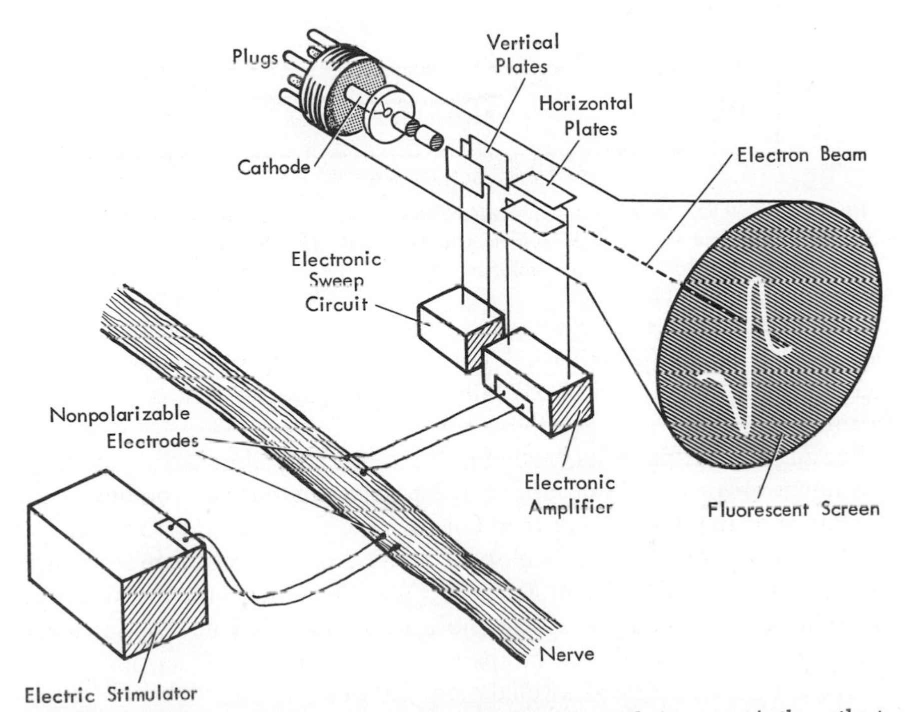

Figure 2–1. The instrument of choice for recording potentials in nerves is the cathode-ray oscilloscope, illustrated here. A cathode produces an electron beam, which is brought to a focus at some point on the fluorescent screen and may be viewed or photographed as a spot of light. A potential difference between the vertical plates causes the spot to shift horizontally from the left of the screen to the right at a certain velocity. Knowing the velocity, one can use this movement as a time measurement. A potential difference between the horizontal plates causes the spot to shift vertically. These plates are connected to an amplifier, which in turn is connected to the nerve by pickup electrodes. When the nerve impulse passes the proximal lead electrode, the electrical disturbance is amplified causing a potential difference in the upper horizontal plate, which causes an upward deflection of the spot, which rises to a maximum and then declines. The impulse reaching the distal lead electrode causes a charge on the lower horizontal plate, which causes a deflection of the spot downward. Thus the action potential which produces a diphasic wave when two electrodes are used, may be recorded. (From Grollman, Sigmund. *The Human Body*, New York: The Macmillan Co., 1964.)

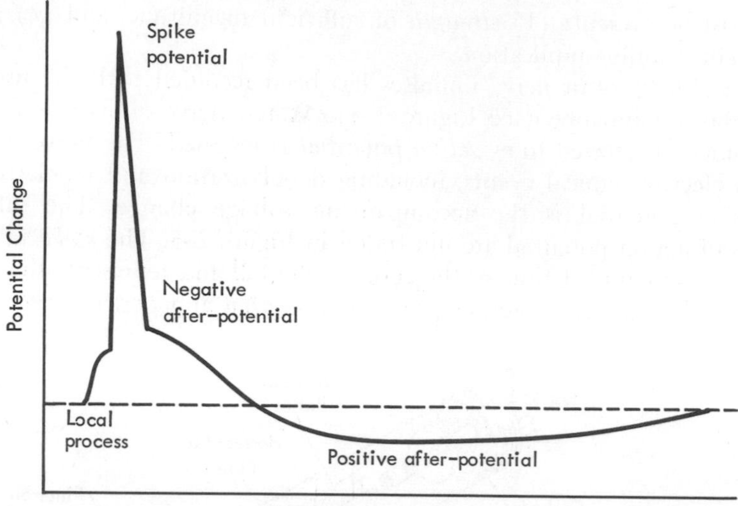

Figure 2–5. Diagarm of action potential showing its three components: the spike, the negative after-potential, and the positive after-potential. The hatched line represents the base line or zero potential. (From Grollman, Sigmund. *The Human Body,* New York: The Macmillan Company, 1964.)

tial components of the wave follow the spike in that order and apparently represent the crossing of electrically charged particles across the neuron membrane.

For all practical purposes, assuming the nerve fiber obtains enough oxygen and nourishment it will not fatigue. Even isolated axons can conduct tens of thousands of impulses before they fail to work (Katz, 1961). General body fatigue, caused by other physiological factors, occurs before nerve fatigue. Muscles are still ablė to contract, nerve fibers conduct, and the myoneural junction can still function during the general body fatigue associated with typical exercise. Considering all parts of the neural transmission system, fatigue in the nervous system would occur first at a synapse.

The Greek word *synapse* means *to clasp,* and within the nervous system it refers to the site where an impulse crosses from one neuron to the next neuron. Sherrington is given credit for the concept of a synapse. Certain electrical and chemical changes occur in this area that allow the impulse to pass from the axons of one neuron to the dendrites or cell body of another. There is evidence that the synapse actually represents a gap between two nerve cells. Figure 2–6 illustrates a synapse occurring between two neurons.

Central Processing. The central nervous system is the recipient of the electrical impulses and the transmitter of others. The brain acts as a control device and assorts and analyzes information, retains some, and sends forth "orders" for action. Through cranial and spinal nerves the peripheral system

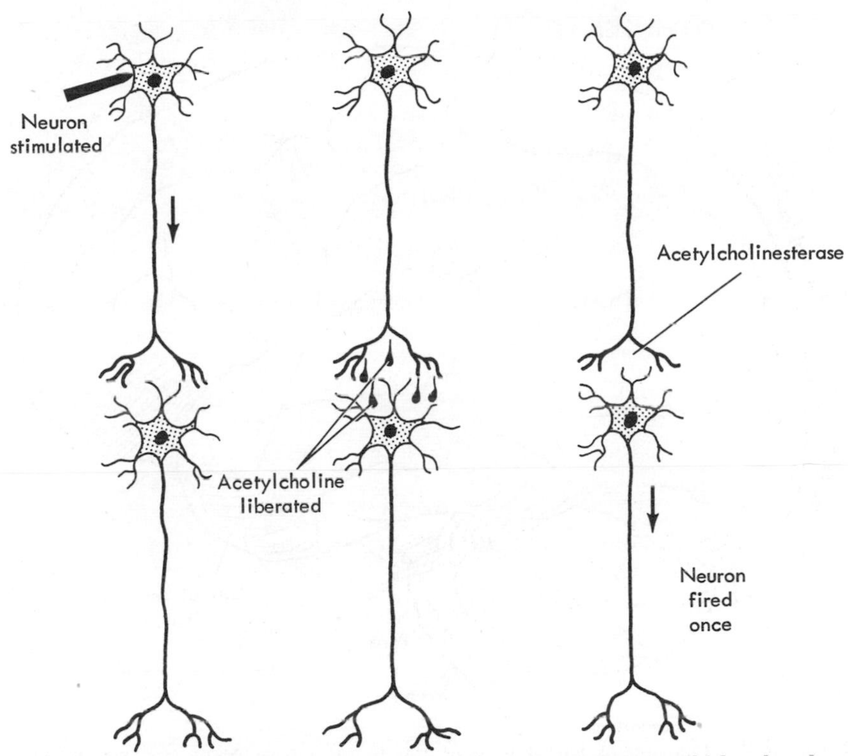

Figure 2–6. A series of diagrams depicting the chemical changes which take place at the synapse as the impulse passes from one neuron to another neuron. (From Langley, L. L., and Cheraskin, E. *Physiology of Man*, New York: Reinhold Publishing Co., 1965.)

conducts impulses between the central nervous system and the peripheral effectors (muscles, organs, glands). It makes good sense to realize that there are simple and more complex, operating computers. Likewise, lower and higher forms of organisms exhibit similar general neural characteristics, with the more advanced animals better able to demonstrate more complex behavior. On the evolutionary scale, the more advanced animals generally have a greater brain weight to total-weight ratio, although brain weight to spinal-cord weight is probably a better measure of the organism's intelligence. Man has a much greater development of the terminal end of the nervous system than lower forms of living organisms. Also, complexity of the brain convolutions increases as one progresses along the phylogenetic scale. The large brain and complex convolutions are correlated with better developed mental processes and ability to perform the most complicated functions.

Although there are many parts of the brain, for the sake of convenience, most of them will be left out of our discussion. Of apparent significance in learning and performance are such structures as the cerebrum, cerebellum, and medulla. These structures combined appear to have the dominant say on what and how much of the incoming data are processed.

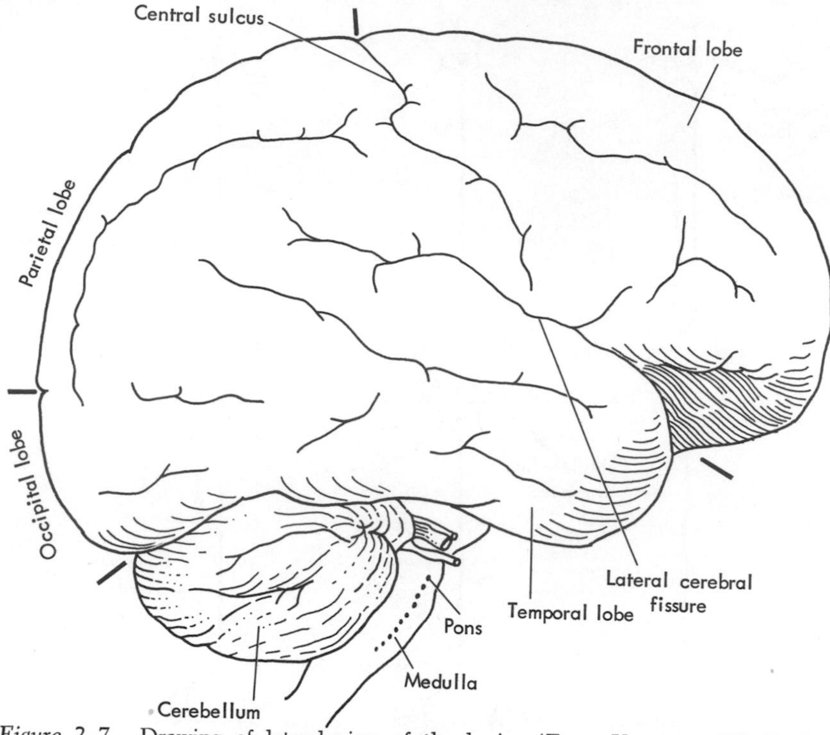

Figure 2–7. Drawing of lateral view of the brain. (From Youmans, W. B. *Human Physiology,* New York: The Macmillan Co., 1962.)

Figure 2–7 indicates the relative position of those structures in the brain described in this chapter.

The *cerebrum,* divided into two hemispheres and containing four lobes each, is the largest part of the brain. The outer surface of the cerebrum called the cortex contains many convolutions, grooves, and fissures, the most prominent of which are used to divide it systematically into areas. This surface is gray in color (*gray matter*) and contains nerve cell bodies. The interior is composed of white and some gray matter, with the *white matter* consisting of nerve fibers (axons) in bundles, called *tracts.* The fatty myelin sheath surrounding these fibers gives them their white appearance.

The four lobes found in the cerebral hemispheres and the general functions of each are (1) *frontal*—primary motor area; (2) *temporal*—auditory area; (3) *occipital*—visual area; (4) *parietal*—somesthetic or sensory area. Figure 2–7 illustrates the relative location of each lobe in the cerebrum, whereas Figure 2–8 depicts the brain in relation to the head. The cerebrum is the *chief processor,* the master signal caller. It will be necessary to examine the structure and functions of the cerebral cortex closely, especially the motor and sensory areas, later, under the heading, Complex Movement.

The *cerebellum,* containing two hemispheres and an outer surface of gray

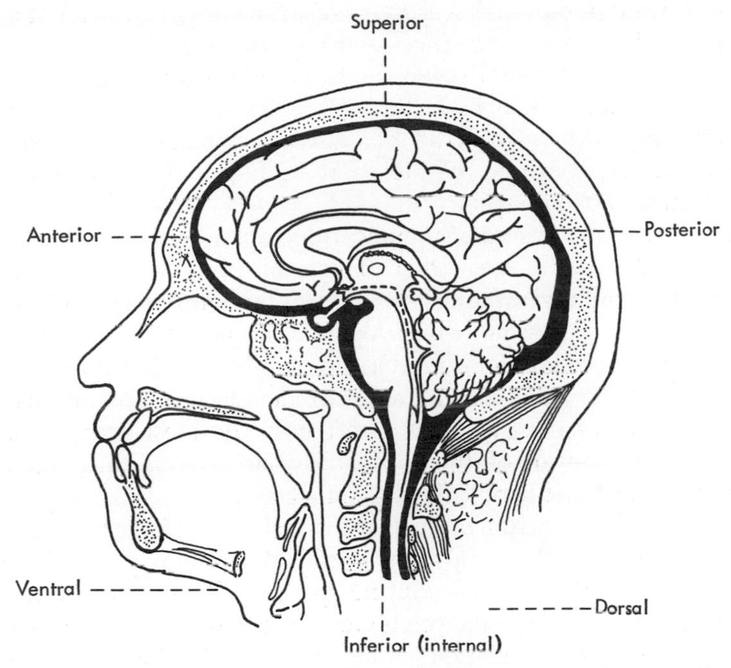

Figure 2–8. The brain in relation to the head. Note anatomical terms often used in describing direction in the nervous system. (From Ranson, S. W., and Clark, S. L. *The Anatomy of the Nervous System*, Philadelphia: W. B. Saunders Co., 1959.)

matter and an inner surface of white and gray matter, appears to be quite similar in structure to the cerebrum. The cerebellum, which contains about ten per cent of the brain's total mass, is second to the cerebrum in size of structure.

There is an intricate relationship between the cerebellum and cerebrum in the coordination and refinement of motor activity to produce skilled movement patterns. Tactile, visual, and auditory areas are located here that correspond to the cortex centers. Proprioceptive information from all muscles concerning posture, equilibrium, and movement come to the cerebellum, which in turn exerts a certain amount of control over these factors. An intact cerebellum is necessary for the harmonious control of the various muscle groups in the body. Injury to this region in the brain may result in uncoordinated and poorly timed movements, a poor sense of balance, or tremors. Snider (1958) states that the cerebellum is localized in the extreme front and rear surfaces, in other words, that these areas have specific controlling functions. He suggests that it is necessary to remove large areas of the cerebellar cortex before there will be severe loss of muscular coordination.

The spinal cord is directly continuous with the *medulla oblongata,* which is the lowermost portion of the brain. Because of this fact, it is a connecting pathway for impulses exchanged between the spinal cord and brain and functions in many motor and sensory mechanisms. Approximately two-thirds of the nerve fibers cross over (*decussate*) at the medulla, thus explaining why one side of the cerebral cortex controls the opposite side of the body. The medulla contains many of the vital reflex centers; for example, the respiratory center, which regulates the rate of inspirations and expirations; the cardiac center, controller of the heart beat; and the vasomotor center, which influences blood pressure.

Because of the many intercommunicating cables found in the brain, all parts are tuned in with each other. Tracts of white tissue serve as these cables. In the cable organization, there are subsystems responsible for computing and data processing which operate in orderly and computerlike fashion. It is not necessary for all mechanisms to be in active operation for all the functions of the body, an indication of the efficiency of the machinery. In fact, as a general rule, we may expect only the most complex behavior to be under the control of the higher nervous system, since most basic, unwilled movements are handled by the spinal cord.

Through scientific experimentation, areas of the brain have been designated as terminal points for the input signals from the various parts of the body. By removing (*extirpation*) or destroying specific cells or studying the action potentials of various cells in the cerebrum, it is possible to determine cerebral area functions. Also, stimulation of certain areas of the cortex results in movements in certain body parts.

Electrical Activity. Functions of the various areas in the cerebral cortex have been extensively studied through instrumentation. One of the forerunners in the study of brain electrical activity was Hans Berger, and his work led to the development of the *electroencephalograph* (see Figure 2–9). An electroencephalogram (*EEG*) is the recording of electrical waves of the

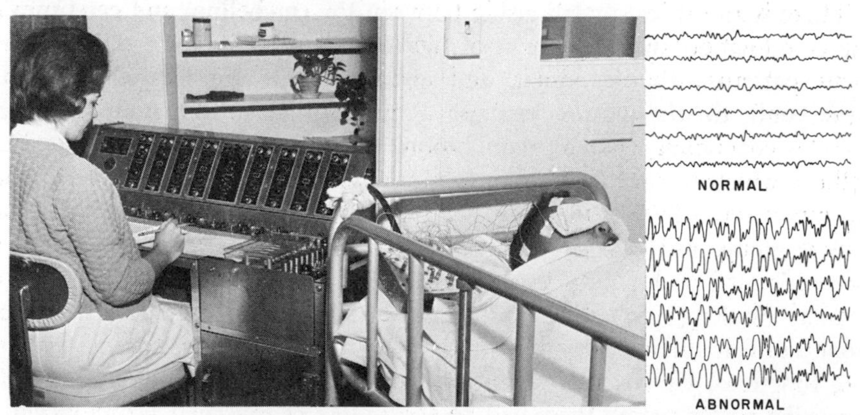

Figure 2–9. Diagram illustrating the recording of electroencephalograms. Technician sits at the console of the electroencephalograph recording the electroencephalogram of a young patient. Both normal and abonrmal tracings are shown. (From Grollman, Sigmund, *The Human Body*, New York: The Macmillan Co., 1964.)

brain obtained from electrodes attached to the scalp. These waves appear at different frequencies and amplitudes and, among other things, indicate changes in body activity. As the state of a person changes from relaxation to activity, the electric potentials (*wave patterns*) of the brain also change.

The shape in voltage waves in the brain determine the state of the organism. Although the operation of the brain is probably chemical, voltage changes are presently what we measure. Alpha, beta, and delta waves have been recognized and are designated according to the number of cycles occurring per second. Slowest waves, possibly less than one a second, are called *delta waves.* These are usually obtained during sleep. *Alpha waves* occur at a rate of about eight to thirteen times a second and are the most common, representing inattentive but waking states. During increased activity and tension, alpha waves give way to the small irregular *beta waves,* and these fast waves may be timed at over fourteen cycles per second. The electroencephalogram has many clinical and diagnostic usages and usually indicates the nature of activity in specific sections of the cortex under varying degrees of behavior and movement.

Computer and Human Differences. By no means should the computer-neural analogy be thought of as perfect nor even near perfect. Similarities have been brought out, in simplified fashion, for the purpose of approaching the study of the nervous system consistent with the theme of the book. At the present time, the complex behavior of the human organism can in no way be completely accounted for by electronic principles in a mechanistic analogy.

How does one program emotions in a machine? Humans typically respond to a given situation in an emotional state which may vary from occasion to occasion. How does one learn or remember? A machine is programmed by a human to react in a particular way to a particular input. It does not, in a sense, have to learn anything. The machine must respond in a predictable manner, whereas the human organism appears not to be a deterministic model of behavior.

There are some things the machine can do better than man, and vice versa. Certainly, the machine can calculate more accurately and at a faster rate than any human. All aspects of the input must be in order if the machine is to relay the desired output while human performance may attain objectives with parts of ideas or fragments of stimuli or even abstractions present. In other words, the data can be incomplete but still the brain can operate successfully; machines cannot.

The machine is limited in function by man's ability to construct; his knowledge and understanding of machine dynamics. Connections in the nervous system are vastly more complicated than the simple cabling arrangement of the computer. This, in essence leads to the final point. The human brain is much more complicated, sophisticated, and versatile than any machines that have been built so far.

Coordinated Movement

The type and nature of output from the control system ranges in many directions, although in the motor-learning situation it is expected that co-ordinated, effective movement is that which is desired. The human organism is capable of demonstrating an assorted array of motor patterns from the most elemental motor acts to the most complicated stunts. As an example of the nervous system's efficiency, sensory information is usually rearranged in lower levels of the system. There is an interconnection and rearrangement in the interneurons of the spinal cord and brain stem before the data arrives at the cerebral cortex. Not all responses or movements need be mediated by past experiences and thought processes. Not all stimuli need be recorded in the cortex.

Some simple receptor-effector loops located outside and inside the brain free the cerebrum for other work. These circuits are associated with certain bodily activity which transpires as if automatic. Consider for example the reflex, the most simple of motor movements. Reflexes do not usually require the attention of the higher levels of the nervous system.

Reflexes. *Reflex arcs* constitute the pathways involved in a simple reaction to a stimulus, usually not requiring the functioning of the higher centers of the nervous system. In the beginning of the twentieth century the outstanding physiologist, Sherrington (1858–1952), experimented on the nature of reflex transmission and the reflex at the spinal level, and his efforts still have tremendous impact on present thinking about the nervous system. Reflex arcs may contain two, three, or more neurons. In any case these reflex arcs result in somewhat consistent responses, usually unconscious in nature, to the same stimuli. Because a reflex is an unconscious response, it can be conditioned to be highly predictable.

The reflex arc, in its simplest form (two-neuron), contains five parts:

1. *Receptor:* specialized sensory nerve ending.
2. *Afferent neuron:* sensory transmitter of impulse from the receptor to the gray matter in the spinal cord.
3. *Synapse:* a gap in the anterior horn of the cord where an afferent and efferent neuron are in functional proximity.
4. *Efferent neuron:* motor neuron, passing the impulse from the cord to an effector.
5. *Effector:* organ responsible for response.

Examples of a two-neuron reflex arc are the *postural reflex* and *knee jerk reflex* (see Figure 2–10), both of which are classified as *stretch reflexes.* In the stretch reflex, or postural reflex, inhibiting impulses are sent to antagonist muscles while appropriate muscles contract in order to maintain body stability. When an extensor muscle contracts and the flexor relaxes or vice versa, we have a condition known as *reciprocal innervation.* As to the actual stretch reflex, the process may be described in the following way:

> Stretch reflex: spindles stretched → afferent impulses to spinal cord → innervation of alpha neurons → reflex contraction of the appropriate muscle fibers (Ralston, 1957).

The knee jerk reflex involves the stimulus of tapping the patellar tendon and response of leg extension. During stimulus application, the quadriceps muscle is stretched causing the stimulation of receptors in the muscle and resulting in a reflex shortening of this muscle. Basic reflexes such as the knee jerk reflex can be used for diagnostic purposes; for if there is some disturbance in the reflex pathway, the reflex will not be reproduced normally. Some reflex acts can be facilitated intentionally. A clenching of the fists before the patellar tendon is struck would result in a greater response, hence the reason for an examining doctor to insist on complete relaxation of his patient before the test.

Certain reflexes are inborn, those needed for chewing and swallowing, simple defense reactions, defecation, micturation, and the like. Previous learning experience is not necessary for these responses, hence they are unconditioned. Others are *conditioned* or *acquired* (learned) reflexes. An example of the latter is best represented by the reasearch of Pavlov, who contributed extensively in developing methods by which new responses medi-

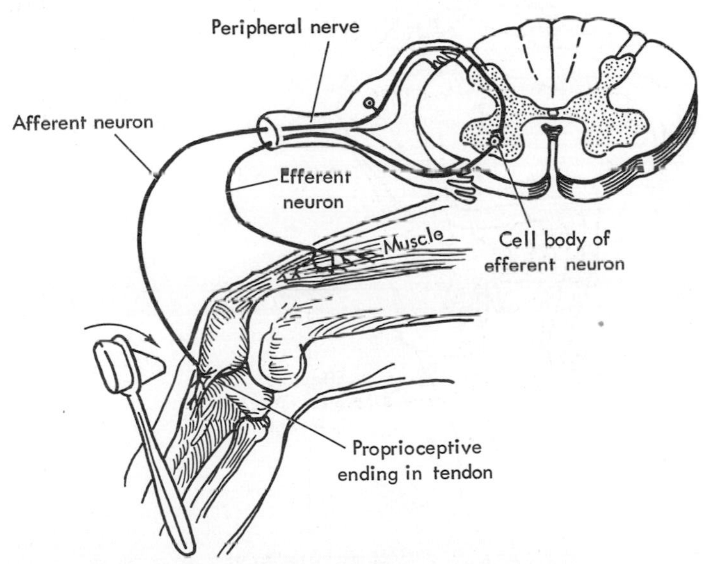

Figure 2–10. Simple reflex arc (knee jerk). The four fundamental parts of a reflex arc are shown: (1) a receptor—proprioceptive ending in tendon; (2) a sensory transmitter—the afferent neuron; (3) a motor transmitter—the efferent neuron; (4) the effector—the muscle. (From Grollman, Sigmund. *The Human Body,* New York: The Macmillan Co., 1964.)

ated by the cerebral cortex could be studied. Salivation accompanies food as well as its anticipation in a hungry animal. Pavlov rang a bell each occasion he fed the dog involved in his experiment. After a number of trials in which the bell and food were presented together, the food was eliminated but each time the bell rang, the animal salivated: thus, a conditioned reflex.

Other reflexes are concerned with body protection via withdrawal and are termed *flexor reflexes.* The sharp withdrawal of the foot from contact with a sharp object is an example of a flexor reflex.

The complex reflex arc is exemplified by the withdrawal reflex. Figure 2–11 illustrates foot withdrawal from a painful stimulus. Although only a few localized receptors are involved, it is interesting to note the *spread of effect* (a generalized reflex response involving many effectors). Notice how many parts of the body actively respond to a stimulus that activates but a few skin receptors. This startle reflex appears to be a "stored-program" reflex, as an organized set of reactions occur without consciousness.

Incorrect withdrawal reflexes have been obtained in a series of experiments by Sperry (1959). After crossing sensory nerves of rats and frogs, extensive

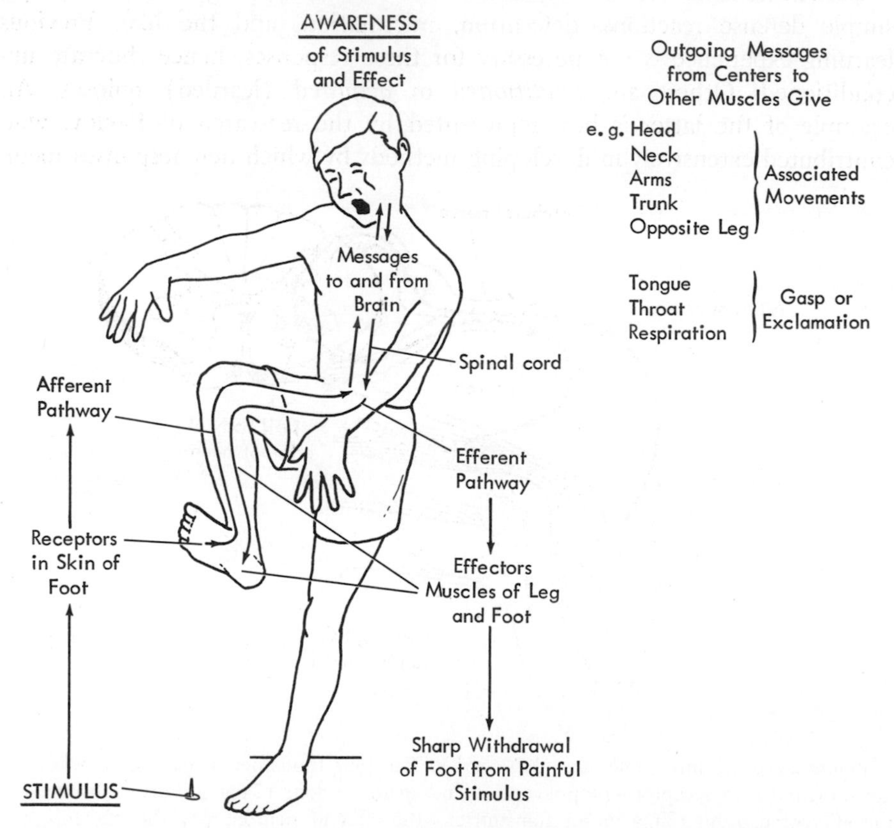

Figure 2–11. Reflex action demonstrating many reflex arcs. (From McNaught A., and Callander, R. *Illustrated Physiology,* Baltimore: Williams and Wilkins Co., 1963.)

training still had no effect in re-educating their motor systems. During the rearrangement of nerve connections, rats would withdraw the right foot in response to an electric shock to the left foot. These results seem to indicate that although higher nervous system centers are capable of extensive learning, the anatomical arrangement of the lower ones are implastic. They cannot be modified much by use or training. Spinal reflexes do recover to some extent following disease or injury in the spinal cord. Damage to the spinal cord, however, will cause a total loss of sensory input and voluntary physical movement.

Simple reflexes are wired-in nerve circuits; the action is not premeditated, nor has it been learned. Other reflexes are learned and are associated with more complex behavior than heretofore discussed. Certain movements in sports situations, although termed reflexive, go far beyond the simple processes discussed thus far. Take, for instance, the almost-automatic responses needed for success in sports. After slight deliberation, responses must be made in automatic fashion to given stimuli: (1) the batter interprets the nature of a pitch, its accuracy and type, in less than a second; (2) the wrestler under control attempts to escape when the referee blows his whistle, before his opponent can react to impede his sudden movement; (3) the hockey center must decide whether to pass the puck to a forward or shoot it at the goalie himself, all in a fraction of a second; and (4) the fooball quarterback decides, in the face of on-rushing linemen and while he is on the move, if it is wiser to hand-off, run, fall down, or pass and pass to whom.

These responses and many more are required in dynamic sports situations. The total situation is ever changing and unpredictable, but the performer reacts almost instantaneously nevertheless. Except under conditions of high certainty, there is always some temporal lag in performance. In other cases, the environment is relatively stable. The athlete is prepared for his task, and he attempts to perform a series of acts in a skillful fashion. The diver, the gymnast, and the trampoliner condition themselves to display routines that appear automatic. If we define a reflex as an automatic performance of a complex sequence of spatially and temporally related motor patterns (Wooldridge, 1963), then sports contain examples where reflexes are demonstrated. Then again, other writers (e.g., Miller, Galanter, and Pribram [1960]) find fault in explaining any form of human behavior, let alone reflex action, in reflex arc terms. Perhaps even reflex action is far more complex than we think. According to Miller et al., behavior is controlled in terms of the order in which a sequence of operation is to be performed. All action is guided by a "plan," which they liken to a computer program.

Athletic situations are filled with examples of predetermined performances to predetermined stimuli. One might even go so far as to believe that there are stored programs (organized memory traces) in the brain. When sensory data are filtered into the nervous system, the appropriate program would be activated. Evidently, these programs become effective with repetition (practice). Most daily activity and athletic activity does not involve simple movements and responses, for frequently we have to select an appropriate response for a given stimulus. Since these actions go beyond the complex reflex stage, the highest levels of the nervous system become involved.

Complex Movement. The development of the cerebral cortex is correlated with man's intellectual superiority over other animals. This structure of the highest order is necessary for refinement of movements, for precision and effectiveness. The cortex itself is not necessary in all motor activity, for gross bcdily movements are but slightly interfered with by the loss of cortical function. However, we are referring here to the most gross of movements, such as walking, crawling, and moving a hand in prescribed directions, and obviously the learning and often the performance of athletic skills demands cortical involvement.

The cerebrum contains motor, sensory, and association areas, which interact during most coordinated complex movement (see Figure 2–12). Between various species, structural differences in the brain are related to differences in physical characteristics. For example, a bird has large-sized optic lobes but small olfactory lobes; vision, not smell, is important to the bird. There is a

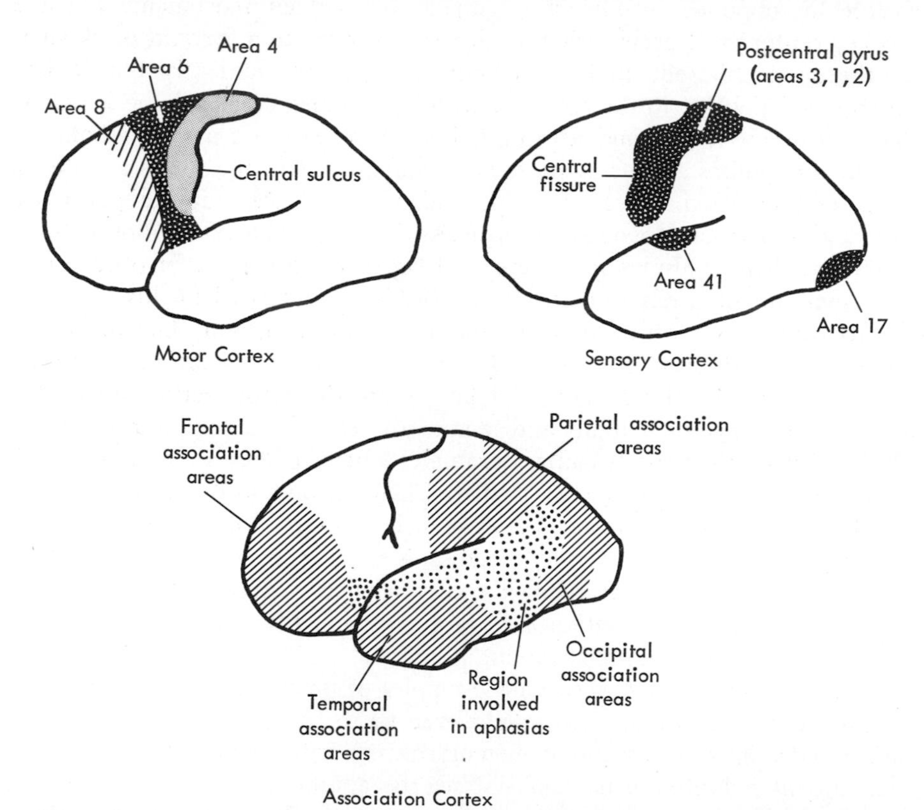

Figure 2–12. The primary motor, sensory, and association areas of the cortex. (From Gardner, E. *Fundamentals of Neurology*, Philadelphia: W. B. Saunders Co., 1963.)

relationship between the number of cells in the motor area allocated to a particular portion of the body, the number of motor units in an effector, and the complexity of movements related to that area. Hence, relatively fewer cells control feet and leg movements whereas a much greater motor area is related to finger and lip motions. Figure 2–13 indicates cerebral control over various parts of the body.

The upper part of the motor region stimulates the lower extremities, the middle sends impulses to the trunk, whereas the lower part is concerned with facial and head movements. Although the motor cortex exerts influence on the various parts of the body, integrated functioning will occur only if surrounding cerebral areas are in place. The nervous system is extremely complex and integrated, requiring coordination between the neural structures involved in a particular act.

The cerebral cortex plays an important role in voluntary movements as contrasted with reflex movement, which is usually regulated at lower levels of the nervous system. Penfield (1954) has described the function of the motor cortex in willed movements and the effects on the body if damage occurs there. One side of the motor area controls movement in the opposite side of

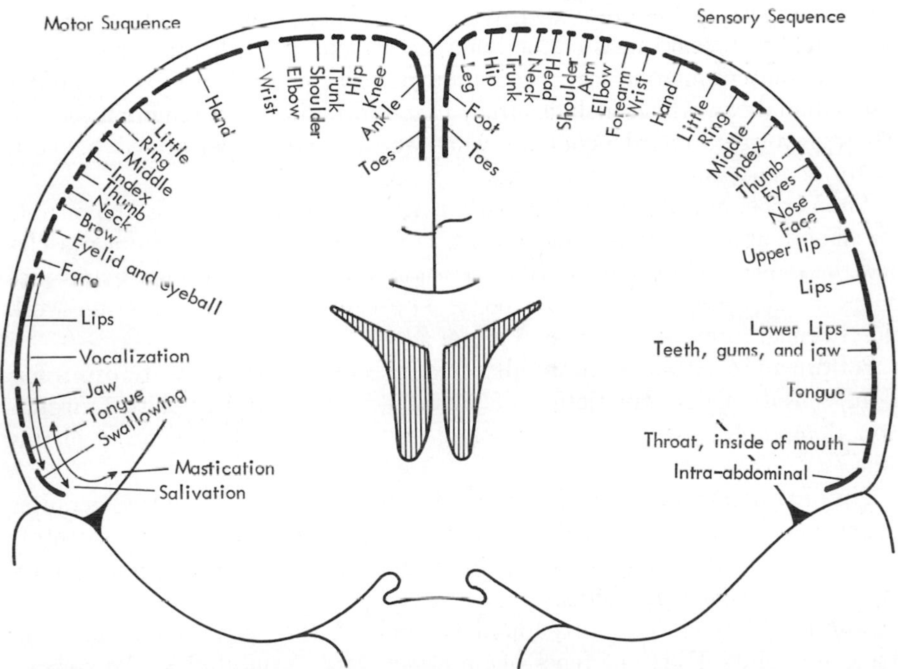

Figure 2–13. Cross-section of the cerebrum through the sensorimotor region with the motor and sensory sequences indicated. The lengths of the solid bars represent an estimate of the average relative cortical areas from which the corresponding responses were elicited. (From Penfield, W., and Rasmussen, T. *The Cerebral Cortex of Man,* New York: The Macmillan Co., 1950.)

the body. If, for example, there is a damage to some cells in the left cerebral hemisphere's motor area, possible paralysis may be inflicted in the corresponding muscles on the right side of the body. The reason for this fact is that nerve pathways cross over at the medulla or spinal cord level on their way down to specific effectors. Although it is possible for some recovery to take place in the form of gross movements, finger skills very rarely if ever return.

The various sense areas of the cortex are just as important as the motor cortex in skilled movement. Sense impulses for vision are distinguished in the occipital lobe, whereas those for audition are distinguished in the temporal lobe. Muscle sensations are interpreted in the somesthetic or sensory area of the parietal lobe, located posterior to the motor area. Representation of the different parts of the body in the somesthetic area is similar to the representation in the motor area. The somesthetic region is concerned with such sensations as touch, pain, pressure, and body position. Although a habit abolished by the removal of certain areas in the cerebral cortex can be relearned, damage to the sensory areas of the brain cannot be compensated for by any amount of retraining. Figure 2–14 represents cortical functions in the sensory, motor, and association areas.

Association areas, which comprise the bulk of the cortex, are thought to be responsible for memory, speech, reasoning, intelligence, and thought and are not as localized as the other areas described. These functions are not usually designated to specific areas of the brain, as evidenced by the fact that such a process as discrimination learning is thought to be controlled in the posterior association areas, which includes the parietal, occipital, and temporal sectors. There is a great interdependence when most acts are performed between motor, sensory, and association areas of the cerebrum.

The cerebellum offers an automatic control function, for it is responsible for smooth and coordinated movement. It receives information from muscles and the semicircular canals on body position and rate of movement, and produces a stabilizing effect on the body. The cerebellum and cerebrum work closely on all forms of coordinated motor acts.

Performance output is the result of sense reception, impulse transmission along sensory paths, stimulation of neural structures, and impulse transmission along motor paths. Let us elaborate on the mechanisms involved in this process.

The first action necessary before an impulse can be transmitted requires the stimulation of an input device or receptor. Based on location, receptors may be classified into four categories: proprioceptors, exteroceptors, interoceptors, and distance receptors.

Proprioceptors are receptors found throughout the body in muscles, tendons, and joints. Different types of proprioceptors are located in these structures; for example, *neuromuscular spindles* in the muscles, *Golgi tendon organs* in the tendons, and *pacinian* corpuscles and *Ruffini* endings in tissues surrounding the joint. Neuromuscular spindles are stimulated when a muscle is stretched and cause the muscle to contract reflexly. Proprioceptors provide

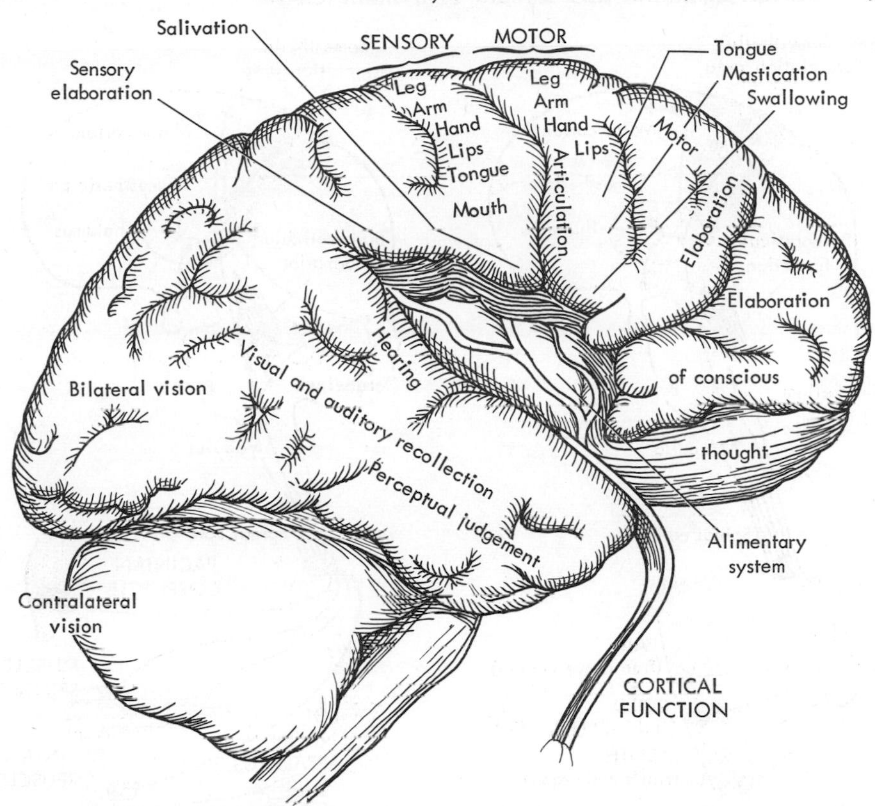

Figure 2–14. Cortical function. This illustration serves as a summary restatement of conclusions, some hypothetical (e.g. the elaboration zones), others firmly established. The suggestion that the anterior portion of the occipital cortex is related to both fields of vision rather than to one alone is derived from the results of stimulation. (From Penfield, W., and Rasmussen, T. *The Cerebral Cortex of Man*, New York: The Macmillan Co., 1950.)

information to the body about changes in body position and movement; they also detect pressure. Along with the impulses from the inner ear, proprioceptors are responsible for the so-called *kinesthetic sense*, the awareness of body and limb position in space. The *labyrinth* of the inner ear contains proprioceptors that provide information about the movement of the head. It is a source of movement sensation.

Exteroceptors are receptors on the skin and provide information about the immediate external environment. These structures function in distinguishing light touch (tactile receptors), pressure (pressure receptors), warmth and coolness (thermal receptors), and pain (pain receptors). Specific types of receptors are associated with each of these sensations, many of which have proprioceptive functions as well. The Ruffini end organs respond to warmth, the Meissner corpuscles to light touch, the pacinian corpuscles to pressure, and Krause's end bulbs to cold. Figure 2–15 compares proprioceptive and exteroceptive sensation transmission.

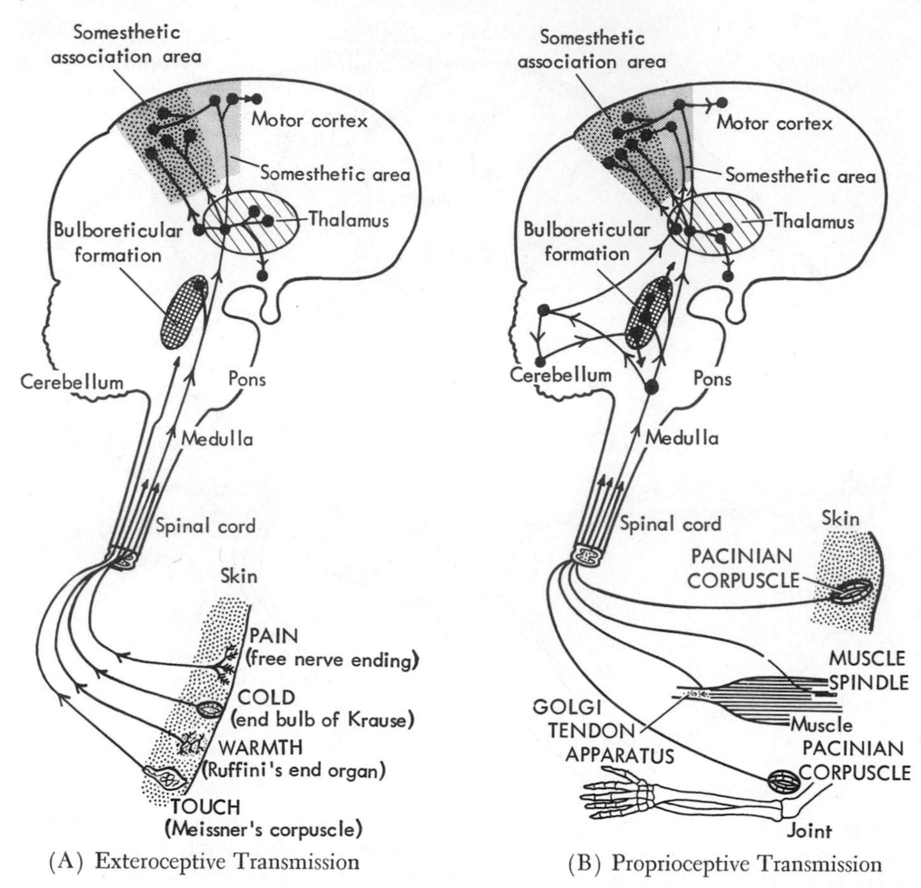

(A) Exteroceptive Transmission (B) Proprioceptive Transmission

Figure 2–15. Transmission of exteroceptive sensations and proprioceptive sensations to the brain. (A) Exteroceptive Transmission. (From Guyton, Arthur C. *Function of the Human Body,* Philadelphia: W. B. Saunders Co., 1963.); (B) Proprioceptive Transmission. (From Guyton, Arthur C. *Textbook of Medical Physiology,* Philadelphia: W. B. Saunders Co., 1966.)

Interoceptors are sense organs found in the viscera and are responsible for detecting information about the internal environment. Mainly they are free nerve endings found in such internal structures as in the walls of the heart and blood vessels, in the lungs, and mesentary. Such visceral sensations as pain, hunger, and thirst are initiated by the interoceptors.

Distance receptors include the eyes, ears, and nose, and they provide information on the remote environment. It is convenient to discuss the senses of sight, smell, equilibrium, hearing, and taste (called the *special senses*) separately because of the more detailed information available on the mechanisms involved in these functions. The author recommends that the reader examine some of the references found at the end of this chapter for a more extensive review of these senses.

After input, the impulse travels along a pre-established path to the appropriate part of the brain. Typical sensory pathways include a three-neuron relay: neuron I going to the spinal cord, neuron II extending from that point to the thalamus, and neuron III communicating with the sensory area of the cortex. One of the most important of the sensory tracts is the *spinothalamic tract,* responsible for feeling pain and temperature changes. Its path is as follows:

Neuron of the first order (I): skin receptors → posterior column of spinal cord →
Neuron of the second order (II): posterior column → decussates → thalamus
Neuron of the third order (III): thalamus → sensory area of parietal lobe in cerebral cortex.

Following sense activity, certain areas in the brain issue orders to the various parts of the body. Voluntary activity is initiated in the higher centers, although the site can only be conjectured. It has been found that stimulation of any part of the motor cortex does not result in skilled acts, leading Paillard (1960) to speculate on the presence of an intermediary system, capable of controlling the motor cortex but receiving its stimulation from some other area of the nervous system. Involuntary or reflex movements have their origin at lower levels of the central nervous system. A method of classifying motor pathways is based on the way their fibers enter the spinal cord. Two motor systems, pyramidal and extrapyramidal, are distinguished in this manner. These two systems are responsible for volitional movements.

The *extrapyramidal pathway* is extremely complicated, eventually affecting gross, coordinated movements of the body. These patterns require the contraction and relaxation of a number of muscles. The pathway involves motor and other areas of the cortex, basal ganglia, the cerebellum, other parts of the brain, and numerous tracts in the spinal cord. Damage to the cerebellum, for instance, results in difficulty in standing erect and performing simple movements.

The *pyramidal path* is simple and direct. It is responsible for fine, discrete movements involving such areas of the body as the fingers, toes, facial muscles, and lips. A specific area of the cerebral cortex contains unique cells called *Betz cells* which connect to large, fast-conducting axons. The large axons enable the impulses to travel a great distance at rapid speed. The fibers from the cortex meet at the medulla and the crossing is pyramidal in shape and appearance, hence the name of this system, although it is also referred to as the *corticospinal pathway.*

It is one thing to have the necessary paths and orderly cabling arrangement as well as neural structures, but perhaps more should be said about the selection of appropriate responses. In other words, the action of certain parts of the nervous system determines consciousness, alertness and preparation for activity, and will have a bearing on the nature of the response.

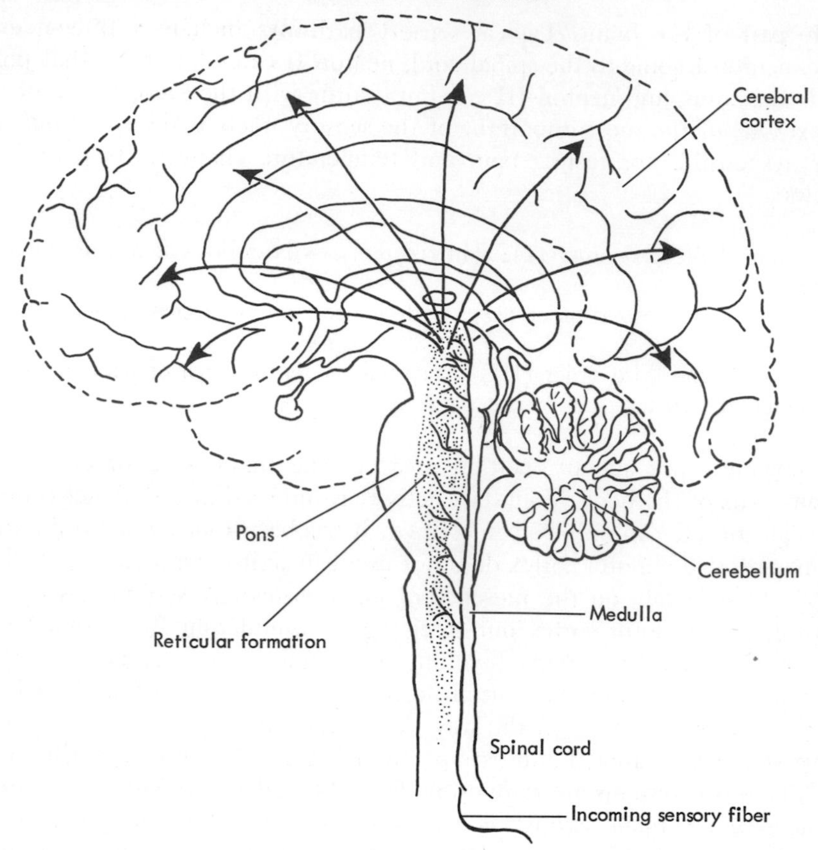

Figure 2–16. Section of brain showing the reticular formation. It is composed of interlacing fibers and nerve cells which form the central core of the brain stem. Incoming fibers from the spinal tracts send collaterals into the reticular formation. Arrows indicate the general arousal of higher brain centers which the reticular area controls. (From Kimber, Diana Clifford, and others. *Anatomy and Physiology*, 15th ed., New York: The Macmillan Co., 1966.)

These functions have been attributed to the *reticular formation* of the brain stem, also known as the *reticular activating system.* The reticular formation is a mesh of motor nerve cells, distributed from the top of the spinal cord to the thalamus and hypothalamus, that receives as well as distributes impulses to the lower as well as the highest centers of the central nervous system (see Figure 2–16). The main function of the formation appears to be that of alerting the individual, of placing him in a condition of arousal.

When an individual is in a sleeping state, little activity occurs in the reticular formation. However, stimulation of this center has an effect on the cortex and results in its awakening. Many of the afferent pathways feed into the reticular system, and if the impulses are strong enough they will pass on to the hypothalamus, thalamus, and finally, to the cortex. Damage to the upper portion of the reticular system may result in extensive sleepiness or even pathologic sleep.

Some writers have attributed great significance to this formation. In fact, it has been termed a program-selection mechanism that determines the nature of a response. As a response selector, the reticular system assigns priorities to messages, determines which are important, and selects the appropriate responses in order of importance. Nearly all incoming and outgoing impulses of the brain pass through the reticular formation.

With the influence of the cerebrum, cerebellum, reticular formation and other areas of the brain, the output of the nervous system, displayed in the form of complex coordinated movement, is made possible. However, learning is a prerequisite before most meaningful and effective behavior occurs. Let us now turn to the learning mechanisms and attempt to determine where and how learning takes place.

Learning

The maturational status of the nervous system, hereditary factors, and the previous experiences of the organism contribute to learning potential. Generalized behavior patterns depend on the physical construction of the system, or shall we say, on the arrangement of neurons. Genes determine the manner in which neurons are interconnected; so, in a sense, we, like computers, are prewired.

Neurons are all in the appropriate place due to heredity. These wired-in networks, similar within members of each species, contribute to the basic reflexes necessary for survival. The behavior and performance skills which distinguish and characterize each individual are determined by personal experiences and genetic factors other than those which merely contribute to the organization of the neural cables. In order to explain learning potential, we must look to such heredity predeterminers as brain size, cortex convolutions, and chemical arrangements in the brain cells.

Acquisition. There is evidently no one learning center in the brain. Rather, there are different areas that contribute to the learning of various kinds of matter. Once the appropriate learning mechanisms have been activated and tuned in, the learning of a motor skill requires the interaction of those areas in the brain responsible for sense reception, perception, thought, and action.

An experiment by Lashley (1935) indicates the effect of cerebral damage on the learning and performance of a motor skill. He trained normal rats and rats with cerebral lesions on five different latch boxes. When performing on a simple latch box, rats with up to 58 per cent damage were unaffected. More advanced tasks were difficult to learn for the rats with cerebral lesions. Lashley concluded that the amount of retardation was proportional to the surface extent of the lesion. Larger lesions had a greater effect on more difficult tasks.

Simple conditioning does not seem to involve cortical processes, for Lashley's rats learned simple tasks without apparently having cortical involvement. These findings may be interpreted as implying that lesions in the motor cortex probably affect exploratory movements, adaptive movements, insight, and the like, but not the mechanism of association.

Certain areas in the brain may act as controllers, but in many cases, other parts of the nervous system are capable of reasonable substitution. Another point to consider is that cortical neurons are not in charge of specific muscles but rather specific muscular activity. As was mentioned previously, oftentimes the cortex functions in making an act skilled, but this act may occur in crude fashion without cortex involvement.

When a reflex is conditioned, that is, not inborn, the act must be repeated over and over until an automatic association between stimulus and response is made. The stimulation of specific patterns of sensory neurons in the brain is followed by specific patterns of activity. Repetition leads to the so-called "connection" of appropriate responses to given stimuli. The process appears to become automatic, with no need for thought or consciousness.

The learning of an athletic skill encompasses the establishment of a series of successive conditioned responses. Each new practice trial is usually performed within a frame of stored past experiences and movement patterns and immediate objectives. Perhaps motor learning involves the following neural processes:

> Performance → sensory input → feedback of signals (visual, emotional, proprioceptive, and the like) → strengthening or weakening of neural connections.

Notice the mention once again of a term that was briefly introduced earlier in this chapter: *feedback*. It refers to the information the individual gains from his performance which permits him to profit from the experience. Hopefully, the information will be accurate, although some researchers have suggested that the sensory pathways are subject to error. Although sensory pathways may be interfered with and thereby modify input patterns, fortunately, the interference is not usually detrimental to performance. Feedback as an important feature of learning and performance will be discussed in greater detail in other chapters of this book. Suffice to say here that without feedback, without the organism's knowing how or what it is doing, progress, to say the least, would be impeded in many forms of activity.

Memory. The speed with which we learn something and learning efficiency in general depend to a large extent on that which is remembered from previous similar experiences. Events are stored for future use. The location and nature of memory traces are difficult to ascertain, but they appear to be widely dispersed throughout the brain.

Breakthroughs in understanding memory and intelligence have been made from the findings of recent research concerned with these problems. Studies on rats, fish, and flatworms indicate an increase in RNA (ribonucleic acid) which is the genetic material in each brain cell's nucleus, in the cells, as learning takes place. Neurons produce RNA, with more cell activity resulting in more of this substance. RNA has even been termed *the memory molecule* by some scientists, even though research is still scanty in this area. Rats trained at problem solving, besides demonstrating an increase in their RNA and protein contents in the brain cells, also had heavier and larger brains. If RNA is the learning secret, there are great implications for improving learning abilities and performance in those individuals who previously were thought to be hopeless. Possibly, the administration of additional amounts of this substance to them would benefit their learning potential.

No one part of the brain can be called the central repository of stored information, and, as we have just seen, neuronal activity increases the RNA in all brain cells. However, as indicated by research evidence, the temporal lobes of the cortex are involved in the recall of many previous experiences. Penfield and Roberts (1959) write that "in this mechanism of recall and comparison and interpretation...the interpretive cortex of the temporal lobes plays its specialized role." Electrical stimulation of portions of these lobes sometimes results in the sudden remembrance of events that occurred many years prior. Perhaps, just perhaps, the temporal lobes constitute that portion of the brain most responsible for memory. We will have to wait for more scientific findings before such a belief can be accepted.

The later performance of once-learned skills is also dependent on the physical condition of the wiring. What happens when there is damage to a wire or two? Regeneration of nerve cells is only believed to be possible if at least the cell body (and its nucleus, which is the center of repair) is intact and a neurilemma sheath surrounds the fibers. Since neurons in the central nervous system lack a neurilemma, regeneration is only possible in the peripheral nervous system. Nerve cells that are completely destroyed cannot be replaced, but other neurons may be able to take over their function, to certain degrees. This ability will be dictated by the period in the individual's life when specific nerve cells are destroyed as well as the specific cells involved. Cells may die due to such factors as injury or disease, and if certain patterns of movement have been established before this occurs, there is a better chance neurons in surrounding areas will be able to compensate for their loss of function. A baby is handicapped to a greater extent than a more mature child or adult as he has not yet had the opportunity to develop skilled motor patterns. Greater experience and education result in more and varied learning patterns. Less behavioral deterioration thus might be expected to occur after brain damage in older and/or highly educated people.

Memory is theorized to be of two types: the long term and the short term. It is interesting to speculate why we remember so well certain things we did in childhood and yet have forgotten others. Also, why are motor skills often retained for a lengthier period of time than are once-learned literary passages? Are there different memory mechanisms involved in the operation of, say, long-term retention versus short-term retention? One fact remains sure at the present time: we cannot isolate or localize a memory trace, regardless of its nature. It does appear, though, that during the retention process of whatever is to be retained, a multiple representation in the cortex is established. That is to say, various portions of the cortex are capable of relaying previously-gained information to the individual when he needs it.

Neurophysiological Theories of Learning

Neuropsychological and neurophysiological theories of learning have been advanced throughout the twentieth century. Physiological psychologists have attempted to bridge the gap between physiology and psychology in order to explain learning and behavior from a combination of both viewpoints. Because of the lack of universal acceptance of many propositions in various areas of psychology and physiology, the problems these theorists are faced with are readily apparent.

Physiologists attempt to describe learning through various neural mechanisms and processes, whereas psychologists are more interested in observable behavior. Lashley (1958) is of the opinion that psychologists have inhibited neurologists in formulating learning theories. He writes:

> Psychologists are mostly pedagogues, engaged in forcing useless information upon unwilling students, and, as a result, they have concluded that drill, repetition, is essential for learning. Actually, they themselves, after they have passed their Ph.D. examinations, have probably never memorized anything by rote again. The basic problem of learning is what we call "incidental memory," learning in one trial. We have to seek the explanation of learning and memory somewhere else than in repetition. All of the neurological theories dealing with the learning process, that I have seen, have assumed an effect of repetition on synaptic nerve endings, but the fact is that most learning does not involve repetition.

Although a number of neurological theories do account for learning by referring to changes in synaptic regions, certainly others have presented different explanations. Actually, theories may be classified as being materialistic or subjective, since there is a dualistic point of view on how to go about understanding the nervous system's role in learning. Those theorists who are materialistic talk about the nature of the nerve impulse, reverberating nerve chains, changes at the synapse, and reflex physiology. These theorists are primarily physiologists. Subjective theorists are primarily psychologists who refer to the mind and experience. To them, the physiological basis of mind occurs between the sensory input and motor output. Mind is not described other than as being an organizer and integrator of activity.

A number of physiological theories fall into the general category of describing learning as a *change in the central synapses.* According to these anatomical theorists, the synaptic resistance is lowered when the same circuits are used repeatedly in a learning situation. Eccles believes that the axon terminals swell, Hebb argues that axon terminals multiply and synaptic knobs become larger during stimulation, and Konorski states that axon terminals enlarge. Some biochemical theorists hold the idea of the release of chemical substances at the synapses, which allows nerve transmission to be more effective.

A theory related to this synaptic theory is that of *reverberation.* Learning supposedly causes changes in the neural circuits and results in reverberating chains of impulses that linger after the response has been made. Learning is a dynamic process causing a continuously circulating pattern of impulses in closed neural chains. A similar situation quickly activates the appropriate chain, which has been reverberating, and the appropriate response is made.

Ritchie (1959) believes in the development of paths, i.e., neuronal patterns, during learning. Repetition of the activity strengthens the pathway. Because the central nervous system constantly practices its skills and continually discharges impulses, even after years of no physical practice, one can still perform a motor skill due to this phenomenon. He feels that nerve cells show spontaneous activity, that they unconsciously strengthen simple patterns. Other learned skills only compete if closely related, since neuronal circuits are quite different—they will not bother the pathway of the just-learned skill unless they are very similar.

Other theories, also physiological in nature, have been advanced. Hellebrandt (1958) describes the physiology of motor learning, and after an extensive review of the literature, cites three theories of motor learning. As for skill development, she points out that cerebration is necessary at first for willed movements. Later, as skill is attained, the act becomes almost automatic, minimizing the need for cerebral involvement.

Through the years, two schools of thought have been advanced to explain the manner in which the brain functions. As Luria (1966) writes, one group believes in the separateness in function of each part of the brain. He calls the people in this group localizationists, for they state that a function in a particular area of the brain can be localized. There is a second group which believes that the brain works as a whole, as a single entity.

Luria rejects both viewpoints in favor of the concept of the dynamic localization of functions. The following quotation will serve to exemplify his platform. "The motor act is not the 'function' of any one localized group of nerve cells situated in the cerebral cortex but is a complex functional system, whose working is controlled by many factors."

The brain, Luria believes, functions as a series of systems. Cerebral reflexes are the basic elements of behavior. He describes the reflex character of all processes, from the natural reflexes of the infant to the formation of complex systems of reflex connections. The formation of many functional systems occurs. The brain functions as a whole but at the same time is a "highly differentiated system whose parts are responsible for different aspects of the unified whole."

Luria emphasizes the influence of sensory information in motor activity, for the organism compares it to the intended output. Voluntary movement requires continuous sensory feedback-information from the muscles and joints. Complex movement needs a flow of kinesthetic afferent impulses to direct motor impulses which in turn will give rise to appropriate movements. Besides kinesthetic impulses, the optic-spatial afferent system is also important in effective movement, Luria writes.

Lashley (1964), like Luria, sees little value in considering the localization of function in the brain. However, contrary to Luria, Lashley feels the reflex theory is inadequate as the basis for the explanation of all behavior. He is very much against a concept that the integration of a motor act comes from a chain of reflexes. He also rejects the concept that the learning process is dependent upon definite anatomical paths specialized for particular neural integrations.

Rather, Lashley is of the opinion that higher-level activity is a function of some more general, dynamic organization of the brain. Before he died, this highly-respected physiological psychologist claimed that our interest should be in the dynamic relations of parts of the nervous system rather than in details of structural differentiation. There are no special cells for special functions, he writes. Patterns of energy, not localization, determine behavior. The unit of neural organization is not the reflex arc, to Lashley, but the mechanism by which reaction to ratios of excitation is produced. The brain cells react to patterns or combinations of excitation.

He (Lashley, 1951) writes furthermore that the cortex is a great network of continuously active reverberating circuits. Each new stimulus affects the system by changing the pattern of excitation throughout the entire system, not by exciting a new isolated reflex path. The brain is a dynamic, constantly active system; in fact, a composite of many interacting systems.

With regard to complex movement, Lashley believes that sensory control is not active, such as in the performance of a pianist. The pianist's movements are too quick for proprioceptive feedback or visual reaction time to the reading of notes of music. He postulates a central nervous mechanism which controls motor patterns and that "fires with predetermined intensity and duration or activates different muscles in predetermined order."

Many interpretations have been provided to explain the effect of learning on the nervous pathways, and theorists tend to agree that when impulses continually travel the same pathways, there is less resistance at the synapse. Habits and memories are formed from repetitious impulses traveling the same routes, with the result that patterns become fixed. Whether learning should be thought of as a building up of a series of conditioned reflexes or the utilization of the appropriate neural pattern which was there all the time, is a question raised by Hellebrandt and one perplexing to theorist and student alike. However, it is interesting to note here (and in greater detail later) the importance the physiology of the nervous system plays in current learning theories concerned with cybernetics and information theory.

Penfield (1959) has taken issue with the idea that the cortex reflects the highest integrating center within the central nervous system. He points out that the brain has a central coordinating and integrating mechanism that integrates the functions of the hemispheres. It is supposedly a subcortical system, with no precise location. This central integrating system he terms the *centrencephalic* system, which controls the activity within the cerebral cortex. He appears to be referring to the recticular formation.

For example, Penfield describes the motor area of the cerebrum as "an arrival platform and a departure platform." It transmits impulses which arise in the centrencephalic system and goes on to effectors.

Paillard (1960) has physiologically interpreted skilled movement as being represented by coordinated voluntary movements. The act includes the economic and accurate use of specific muscles. Two pathways underlying skilled movements are presented. The lower motoneuron keyboard is controlled by the medulla and spinal cord, both structures being sensitive to body changes and thus in an ever-changing state. The upper motoneuron path involves cortical motor function. The pyramidal tract is the chief executor of the skilled movements, and the motor-cortical keyboard directly controls the discharge of the spinal motoneurons. A motoneuron is a final common path for actions.

Paillard emphasizes the role of sensory impulses in initiating and controlling motor performance. Finally, he states that learning does not result in a new motor pattern, materializing out of nothing. The process involves the disruption of pre-existing units, then the selective choice of appropriate motor combinations, and ultimately a new unit. In learning, perceptual processes are first emphasized, then a reorganization of movement patterns. Automatization, perhaps caused by repetitious practice, is experienced when control of the act is at the lower levels of the nervous system. Motor-learning capacity, Paillard mentions, is related to the coordination of higher and lower motor arrangements.

Held (1965) also stresses the importance of sensory information in motor activity. He states that there is a close relationship between signals from the motor nervous system, which produce active movement, and the consequent sensory feedback. Sensory feedback accompanying movement, termed *reafference,* is vital in perception, hence learning. He attributes this single mechanism to helping a newborn baby develop coordination.

The effect of sensory activity on purposeful movement is noted by Guyton (1966). Sensory *engrams,* which are memory traces, result from willed movement. According to Guyton, the motor cortex does not control activities, for the patterns of activity are located in the sensory area. The motor area merely follows these patterns. If performance is bad, signals are sent to the motor cortex from the sensory area to change the movement.

Some skilled movements are performed very rapidly, with no time for sensory feedback. In these cases, Guyton states that the motor and premotor areas of the frontal lobe would control quick movements. Research has indicated that ablation of these areas causes an inability to perform rapid, coordinated movements.

Many theorists feel that it is erroneous to think about learning as specific to the cerebral cortex. Other parts, such as the reticular formation, apparently contribute to the learning process as well. In addition, consideration is given by theorists to the pleasure and pain centers of the brain. Because of detailed research and investigation, these centers can now be isolated and studied. Reward and punishment have psychological as well as physiological implications, and may be studied from both points of view. After considering the present evidence, it is no longer acceptable to think of learning and performance in terms of electrical impulses alone, but rather as the result of chemical changes and increases in the RNA and protein contents found in the cells. The chemical-electrical activity in the brain accompanying learning, memory, and the ability to recall for immediate performance is the basis for some nerve theories being developed.

Summary

Perhaps a summary on the neural process and its role in learning should be quoted from another author who has candidly expressed his feelings on the matter. "People in the past have ruefully commented upon the primitive state of our knowledge about the neural basis of learning, and, as this review makes clear, such comments are fully justified." (Galambos, 1960). This writer is not quite a pessimistic, but nevertheless recognizes the need for a much more factual basis in describing the role of neural mechanisms in learning and behavior.

The approach taken in this chapter to explain the neural activity that occurs during learning and coordinated movement has been to compare the computer's operations with the way a human being functions. General similarities exist in operation but mechanism dissimilarities are more apparent. Nevertheless, it has been quite convenient, and hopefully, beneficial, to make this analogy. Where appropriate and relevant, physiological information may be found to explain more fully certain operations of the nervous system.

Intelligent movement is based on a series of stimuli, neural integration, and appropriate responses. Responses may be initiated at any level of the central nervous system, with all volitional acts controlled by the highest centers. Basic reflexes, habits, and well-learned acts can be performed at subcortical levels and without consciousness, whereas the learning of complex acts requires the coordination of the highest centers in the nervous system. A number of physiological theories have been advanced to explain the learning process, and it will interest the reader to compare these theories with the psychological theories found in Chapter 8.

References

GALAMBOS, ROBERT, and MORGAN, CLIFFORD T. The Neural Basis of Learning, in FIELD, JOHN (ed.), *Handbook of Physiology: Neurophysiology,* Vol. III, Baltimore: Williams and Wilkins Co., 1960.

GUYTON, ARTHUR C. *Textbook of Medical Physiology,* Philadelphia: W. B. Saunders Co., 1966.

HELD, RICHARD. Plasticity of Sensory-Motor Systems, *Scientific American,* 213:84–94, 1965.

HELLEBRANDT, FRANCES A. The Physiology of Motor Learning, *Cerebral Palsy Review,* 19:9–14, 1958.

KATZ, BERNHARD. How Cells Communicate, *Scientific American,* 205:209–220, 1961.

LASHLEY, KARL S. The Behavior of the Rat in Latch-Box Situations, *Comp. Psychol. Monogr.,* 11:5–40, 1935.

LASHLEY, KARL S. *Brain Mechanisms and Intelligence,* New York: Hafner Publishing Company, 1964.

LASHLEY, KARL S. Cerebral Organization and Behavior, in SOLOMON, HARRY C.; COBB, STANLEY; and PENFIELD, WILDER (eds.), *The Brain and Human Behavior,* Baltimore: Williams and Wilkins Co., Inc., 1958.

LASHLEY, KARL S. The Problems of Serial Order in Behavior, in JEFFRESS, LLOYD A. (ed.), *Cerebral Mechanisms in Behavior,* New York: John Wiley & Sons, Inc., 1951.

LURIA, ALEXANDER R. *Higher Cortical Functions in Man,* New York: Basic Books, Inc., Publishers, 1966.

MILLER, GEORGE A.; GALANTER, EUGENE; and PRIBRAM, KARL H. *Plans and the Structure of Behavior,* New York: Henry Holt and Co., 1960.

PAILLARD, JACQUES. The Patterning of Skilled Movement, in FIELD, JOHN (ed.), *Handbook of Physiology: Neurophysiology,* Vol. III, Baltimore: Williams and Wilkins Co., 1960.

PENFIELD, WILDER. Mechanisms of Voluntary Movement, *Brain,* 77:1–17, 1954.

PENFIELD, WILDER, and ROBERTS, LAMAR. *Speech and Brain-Mechanisms,* Princeton, N.J.: Princeton University Press, 1959.

RALSTON, H. J. Recent Advances in Neuromuscular Physiology, *Amer. J. Phys. Med.,* 36:94–120, 1957.

RITCHIE, RUSSELL W. *Brain, Memory, Learning,* London: Oxford University Press, 1959.

SNIDER, RAY S. The Cerebellum, *Scientific American,* 199:84–90, 1958.

SPERRY, R. W. The Growth of Nerve Circuits, *Scientific American,* 201:68–75, 1959.

TASAKI, ICHIJI. Conduction of the Nerve Impulse, in FIELD, JOHN (ed.), *Handbook of Physiology: Neurophysiology,* Vol. I, Baltimore: Williams and Wilkins Co., 1959.

WOOLDRIDGE, DEAN E. *The Machinery of the Brain,* New York: McGraw-Hill Book Co., Inc., 1963.

Annotated Student References

FIELD, JOHN (ed.). *Handbook of Physiology: Neurophysiology.* Volumes I, II, and III, Baltimore: Williams and Wilkins Co., 1959, 1960.

One of the most complete and authoritative works ever undertaken in a given area, containing contributions from scientists all over the world on all aspects of neurophysiology.

FULTON, JOHN. *Physiology of the Nervous System,* New York: Oxford University Press, 1949.

Contains a descriptive presentation of research on the physiology of the nervous system and is one of the best earlier attempts at a comprehensive overview of neurophysiology.

GARDNER, ERNEST. *Fundamentals of Neurology,* Philadelphia: W. B. Saunders Co., 1963.

Good basic text, simply written, which provides a general background for more advanced works.

GEORGE, F. H. *The Brain as a Computer,* London: Pergamon Press, 1962.

The brain-machine analogy is made in considering psychology and neurophysiology behavioral principles.

GUYTON, ARTHUR C. *Textbook of Medical Physiology,* Philadelphia: W. B. Saunders Co., 1966.

Although basically a text for medical students on all areas of physiology, there is an abundance of up-to-date material on all aspects of the nervous system.

KATZ, BERNHARD. How Cells Communicate, *Scientific American,* 205:209–220, 1961

Simply written, deeply penetrating discussion on nerve cells: their structure and functions.

MILLER, WILLIAM H., RATLIFF, FLOYD, and HARTLINE, H. K. How Cells Receive Stimuli, *Scientific American,* 205:223–238, 1961.

Detailed description of the nature of receptors and how impulses are transmitted.

NETTER, FRANK H. *Nervous Systems,* U.S.: CIBA Pharmaceutical Co., 1964.

Excellent colorful illustrations and descriptions of all aspects of the nervous systems.

SCHADÉ, J. P., and FORD, DONALD H. *Basic Neurology,* New York: Elsevier Pub. Co., 1965.

An introductory textbook, very well illustrated, combining and relating information concerning neuroanatomy, neurophysiology, neurochemistry, and neuropsychology.

WOOLDRIDGE, DEAN E. *The Machinery of the Brain*, New York: McGraw-Hill Book Co., Inc., 1963.

An easily comprehensible and interesting description of higher mental activity, with man being compared to a computer.

3

Basic Considerations in Motor Learning and Performance

In order to demonstrate learning in the form of successful performance, the development, implementation, and control of a wide range of physical, motor, cognitive, perceptual, and emotional mechanisms are a necessity. Each skill reflects the need for varying degrees of physical, mental, and emotional involvement. Although in some cases it may appear that certain skills are performed purely physically (running the dash) or cognitively (in the form of mental rehearsal), in reality there is always an interaction of both these processes. The human factors underlying motor-skill learning and performance are presented in this chapter. Specific reference is made to the various physical and motor attributes, special senses, intelligence, and perceptual mechanism, the effectiveness of which might very well be determined by the emotional climate surrounding the act. Therefore, consideration is also provided for the emotional states that vary from individual to individual and their potential impact on learning and performance.

The performance of various skills may be handicapped for many reasons, such as, inadequate physical qualities necessary for the skilled movement. All the appropriate teaching methods and understandings of the learning process will be of little use to the educator if the performer does not have, say, enough strength to undertake the task. Although specific acts require the exploitation and emphasis of unique qualities, certain general conditions operate consistently from task to task. Let us now turn to these general considerations associated with human physical characteristics and motor qualities underlying skilled performance.

Physical and Motor Considerations

Physical educators have attempted for many years to determine those physical and motor factors underlying general performance success as well as the attributes specific to certain sports. Even the terms *physical* and *motor* have been used interchangeably in research literature, and clear distinctions between these terms are not usually observed. The dictionary refers to *motor* as "that which produces action" and *physical* as "pertaining to the body." Body action and activity certainly would underlie any so-called physical or motor test. Numerous physical and motor-fitness tests, as well as motor-ability, motor-capacity, and motor-educability tests have been constructed. The literature is replete with them. Motor and physical traits have been distinguished, but as yet, there is no agreement as to the elements that constitute physical fitness or motor ability. It would therefore be rash confidence for one to list the physical characteristics and motor abilities necessary for success in motor–skill learning. However, research has indicated the value of certain contributing factors to potential motor-skill success that play a prominent role in performance.

Psychologists, notably Guilford (1958) and Fleishman (1954), have investigated psychomotor abilities through the factor–analysis method. Although the terms *psychomotor abilities* and *general motor abilities* are often used interchangeably, *psychomotor abilities* are usually considered to be more refined than general motor abilities, involving a higher degree of perceptive and judgment responses. These abilities are represented by skills composed of finely coordinated movement patterns. Abilities that are psychomotor in nature are needed by Air Force personnel in flying, for example, and many investigations of tests and performances necessary for qualifying as a skilled pilot may be found in psychological literature. According to Guilford, three kinds of tests have been devised to measure psychomotor abilities. There are physical fitness tests, printed tests to measure finger-hand movements, and apparatus tests, which can overlap the functions of the preceding two. Guilford favors apparatus tests for the measuring of psychomotor abilities. He has isolated such factors as speed, strength, impulsion (a movement initiated from a starting position), precision (static and dynamic), coordination, and flexibility as constituting psychomotor abilities. The traits that contribute to the learning of motor skills with which physical educators are concerned overlap considerably with those apparently connected with psychomotor skills.

The physical characteristics and motor traits to be considered in this chapter include: body build; height and weight; strength; endurance; flexibility; balance and coordination; reaction, movement, and reflex times; and kinesthesis. Since the physical qualities have been covered in detail elsewhere, strength, body build, endurance, flexibility, and height and weight are treated briefly in this section. Balance, kinesthesis, coordination, and speed of movement are abilities often utilized in physical education and psychological research, but in most sources a comprehensive analysis of these factors has been inadequate. A more detailed description of them as well as devices used in their measurement are therefore presented here.

Body Build. The idea of classifying man according to his physical structure is by no means new. From the days of Hippocrates body types as *phthisic habitus* (long and thin) and *apoplectic habitus* (short and thick), to the early 1920's and Kretschmer's *pyknic* (squat and compact), *asthenic* (thin, anemic in appearance), and *athletic* (muscular) types, and finally including Sheldon's (1940) concept of *somatotyping*, various methods of body typing have been employed. Sheldon's method and the suggested modifications initiated by various researchers, e.g., Cureton, have become widely recognized as the most promising and accurate means of body classification.

In order to classify individuals, Sheldon designated three components: *endomorph* (round and soft body), *mesomorph* (muscular and masculine looking), and *ectomorph* (tall and thin, linearly constructed). Individuals are photographed, and then are rated by judges on a 1–7 scale for each component according to the degree of component dominance. The somatotypes are described by three numerals, each of which contains a number ranging from 1–7, with 7 indicating the highest prevalence. The descriptive sequence of numbers refers to the components in the following order: endomorph, mesomorph, and ectomorph. Thus, a rating of 1–7–1 indicates extreme mesomorphy, 7–1–1 extreme endomorphy, and 1–1–7 indicates extreme ectomorphy. In actuality an individual will have certain amounts of each component and is thus not specifically one type. In all, eighty-eight different somatotypes have been recognized.

Of particular interest to recent researchers is the question of whether certain body types are associated with specific activities. For instance, Olympic athletes have been analyzed and categorized according to body structure. During the 1960 Olympics, Tanner (1964) compiled data on 137 track and field athletes; they were somatotyped and classified by event. His results indicate distinct somatotypes for the different events. For example, a somatotype of 3–6–2 was designated to the discus, shot, and hammer throwers; 2–5–3 for the sprinters; 2½–4–4 for the middle and long-distance runners; and 2–6–2 to 2–3–6 for the high jumpers.

Present methods indicate a refinement of original somatotyping techniques, and the usage of somatotypes is widespread. There have been attempts to determine the body types of successful athletes in various sports so as to best predict the achievement one might expect in a given sport. Although there are exceptions to rules, research has shown the relationship of body type to given sports. Cureton (1951) body-typed the 1948 United States male Olympic swimmers and divers, and he reported that the best performers most represented the mesomorphic ideal in body build. In fact, these athletes were significantly taller and heavier than a large sampling of male students from Springfield College and Yale University.

Cureton also studied the 1948 Olympic track and field team and found the highest mesomorphy prevalent in the sprinters, shot-putters, and broad jumpers. Many of the longer distance runners were ecto-mesomorphic. Interestingly enough, after surveying champion athletes representing numerous sports, Cureton found the ecto-mesomorph type most represented.

It is of interest to note the observation of Hirata (1966) at the Olympic Games in Tokyo, who made physical evaluations of the entries to the Games and classified them by event. Among the relations between particular sports and the morphology of the participants were the following:

Sport	Morphology
Basketball	Tall and lean
Canoeing	Large and stout
Cycling	
Long races	Short and lean
Short races	Short and stout
Fencing	Lean
Gymnastics	Small and stout
Hockey	Small and a little stout
Rowing	Tall
Soccer	Small and a little stout
Swimming	
Divers	Small
Free-stylers, Back strokers	Large and lean
Breast strokers, Butterfly swimmers	Stout
Track and Field	
Hurdles	Large and lean
Short dashes	Small
Middle distances	Larger
Long distance, Marathon runners	Small and lean
High jumpers	Large and lean
Long jumpers	Lean and not so large
Pole vaulters	Average
Throwers	Large and stout
Volleyball	
Forward players	Tall and lean
Back players	Small and stout
Water polo	Large and stout
Weight lifting	Stout
Wrestling	Stout

In some sports, it is important to have momentary muscular strength, and a muscular and stout build promotes successful performance for such events as weight lifting, wrestling, short-distance cycling, and throwing events. We might speculate why the average short-distance runners are comparatively small, but the gold-medalist in the 100 meter race, Hayes, is muscular and stout. It would appear that immediate strength is necessary in the race, and

Hayes' build is more favorable to successful performance than is the slender, slighter build.

Longer distance events require more endurance than strength, and the combination of an efficient cardiorespiratory system with a lighter weight results in better performance times. In general, the evidence in this study appears to justify the idea that physique and constitution have an important effect on athletic performance, at least when the athletes have trained to top-level physical condition. Hirata expresses the opinion that the individual with the most adequate physique will win an event when the participants in that event have all trained hard and achieved maximal physical condition.

Other investigations concerning body builds have noted a positive relationship between mesomorphy and motor ability and a negative correlation between endomorphy and motor ability; greater strength and general physical fitness with mesomorphy; and better balance and flexibility with ectomorphy. An important consideration is that *although a certain body type or build may contribute to success in specific activities, it is by no means necessary*. Skill attainment is the result of many complex factors, and a limiting body structure may very well be overcome by an emphasis on other variables.

Height and Weight. Researchers, especially in the 1920's and 1930's attempted to classify physical education students by *age, height,* and *weight.* These factors appeared to be of some value in predicting general athletic performance. However, an increasing number of investigations has offered little encouragement to classify by age, height, and weight. Age is the best predictor of the three as to success in various physical activities, at least during preadolescence and adolescence. Although numerous studies may be located in the literature concerning height and weight and performance, a few studies representative of their general findings are described here. Cozens (1937) stated that there was no relationship between body height and weight of girls with fundamental skill achievement in a variety of sports, whereas Adams (1934) found little predictive value in height and weight to track and field performance of 200 junior high school girls.

Another study by Espenschade (1963) involved the testing of boys and girls, ranging in age from ten to eighteen, in the 50-yard dash, standing broad jump, throw for distance, sit-ups, and pull-ups. Her results indicated low correlations most often not significant, between the test performances and height and weight. When testing 1,559 college men on seven test items, Miller (1952) reported that height and weight measures were unsatisfactory for classification purposes on the basis of low relationships obtained between these factors and the test performances.

It would appear that only at extreme heights and weights will individuals benefit or suffer in certain physical activities. The volleyball player has an advantage in spiking if he is tall, but at the same time may be at a disadvantage in digging a ball that is low to the floor. The huge basketball player demonstrates success near the basket, but at a distance away from the goal, he may lack as good a shot as a smaller man. His size may cause him to lose the speed and agility, which generally characterize the smaller man. Therefore, it may be generally stated that height and weight factors are not valid predictors of athletic success, at least, in physical education classes.

Strength. There is no doubt that in varying degrees, strength underlies all motor performance. In an isolated sense, *strength* may be thought of as the capacity of a muscle or group of muscles to exert maximum pressure against a given resistance in a limited period of time. A weakness in any area of the body may severely limit the coordination and effort needed for the performance of a skill. Thus, a minimum amount of strength is a necessity for motor-skill performance.

Strength has been measured in various ways: lifting of weights, grip strength by the hand dynamometer, the dynamometer for the back and leg, and a cable tensiometer for recording the tension supplied by various muscle groups responsible for thirty-eight joint movements. Figure 3–1 illustrates methods that with the use of the tensiometer Clarke has recommended for testing elbow-extension strength and knee-flexion strength.

Muscular Endurance. The capacity of a muscle or a group of muscles to contract repeatedly against a moderate resistance reflects *muscular endurance.* The individual must maintain a moderate energy output over an extended duration of time. Whether it be muscular or cardiovascular in nature, endurance permits the individual to prolong the performance of an act. Although the constant practice of a skill promotes improvement, a degree of muscular as well as mental endurance is needed in order for the performer to be able to concentrate at length on the skill itself. Many motor skills are arduous to learn and perform, and the development of such physical qualities as strength and endurance delay fatigue, thus permitting attention to be focused for a longer period of time on the skill to be learned.

Flexibility. *Flexibility* is determined by the range of movement of a joint. Mathews and others (1957) mention three factors that limit joint flexibility: the nature of the joint structure; the condition of the ligaments and fascia that surround the joint; and muscle extensibility. These investigators cite the need for a flexible range of motion among athletes, especially in track and swimming.

This premise has been verified by Cureton (1951), who found above-average flexibility in the champion athletes he measured from 1946 to 1948. In one study, he found the 1936 Japanese champion Olympic swimmers to have 31 per cent greater trunk flexion than the American swimmers. In comparing 21 Olympic swimmers with 100 college competitive swimmers, the Olympians proved to be superior in ankle flexion by 11 per cent and by 8 per cent in trunk flexion. Flexibility is a physical quality involved in many skilled motor patterns, and its inadequate development may well be regarded as another possible deterrent to achievement in certain sports.

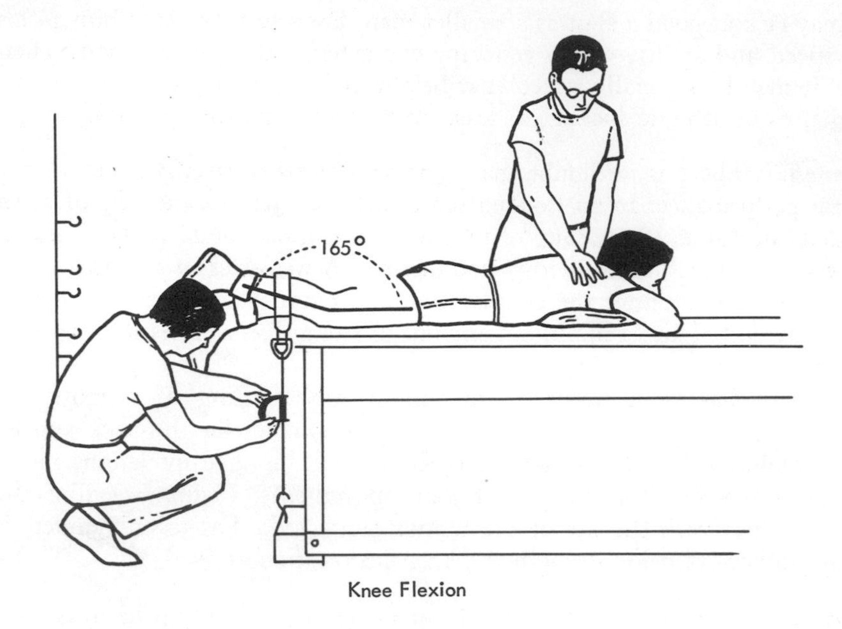

Knee Flexion

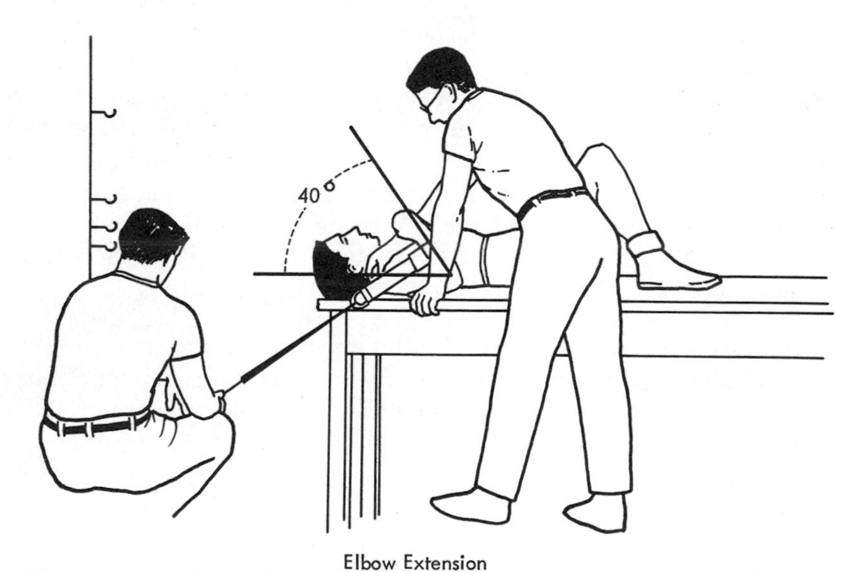

Elbow Extension

Figure 3–1. Two of the thirty-eight suggested methods for measuring strength at the various body joints. (From Clarke, H. Harrison. Improvement of Objective Strength Tests of Muscle Groups by Cable-Tension Methods, *Res. Quart.*, 21:399–419, 1950.)

Balance. The ability to maintain body position, referred to as *balance*, is necessary for the successful performance of sports skills. It is essential in those dynamic sports requiring sudden changing movements, exemplified by the tennis player who has to pursue a ball, regain balance, and then strike the ball. The wrestler, whether standing or kneeling on the mat, has to retain his balance when moving toward or away from his opponent. Each sport demands a particular type of balance. In other words, an individual does not possess one general balancing ability that will enable him to balance himself well for all tasks and under all conditions.

Standing erect under trying or even normal conditions involves an interaction of a number of neurophysiological structures, senses, and pathways. Equilibrium is obtained through the combined efforts of simple reflexes, proprioceptive information relayed to the cerebrum and cerebellum, an activation of the reticular formation, the vestibular apparatus, visual information, and voluntary movements.

The *stretch reflex* (described in Chapter 2) works in sustaining body posture. *Proprioceptors* in various parts of the body contribute to equilibrium: the neck proprioceptors stimulate the reticular nuclei; the head receptors for movement activate the vestibular apparatus; and proprioceptors from other parts of the body stimulate the *reticular pathways, cerebellum,* and *cerebral cortex.* The reticular formation has been discussed in Chapter 2, hence the discussion here is limited to the vestibular apparatus.

The *bony labyrinth,* which is a cavity in the temporal bone, contains the cochlear duct (concerned with hearing), the saccule, the semicircular canals, and the utricle (see Figure 3–2). The *semicircular canals* and *utricle* combined constitute the *vestibular apparatus,* and are sensitive to body movement and position. The canals respond to acceleration or deceleration changes in head velocity. Head movements stimulate proprioceptors and vestibular nerves, which in turn extend to the reticular nuclei and cerebellum, produc-

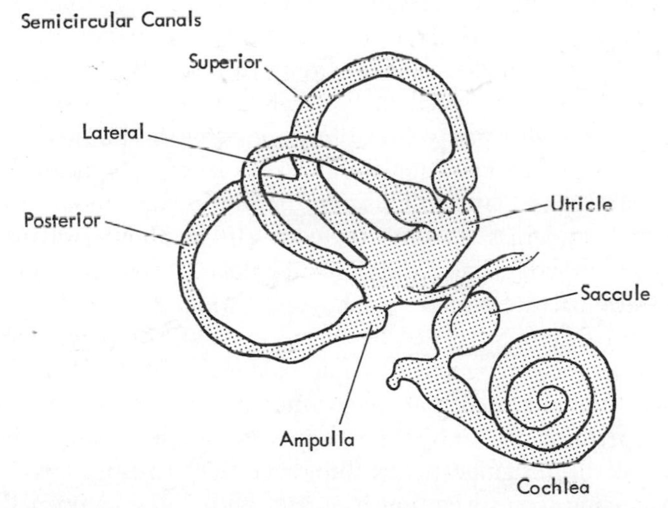

Figure 3–2. Bony labyrinth apparatus. The cochlea is concerned with audition. The semicircular canals, the utricle, and probably the saccule are essential for equilibration. (From Langley, L. L., and Cheraskin E. *Physiology of Man,* New York: Reinhold Publishing Co., 1965.)

ing impulses that are sent to the appropriate muscles for body equilibrium. *Vision* assists in providing information about the body's position with regard to its environment. Even with destruction of the vestibular apparatus, vision can compensate and allow the person to maintain a degree of equilibrium. *Voluntary movements,* directed from a cortical center, allow man to have a conscious awareness of his body's position and to do something about it. Man observes his environment and perceives the changing position of his body and, through conscious effort, can direct the necessary movement adjustments in order to maintain the desired posture.

An interesting point concerning balancing ability is that although investigations have sometimes revealed this factor to be important for athletic success, different tests of balance do not correlate highly with each other. For example, Espenschade and others (1953) found dynamic balance, as measured by the Seashore Beam Walking Test, to be moderately correlated ($r = .62$) with the assigned physical education grades of 287 high school boys. Gross and Thompson (1957) administered the Bass Stepping Stone Test to college students enrolled in swimming classes and noted a highly negative correlation of −.75 with speed in swimming and a correlation of .65 with swimming ability.

And yet researchers like Bachman (1961) discovered no general balancing ability when his subjects performed two novel balancing tasks. An analysis of the data from scores on a stabilometer and a free-standing ladder climb reflected little more than a zero correlation between the two tasks. More conflicting results are offered from an investigation by Singer (1965). Athletes demonstrated poorer balance on a stabilometer than did nonathletes, a surprising revelation since athletes need a high balancing ability in order to perform effectively. Perhaps the balancing ability required on the stabilometer has nothing to do with the balancing ability needed for sports.

Tests have been constructed to determine dynamic and static balancing ability. However, highly positive relationships between the two have not been obtained as is the case when comparing the results of tests measuring dynamic and static strength. Static equilibrium requires continuous, even muscle tension, which underlies standing perfectly still, without swaying. Dynamic balance demands body orientation in off-balance situations. Travis (1945) measured static balance with an ataxiameter (which records body sway while standing) and dynamic balance by means of a stabilometer. He found no relationship between static and dynamic balance. Additional interesting findings of this study indicated that weight, not height, was an important factor in dynamic performance. Subjects with greater weight balanced better. Also, there was a small, insignificant sex difference in balancing, favoring women. Finally, balancing scores were much greater with the eyes open than closed.

Balance required for each skill varies, and is evidently unique to the skill employed. An in-depth discussion of this problem and related ones is presented in Chapter 4. However, it may be stated that there is inconclusive

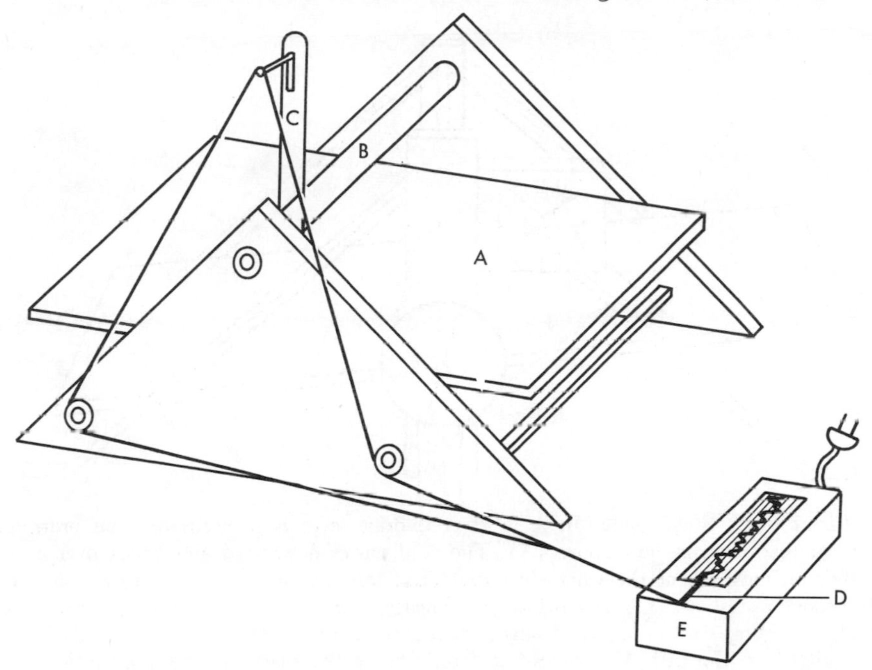

Figure 3–3. Stabilometer A. Subject stands on platform (A) with his feet straddling axle (B). Lever arm (C) is attached to the platform. A cord extends from needle (D) to a point under the rear pulley to and around the far pulley to the lever arm where it is firmly attached. Another cord extends from the lever arm around the near pulley, and is also attached to the needle. The needle records the extent of movement of the platform on graph paper inserted in the electric kymograph (E). (From Singer, R. N. Effect of Spectators on Athletes and Non-Athletes Performing a Gross Motor Task, *Res. Quart.*, 36: 473–482, 1965.)

evidence on balance transference from task to task, task to sport, and sport to sport.

Balance tasks designed in varying degrees of complexity range from the simple balance beams to stabilometers. Basically, a stabilometer requires one to balance on an unstable platform. Investigators have constructed different types of stabilometers for determining balancing ability, and each apparatus has certain advantages and disadvantages not associated with another model. In the Singer study already referred to, he graphically determined time on balance during a specific time period, and the diagram of this stabilometer apparatus appears in Figure 3–3 (Stabilometer A).

A work-adder has been used in conjunction with a stabilometer in certain investigations. A picture and description of this apparatus appears in Figure 3–4 (Stabilometer B). An example of a model quite different in design from A and B is illustrated, and its method of function is explained in Figure 3–5 (Stabilometer C). Finally, Figure 3–6 contains a stabilometer (Stabilometer D) recently designed by the writer and used with great success in his research undertakings.

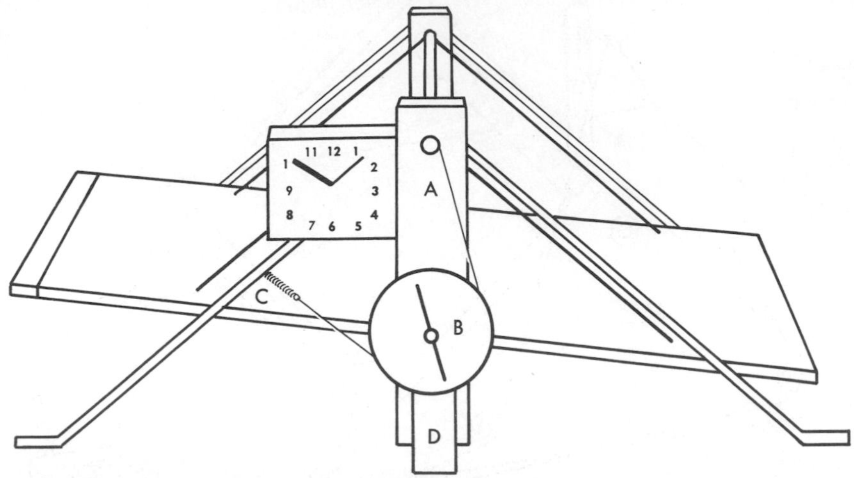

Figure 3–4. Stabilometer B. A short cord drive lever is screwed into the protruding end of the main axle just above (A). The cord passes downward and bends over a large pulley on the back of the work-adder dial (B), terminating at a coil spring fastened to the frame just above (C). A pawl at (D) engages the milled periphery of the work-adder dial, restricting its turning to a single direction so that movement of the platform is cumulated on the dial. Various A-frame rods brace the platform and the vertical posts that rise from the base to carry the main axle. Motion of the board is measured by the work adder. (From Bachman, John C. Specificity vs. Generality in Learning and Performing Two Large Muscle Motor Tasks, *Res. Quart.*, 32:3–11, 1961.)

Coordination. *Coordination* of various parts of the body implies an ability to perform a skilled movement pattern. The skill itself primarily may involve eye-foot coordination, an example of which is kicking a football or soccer ball; or eye-hand coordination, such as throwing an object at a target. Some sports require an overall coordination of the body: a gymnastic routine on the parallel bars requires perfect timing; a football halfback demonstrates agility and speed in movement; and swinging a golf club requires smoothness and rhythm.

Various types of body movements have been used as coordination tests. In answer to the question as to what coordination tests really do measure, the factor-analysis method has been applied by Cumbee (1954) to determine the factors present in tests that measure motor coordination. This statistical method was employed by Thurston in his classical study that attempted to discover the factors really being measured in the so-called intelligence tests. Two-hundred college women were tested in Cumbee's study, and from twenty-one variables of coordination eight were extracted. Although three of the factors were unnamed because they needed further classification, the other five distinguished were: balancing objects, body balance, two-handed agility, tempo, and speed of arm and hand change of direction.

Sometimes the word *coordination* is used interchangeably with *timing, skill,* or *general motor ability*. It has been determined from the research that

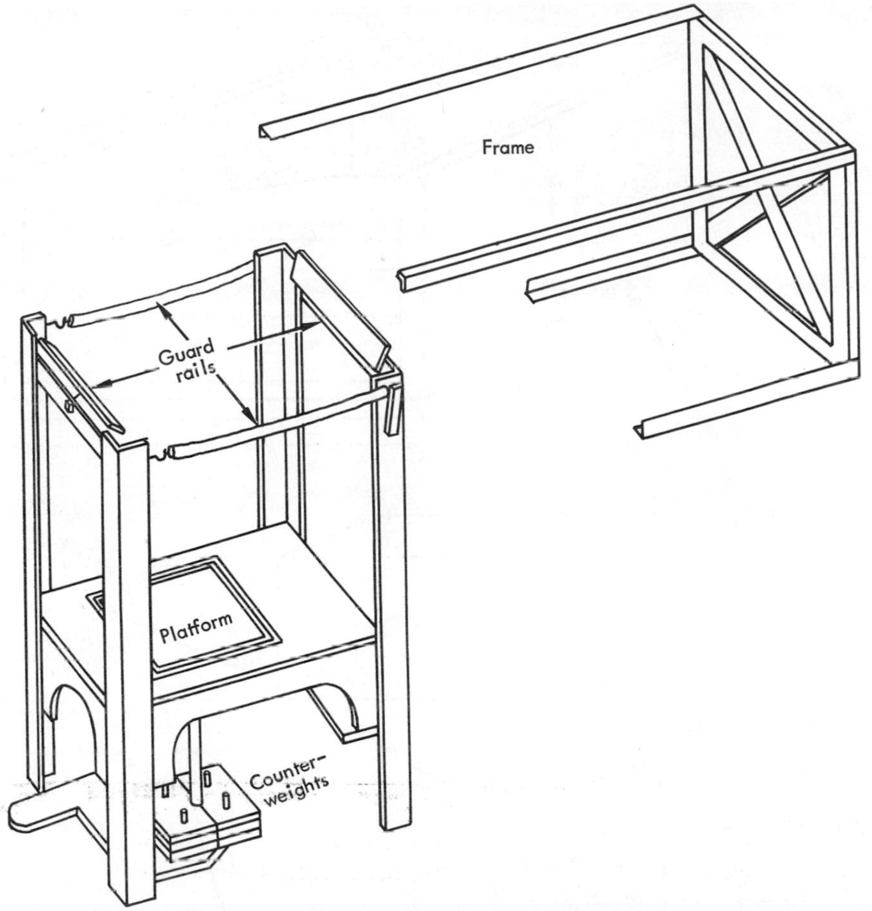

Figure 3–5. Stabilometer C. The subject stands on the platform, and the magnitude of tilt is recorded. Platform tilt of more than 1.5° of the horizontal position opens micro-switches that control the operation of recording dials. Time-on-rails score, that is, the length of time a subject holds on to the guard rails, can also be recorded. (From Witkin, H. A., and others. *Personality Through Perception*, New York: Harper & Brothers, 1954.)

coordination is important to potential athletic success as well as specific to the task achieved. Whether an individual is born with or develops body coordination, and to what extent, as reflected in certain motor skill achievements, is a moot point to be elaborated on in Chapter 4, under "The All-round Athlete."

Many laboratory tasks have been developed to predetermine success in certain fields. In industrial jobs that require manual dexterity, for example, manipulative tasks help in predicting success. An example of a widely-used task utilizing arm-hand coordination (manual dexterity) is the Minnesota Rate of Manipulation Test, whereas the Crawford Small Parts Dexterity Test requires finger dexterity (see Figure 3–7).

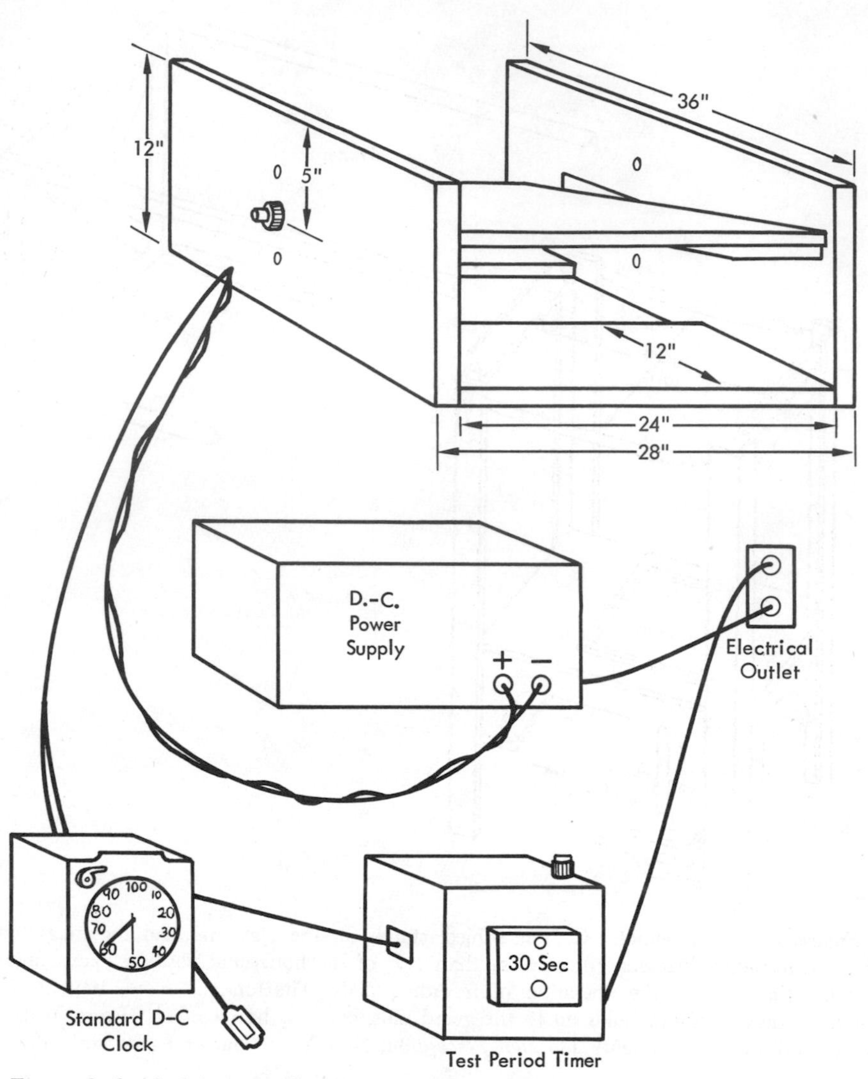

Figure 3–6. Stabilometer D. Time-on-balance score is obtained when steel contacts touch the angle plates opposite the balance platform. The Standard D-C Clock records time on balance while the Test Period Timer, which is connected to the clock, regulates the testing period.

Other devices are used for testing potential pilot success or probable athletic achievement. Also, they serve as a medium for viewing the effects of environmental manipulations and understanding psychological phenomena associated with motor tasks. In physical education, coordinated movements may be demonstrated in target-accuracy skills and in the performance of various stunts. However, the laboratory environment is better for controlling the many extraneous variables apt to confound the field study. This is why

Minnesota Rate of Manipulation Test

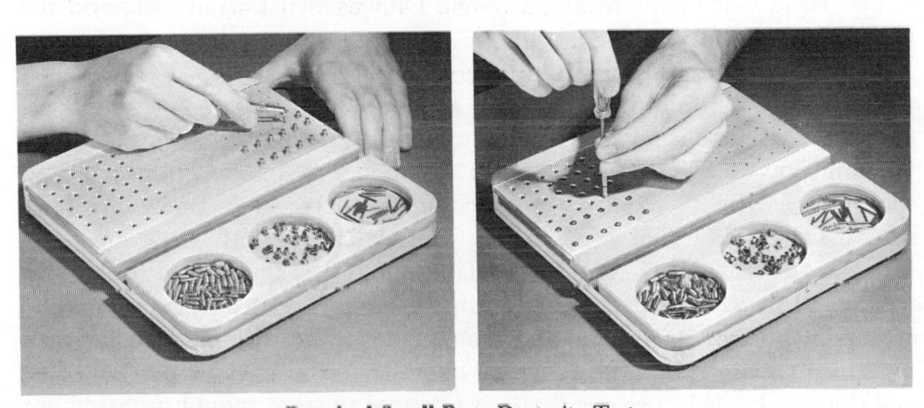

Crawford Small Parts Dexterity Test

Figure 3–7. The Minnesota Rate of Manipulation Test measures capacity for manipulative work. In the five tests that are administered with this equipment, the blocks are turned, moved, and placed in certain prescribed ways. This involves finger movement and hand-and-arm movement. It involves movements with the preferred hand and also with both hands simultaneously. As usage of this test has spread, it now appears that more than speed is involved in gross finger, hand, and arm movements. Also involved are gross body movements, intelligence, vision, and perseverance. (From American Guidance Service, Inc., Minneapolis, 1966.)

The Crawford Small Parts Dexterity Test measures fine eye-hand coordination. Part I measures dexterity in using tweezers to insert small pins in close-fitting holes in a plate and to place small collars over the protruding pins. Part II measures dexterity in placing small screws in threaded holes in a plate and screwing them down with a screwdriver until they drop through the plate into a metal dish below. (From the Psychological Corporation, New York, 1965.)

various types of apparatus have been constructed by those interested in understanding and explaining the learning process, especially as it relates to motor skills. Unfortunately, there is a danger in assuming that the learning of practical skills, those performed in daily life, are governed by the same principles as skills learned and performed in the laboratory. Arguments have been presented for and against both laboratory research and classroom or gymnasium research; but both are needed for a better understanding of the psychology of learning. Both research methods can and should complement each other and not provide fuel for debate.

Laboratory researchers concerned with coordination tasks have constructed ingenious devices for measuring coordination. One of the forerunners in attempting to uncover the factors underlying psychomotor-performance success was Fleishman (1957, 1958a, 1958b). Besides employing previously used tasks in other experiments, he devised other tasks to measure the many aspects of psychomotor skill. They are basically coordinating, positioning, and speed tasks. Figure 3–8 contains a number of these apparatuses that have been widely used in his investigations, as well as the Snoddy stabilimeter, which may be found in many other investigations. These tasks range from the simple to complex: a Response Orientation task, a Rotary Pursuit task, a Two-Hand Coordination task, a Single Dimensional Pursuit task, and the Complex Coordination test.

Although evidence is fragmentary, there has been an attempt to relate such tasks to success in industry, dentistry, and piloting a plane. The tests have demonstrated moderately predictive values in these cases. The Complex Coordination test, which requires stick and rudder movements in response to specific signal lights, has been reported to correlate .40 in predicting pilot success. The Hand-Tool Dexterity test correlated .46 with the actual performance of machinists, and the Metal Filling Worksample correlated .53 with dentistry course grades. Obviously, the more related the task to the actual criterion, the higher the anticipated correlation. Relationships between movements required for the coordination tasks, often used by psychologists, and the coordinated movement patterns desired in sport should probably not be high because of the lack of similarity in the nature of the required responses.

A familiarity with the design and nature of coordination tasks, especially that of the pursuit rotor, will be most profitable for the physical educator interested in reading and analyzing the psychological literature concerning the learning of motor skills. Many deductions from the phenomena related to motor learning, transfer, retention, practice, and the like, have been derived from the utilization of these tasks under manipulated environmental conditions. If he has not done so already the physical educator will also become cognizant of differences within terminology applications between psychologists and physical educators. Whereas physical educators may have regarded sports skills only as motor tasks, psychologists include in this category all previously discussed devices and the responses required for them as well as many others.

Reaction Time, Movement Time, Response Time, and Reflex Time. The track sprinter awaits the starting gunshot. Bam! He's off. Did the time he took to respond to the sound constitute reaction time or reflex time? Is there any difference between these terms? What is movement time? All these terms are often used interchangeably although, in fact, they are not synonymous. Actually these particular times can be isolated and recorded in experimental situations.

Reaction time (RT) involves an integration of the higher centers of the nervous system: perception of the stimulus (a noise, light, or the like) and the initiation of the appropriate movement. It is the elapsed interval of time from the presentation of a stimulus to the initiation of a response. A *reflex* (see Chapter 2) is usually nonvolitional, involving the lower centers of the nervous system. It is an automatic response, predictable, and does not require perceptibility. *Movement time* (MT) may include reflex or reaction time, or, as it is usually viewed in research literature, the time a particular act takes to be completed after it has been initiated. *Response time* is the time it takes to complete the entire movement and includes the other times mentioned here.

Returning to the track situation, the time elapsed from the pistol shot to the sprinter's response is referred to as his reaction time. From that point to the completion of the race, the time recorded is actually his movement time. Obviously, under normal conditions a typical time for the track man includes both his reaction and movement time. However, the initial reaction to the stimulus is as important as running speed, especially in the short sprints, and the time it takes to react to a stimulus may provide information concerning potential success or failure in the event.

If the track man was standing on a shock source at the starting line, the time elapsed from the stimulation to the initiation of movement would be recorded as a *reflex time*. Since a reflex requires neither willed movements nor judgment, it may be expected that an individual's reflex time will be faster than his reaction time.

Time factors then, interest researchers. Under laboratory conditions, the usage of stimulus-response displays has provided much knowledge about reaction, movement, and reflex times. According to some investigators, the first reaction time experiment was initiated in the 1860's by Donders, a Dutch physiologist. Contrarily, others claim that the first reaction-time experiment is associated with the efforts of Helmholtz in 1850. Since then, the technique for measuring reaction time has not been varied much except in the use of more elaborate equipment. The reaction time and the movement time of an individual have been compared to determine relationships between these factors; in other words, to see whether a person with a fast movement time also has a fast reaction time. Studies have also compared the reaction and

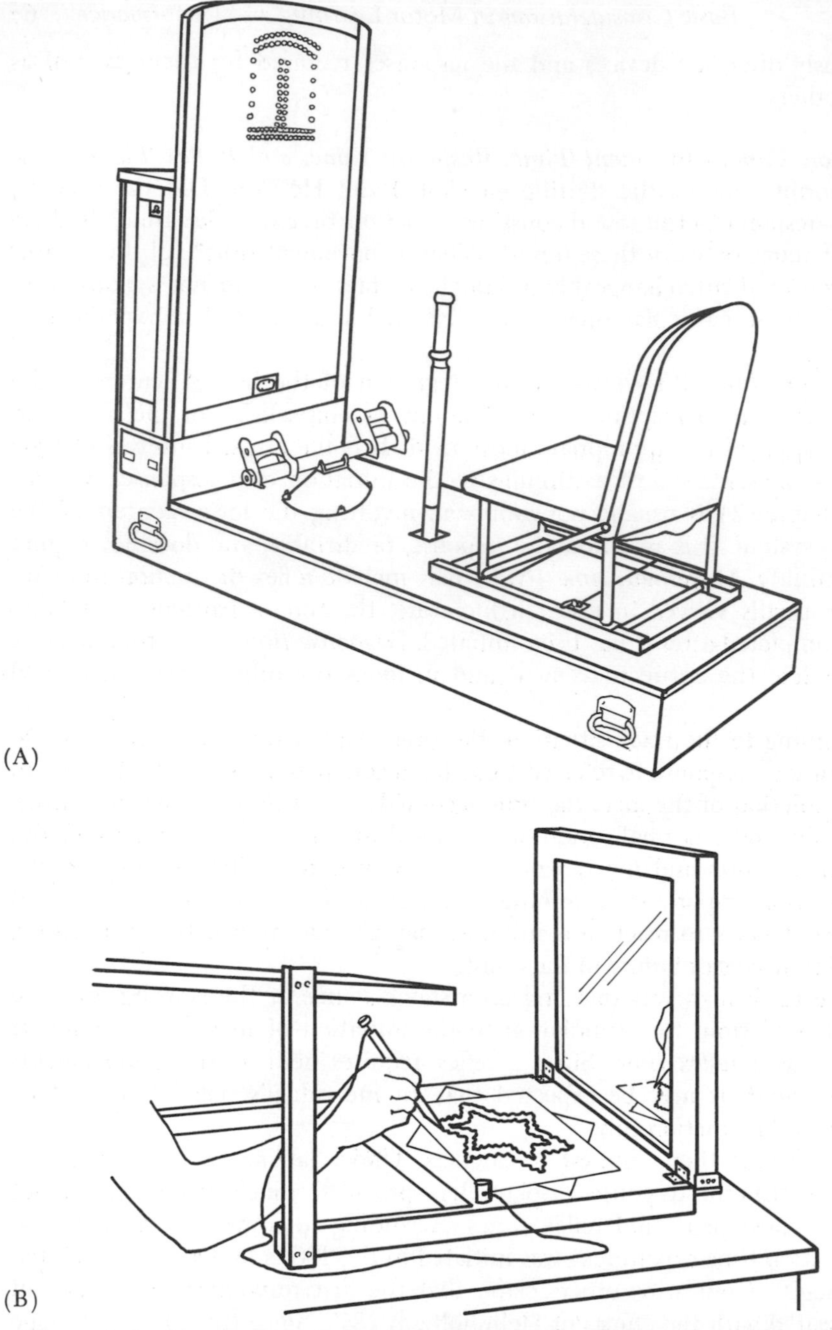

(A)

(B)

Figure 3–8. Coordination Tasks. (A) Complex Coordination test. The subject is required to make complex motor adjustments of stick and pedal controls in response to stimulus light patterns. (From Fleishman, E. A. A Comparative Study of Aptitude Patterns in Unskilled and Skilled Psychomotor Performances. *Appl. Psychol.*, 41:263–272, 1957.) (B) Snoddy Stabilimeter. The star is traced as accurately as possible with the subject viewing it in the mirror. (From Fulton, R. Speed and Accuracy in Learning Movements, *Archives of Psychol.*, No. 300, 1945.)

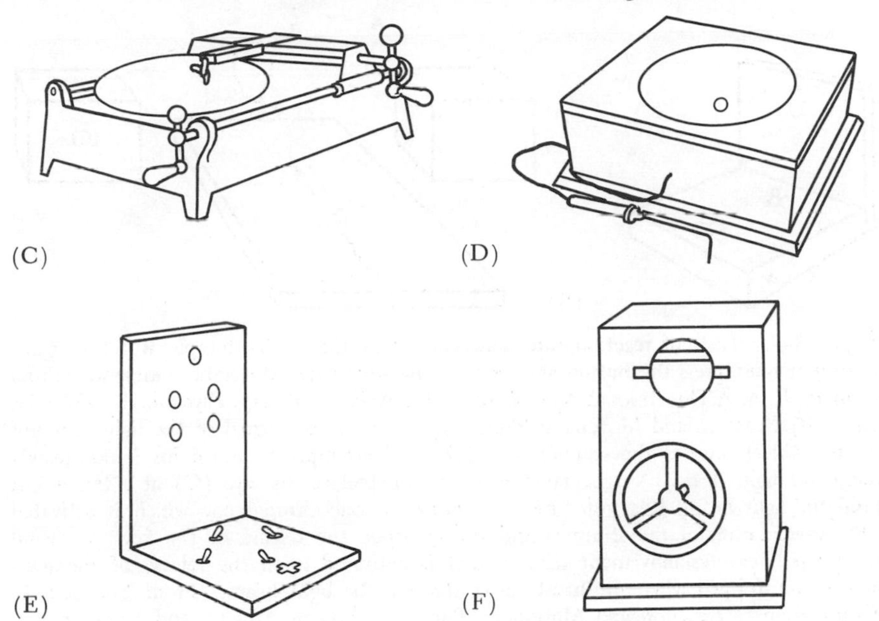

Figure 3–8 (continued). (C) Two-Hand Coordination. Two handles must be controlled and manipulated in order to keep a target-follower on a target disk as the target moves unpredictably; (D) Rotary Pursuit. The stylus is kept in contact with a small metallic target which is set on a revolving phonograph-type disk; (E) Response Orientation. The subject manipulates one of four toggle switches as rapidly as possible in response to rapidly changing light patterns; (F) Single-Dimension Pursuit. The subject makes adjustments to the wheel in order to keep the line in the window centrally located as it moves unpredictably. (From Fleishman, E. A. Dimensional Analysis of Movement Reactions, *J. Exp. Psychol.*, 55:438–453, 1958.)

the movement times of select groups, such as athletes versus nonathletes. Some examples of devices and methods utilized in obtaining these data are shown in Figure 3–9.

The simplest method of deducing reaction time is to have a subject place his finger on a button, with instructions to remove his finger when he views a light signal just above the button. The chronoscope starts with the presentation of a stimulus and stops when the button is no longer depressed. In the choice reaction-time method, the subject may be faced with a number of visual cues and is expected to react to one specific cue. If reflex time is desired, the button may be wired for shock, and the response is a result of withdrawal from a noxious stimulus. Considine (1966) employed both these tasks in his study, and his apparatus is illustrated in Figure 3–9.

Physiologists and experimental psychologists have investigated and suggested theories about the internal mechanism activated during a response. In a recent study, for example, Botwinick and Thompson (1966) proposed that reaction time be thought of as involving pre-motor and motor time. Pre-motor time includes the time elapsed from the stimulus presentation to the muscle

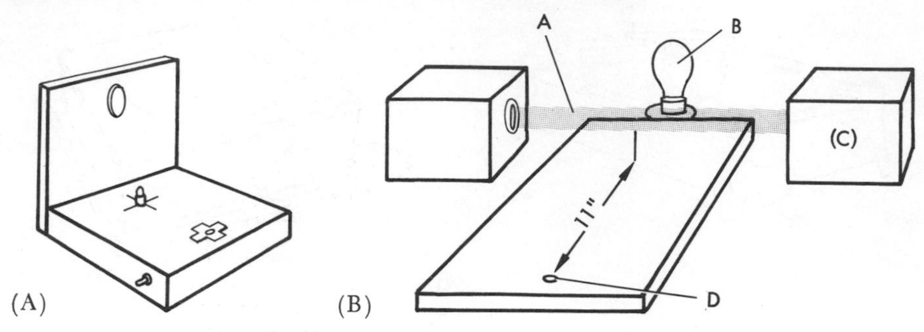

Figure 3–9. Tests of reaction time and movement time. (A) Simple Reaction time. The subject must press the button as quickly as possible when the light comes on. (From Fleishman, E. A. A Dimensional Analysis of Motor Abilities, *J. Exp. Psychol.*, 48:437–454, 1954); (B) Reaction and Movement Time Apparatus. At the signal of the light stimulus (B) the subject releases the reaction key (D) and attempts to move his hand quickly through the light beam (A) generated from the photoelectronic eye (C) at a target just behind the light beam. Reaction time is recorded by one chronoscope which is activated on the presentation of the stimulus and broken upon the release of the key. A second chronoscope measures movement time, and it is activated upon the release of the reaction key and stopped when the hand passes through the light beam. (From Youngen, L, A Comparison of Reaction and Movement Times of Women Athletes and Non-Athletes, *Res. Quart.*, 30:349–355, 1959.)

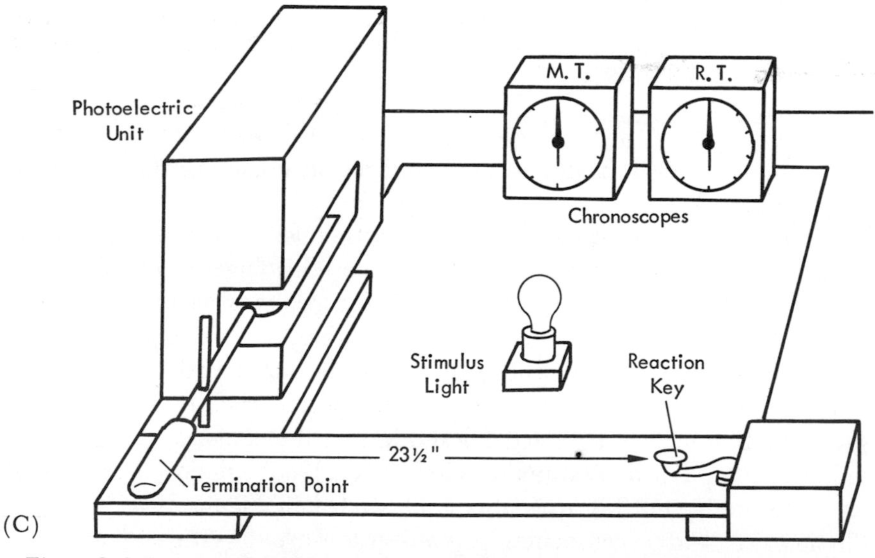

Figure 3–9 (continued). (C) Reaction and Movement Time Apparatus. The reaction chronoscope starts with the presentation of the light stimulus and stops with the release of the reaction key. The speed-of-movement chronoscope is then activated and upon contact with the terminating rod, is deactivated. (From Hodgkins, Jean. Reaction Time and Speed of Movement in Males and Females at Various Ages, *Res. Quart.*, 34:335–343, 1963.)

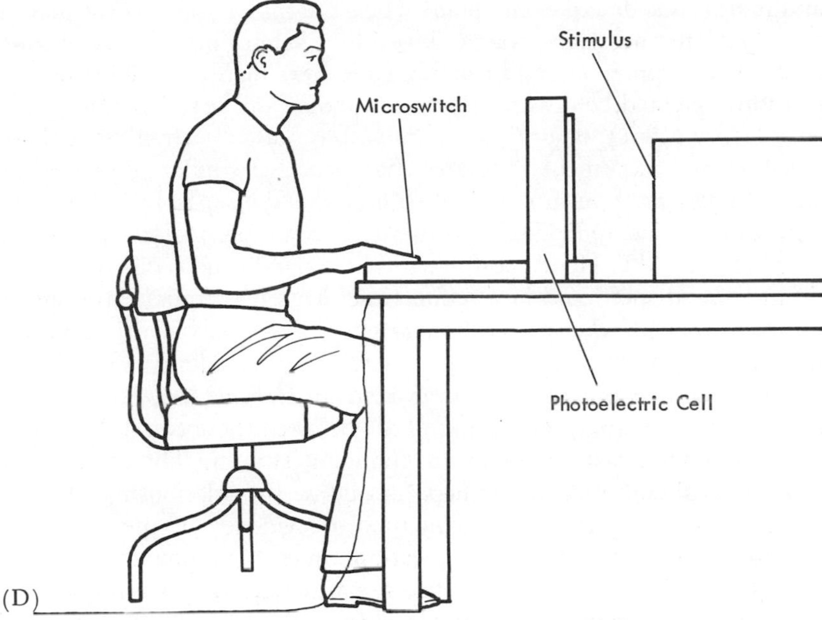

Figure 3–9 (continued). (D) Position of subject in reaction and movement time experiment. A chronoscope is activated simultaneously with a neon stimulus lamp, a microswitch stops the chronoscope and activates another when the subject initiates the response, and his movement interrupts a photoelectric beam and stops the second chronoscope. (From Pierson, William R., and Rasch, Philip J. Isometric Strength as a Factor in Functional Muscle Testing, *Amer. J. Phys. Medicine,* 42:205–207, 1963.)

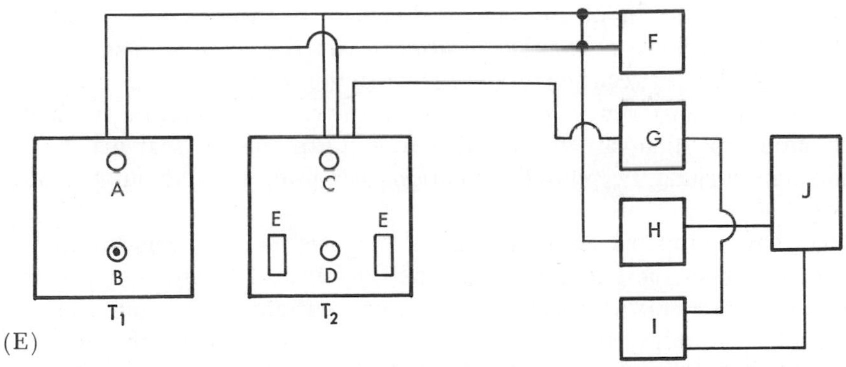

Figure 3–9 (continued). (E) Reaction and Reflex Time Apparatus. (T_1) reaction time test panel; (T_2) reflex action time test panel; (A) light stimulus; (B) contact switch; (C) light (unwired); (D) contact switch; (E) metal strips; (F) chronometer; (G) rheostat; (H) control panel; (I) control junction box; and (J) direct current power supply. When the stimulus is presented (either the light or the shock depending upon which test is being administered), the subject releases the contact button by withdrawing the finger. (From Considine, William. Reflex and Reaction Times Within and Between Athletes and Non-Athletes, Unpublished Master's Thesis, Illinois State University, 1966.)

firing, and motor time describes the point when the muscle fires to the actual response, which, in the study, was a finger lift. Interesting results of this study indicated that pre-motor and reaction time were highly related while no direct relationship could be discerned between motor and reaction time.

Franklin Henry (1961), one of the foremost physical education researchers in the reaction and movement time area, has provided similar physiological reasoning as to why reaction time should be considered a separate factor from movement time. Some individuals postulate a common factor—speed—as underlying RT and MT. Henry postulates that separate mechanisms are involved in movement speed and in reaction time. Muscular forces cause speed of the limb movement whereas reaction latency, a premovement operation of the central nervous system, determines reaction time. Henry and his co-researchers have consistently obtained near–zero correlations between RT and MT, and in the present study, noted an *r* of .02 between these two factors.

Most sports require fast responses to changing stimuli. Therefore, it is natural for physical education researchers to analyze the relationship of reaction time to athletic success. The abundance of evidence in the literature indicates that athletes do have faster reaction times than nonathletes. For instance, Olson (1956) compared athletes, nonathletes, and an intermediate group consisting of intramural and junior varsity players as well as participants in a recreation program. The athletes had the fastest reaction times. Other studies have produced similar results.

Reaction time may be induced by the presentation of light, sound, or touch stimuli. (One source reports reaction times in milliseconds as follows: light 180, sound 140, and touch 140). In a study by Forbes (1945) 178 subjects provided a mean reaction time of 28.26 hundredths of a second to a light stimulus and 19.19 hundredths of a second to a sound stimulus. Although a number of researchers hold the opinion that a person who reacts quickly to one stimulus will do so to another, Forbes obtained only a modest positive correlation of .428 between sound and light reaction times. The intensity and distinctiveness of a particular stimulus, and in the case of sound, its audibility as well, are factors that can alter reaction time. Other factors that may affect reaction time include the subject's attention, age, prior warning, fatigue, and practice.

Studies have compared reaction times of subjects asked to concentrate on the response or on the stimulus. In a practical sense, the situation may be likened to the race start: Should the runner concentrate on the sound of the starting gun (stimulus) or the bodily movements involved in the act (response)? Although much evidence appears to justify the emphasis on motor reaction rather than on sensory reaction, recent conflicting research has also been reported.

Lautenbach and Tuttle (1932) were interested in determining the relationship of reflex time to time recorded in track running events. The reflex measured was the knee jerk. The results of this study indicate a direct relationship between reflex time and running-event time. More specifically, the short-distance men had the lowest reflex time, the distance men had the highest reflex time, and the middle-distance runners obtained reflex times in between the other two groups.

In addition to quick reactions, speed of body or limb movement in a given space is required very often for success in various physical activities. In laboratory tests designed to measure quickness of body and limb movement, athletic performers have tended to realize more favorable results than their nonathletic counterparts. An interesting and logical deduction from the information presented thus far is that an individual who displays a low reaction time may be expected to do likewise in his movement time. Oddly enough, this has not always been the case. In fact, in the bulk of the research to date, reaction time and movement time, even when involving the same limb, have shown to be measures independent of each other. In Chapter 4 it is shown how, on the basis of reaction-time versus movement-time studies, the trend of thinking has followed the concept that the motor abilities represented in any given act are specific for that act rather than generalizing factors.

Kinesthesis. When a student is learning how to swing the golf club for the first time, it is not uncommon for the instructor to tell him to "feel the movement." Information about this awareness of what the muscles are doing and their position during a movement is extremely important to the learner of a new skill. It might also be successfully argued that this muscle sense, called *kinesthesis*, is equally necessary for the successful execution of well-learned skills. Kinesthesis is a consciousness of muscular movement and effort and a keenly developed sense required of beginners and experts alike for proficiency in many motor skills.

The terms *kinesthetic* and *proprioceptive* generally refer to the same sense —providing information concerning the body's position in space and the relationship of its parts. Experimental psychologists usually refer to this sense as kinesthetic, whereas physiologists prefer the term proprioceptive, this term having been introduced by the great physiologist, Sherrington. When the special sense receptors in the muscles, tendons, and joints (called *proprioceptors*) are stimulated, the impulses pass through the posterior column of the spinal cord to the thalamus and finally to the somatic area of the cerebral cortex. If the posterior column is destroyed, there results a loss of sensation in limb movement and position. Coordination of the visual, vestibular, and somatic sensory receptors contributes to the body's orientation in space.

Rose and Mountcastle (1959) present a convincing argument against the traditional belief that stretch receptors of muscles alone are responsible for kinesthesia. These receptors have not been found to provide information about joint position since they discharge over their full frequency range at any muscle length. They state that the joints contain the source of kinesthetic sensations and designate the following receptors located in articular tissue: the Ruffini receptors, which have spray-type endings and are the most common in connective tissue; the Golgi tendon organs, which are less numerous; and the pacinian corpuscles. Whether or not muscle spindles that react to muscle stretch also play an important role in kinesthesis is open to question. Rose and Mountcastle reject the traditional acceptance of their contribution in this sense.

Physical educators have realized the importance of the kinesthetic sense in skill learning for many years. Sir W. G. Stimpson in the year 1887 is quoted by Mrs. Stewart Hanley (1937) on his advice for beginning golfers: "Let the beginner shake himself down naturally before the ball and hit. Till he has done this for a good many days, no advice has either use or meaning." She goes on to indicate a weakness in the imitative method of learning, that of ignoring muscle feel and muscle sense. She emphasizes the need for kinesthetic sensations during the swing and that the beginning golfer should think the swing, not merely imitate it.

Adams and Creamer (1962) have noted the importance of proprioceptor variables in contributing to proficiency in performance. Since movements give rise to proprioceptive stimuli, they provide feedback information which aids in similar future situations. These authors conclude that proprioception has not only its traditional role of information feedback but also a role in response timing, which is extremely important in skilled performance. Leading physical educators in recent years have endorsed the importance of kinesthesis. In fact, some call it the most important of all the senses. Unfortunately, research findings have not been consistent in encouraging this belief.

Prior to 1950, very few investigations concerning the role of kinesthesis in motor learning can be found in physical education literature. Research completed since that time, although not in total agreement, permits these overall conclusions:

1. There is no general kinesthetic sense. Intercorrelations between tests devised to measure this factor are extremely low unless the tests are similar in nature. Kinesthesis appears to be composed of specific factors and is specific to the test and the part of the body involved in the skill.
2. Skilled performers, athletes, musicians, and mechanics, for example, are superior on kinesthetic tests than average or poorer performers.
3. The importance of kinesthesis to motor-skill learning has not been clearly established. For instance, although one investigator noted no significant relationships between kinesthesis and tennis performance, and bowling achievement and kinesthesis, another researcher concluded that multiple-kinesthesis tests correlate significantly with tests of golf putting and driving.
4. Kinesthesis may very well be related to rate of learning. It has been found that fast learners in bowling score higher on kinesthetic tests than do slow learners, and elementary school children who learn many

tasks quickly, do significantly better on tests of kinesthesis than their slower-learning counterparts.

5. There appears to be little or no relationship between tests of kinesthesis and general motor ability tests.
6. Practice can improve kinesthetic perception as well as the acuity of all the senses. For instance, when an individual is blindfolded and practices blindfolded a skill such as the golf swing, he relies more on kinesthetic cues and may improve this sense.
7. Balance is an important aspect of kinesthesis. Balance ability is determined to a great extent by proprioceptive activity, and tests of balance are recommended to be included in any battery of kinesthetic tests.

Tests of kinesthesis vary in nature and bodily involvement. Batteries of tests have been devised by a number of physical educators interested in the kinesthetic sense, notably Scott, Young, and Wiebe. Scott (1955) developed a twenty-eight test battery that she administered to women college students. She noted a specificity in the function of the tests. A twenty-one test battery was administered to thirty college men by Wiebe (1954), who also found a low intercorrelation between the tests and deduced a lack of a general kinesthetic sense. Some tests of kinesthesis are illustrated in Figure 3–10.

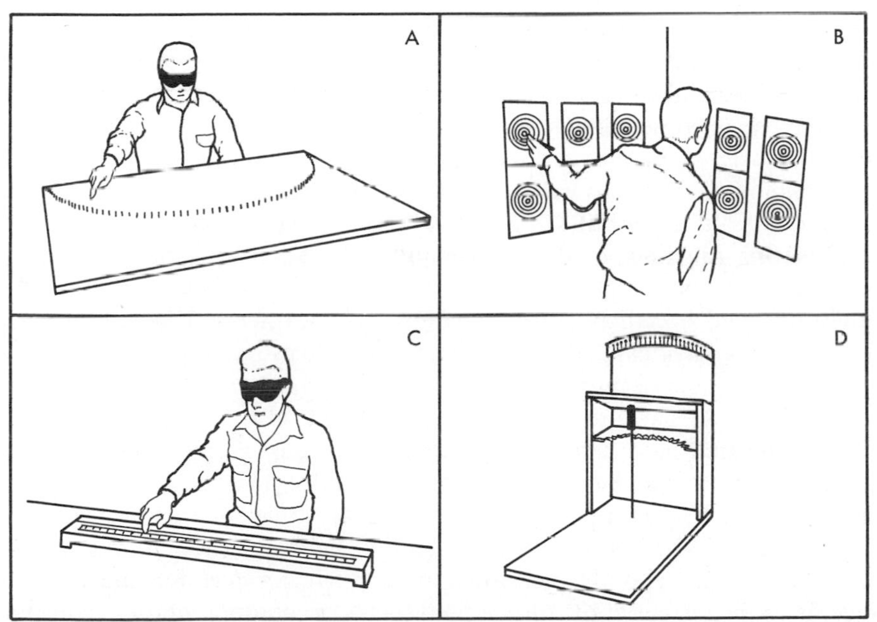

Figure 3–10. Tests of kinesthesis which require kinesthetic discrimination. In these tests the blindfolded subject must **A** reach a certain peg or **B** mark a certain target, in response to verbal instructions. In tests **C** and **D**, he reproduces certain movements with a knob or a stick control. (From Fleishman, E. A. An Analysis of Positioning Movements and Static Reactions. *J. Exp. Psych.*, 55:13–24, 1958.)

Many tests of kinesthesis have been static, involving positional sense. Examples of some kinesthetic tests described by Roloff (1953) are the Balance Stick, Arm Raising, and Weight Shifting tests.

Balance stick. A stick, one inch by twelve inches, is taped to the floor. The subject has to close his eyes and balance on one foot on this stick as long as possible.

Arm raising. The subject is tested on his ability to raise each arm to the horizontal position while blindfolded. Deviations in degrees are measured with a goniometer.

Weight shifting. The subject has to straddle a scale and a block of wood. With the eyes open, he first practices getting the feel of running the scale up one-half his weight in pounds. Then, with eyes closed, he attempts to do the same, and deviations are determined to the nearest half pound.

Other investigators have expressed dissatisfaction with the design of these tests. Henry (1953) created a device that required continuing constant pressure exerted by the subject against a pad while the pressure continually changed under the influence of a cam. This dynamic test brought about an increase or decrease in muscular tension caused by the changing pressure of the cam. In two separate tasks, his twelve subjects were required to adjust to pressure changes or to perceive pressure changes. An objection to most kinesthetic tests was raised by Slater-Hammel (1957), who felt that the tests involved tactile stimulation as well as muscular force. He therefore suggested a task in which individuals had to reproduce a specific muscle contraction. With the use of muscle potentials, he measured the intensity of the muscle contraction after an initial prescribed contraction of 125 microvolts.

In summary, there are a variety of methods and means of measuring aspects of kinesthesis. In a general sense, kinesthesis is believed to underlie many discriminating functions of the body required for successful motor-skill performance: locomotion, perception of pressure changes, balance and body equilibrium, and overall body coordination. Its presence is thought to contribute to an individual's ability to learn as well as perform motor skills. However, this presence must not be thought of as a general factor but rather specific to the skill which requires certain movements of the body.

Recent research has attempted to discover methods of improving proprioceptive activity in teaching for the transfer of skills. There is speculation as to the transfer effect from practicing with a lighter projectile to a heavier one, and vice-versa. Whether a lighter projectile sharpens the proprioceptors' sensitivity and provides the performer with a greater *feel* for the heavier projectile is being currently investigated. This is another example of the interrelatedness of psychology of learning and neurophysiology showing why content matter associated with both disciplines must be studied together in order to obtain more answers to questions raised about aspects of the learning process.

Acuity of the Senses

Whereas physical and motor factors are always emphasized for successful motor-skill performance, the senses are often taken for granted. Those remarkable sense organs that have the ability to detect minor changes in stimuli are indispensably involved in many motor acts. Such senses as taste and smell rarely function as part of the typical performance of motor skills. Hearing, of course, plays an important role in isolated instances, such as responding to the starting gun. (There must have been many an occasion when visiting team players wished this sense could be turned off so that they would not be aware of crowd reactions in crucial situations.) The importance of *vision, equilibrium,* and *proprioception* to skilled performance is obvious.

Vision. There are many facets of vision. Following a moving projectile, and determining peripheral activity, spatial relations, color, and brightness are examples of the function of the visual system. The baseball batter must have eyes keen enough to follow pitches thrown at the rate of 90 mph, the infielder has to follow the ground ball visually and move his body and hands accordingly, and the outfielder is required to detect a little white sphere against a background of people, stands, and lights. Success is more probable for the performer with a visual handicap where the environment is stable and change is brought about by the individual himself, rather than in sports where external events are unpredictable. Respectable scores have been reported by blind golfers and bowlers.

During the initial photoelectronic process of visual activity, retinal potentials are formed. Messages, in the form of impulses, are sent by certain ganglion cells of the retina to the visual region of the occipital cortex (DeValois, 1965). There is a perceptive interpretation of the information in this area. In most sports, this perceptive analysis must occur in a matter of moments if the performer is to react successfully to given stimuli often unpredictable in nature.

Many investigations in psychological literature yield results that stress the importance of vision, in addition to tactile and kinesthetic experience, in learning skills. Evidently, even for skills that require no perception of a changing external field, vision enhances performance. The body utilizes much of its sense information, and even though there may be considerable overlap and unnecessary information, the removal of one sense appears to be somewhat detrimental to performance.

Some people feel that compensation takes place for those people who have lost a particular sense. That is, one or more of the other senses become more discriminatory. However, an extremely early study by Seashore and Ling (1918) does not uphold this theory of sensory compensation—that the loss of one sense modality is made up by the overdevelopment of other sense areas. Two groups of high school students, one blind and the other with normal vision, were compared in tasks requiring an ability to identify the direction of a sound source, to discriminate between intensities of eight tones, to differentiate between weights, and to judge pressures. There were no performance differences between the groups.

Bannister and Blackburn (1931) suspected that the relative placement of the eyes might be a factor in skill achievement. They measured the interpupillary distance of 258 collegiate students and confirmed that those players who had eyes wider apart were better players: they had superior ability in judging relative distances of objects and theoretically therefore better stereoscopic vision. But the experimental methods of this research are open to question. For example, the method of determining player skill status was extremely subjective. It might be interesting to see this study repeated under more controlled conditions.

Kinesthesis. Information concerning the kinesthetic sense seems more limited than that regarding the other senses. A leading reason for this circumstance is the great difficulty researchers have in isolating this sense for study. In spite of the difficulties in obtaining precison in experimentation those receptors responsible for informing the body of its conscious change in position as well as of the relationship of its parts in space have been demonstrated to be necessary for the smooth movements of the skilled act. Probably this sense is appreciated most by persons having visual limitations, for it is this sense they must rely on in order to perform motor skills adequately. Nevertheless, kinesthesis is a sense usually associated with the more gifted performers, and research appears to indicate its greater presence in those people demonstrating outstanding skill in motor activities.

A means of demonstrating the effects of kinesthetic impairment has been offered by Laszlo (1966). By raising the systolic blood pressure 40 mm. Hg. higher than the subject's normal reading with the use of the cuff and having the subject continually tap on a Morse key as quickly as possible, Laszlo found an expected decrease in key-tapping efficiency with a loss of kinesthetic sensation. She also tested her subjects in other ways. Once again, with the cuff on the arm, and head turned away, each subject had his finger touched lightly with a cotton end stick. The finger was also manipulated up or down and the subject was asked to move it up or down. This was done regularly after the cuff was in place for ten minutes. On the average, the subjects lost their tactile sense after 19.2 minutes, their passive kinesthetic sense after 22 minutes, and their active kinesthetic sense after 22.4 minutes. The experimental methods employed in this investigation offer physical educators ideas on how to study the function of kinesthesis when one learns and performs skilled movements. Sensory restriction has provided a means for psychologists to determine sensory involvement in behavior, learning, and perception.

Tactile Sense. Closely related to the kinesthetic sense is the tactile sense. The ability to detect changes of touch and pressure involves many of the same type of proprioceptors involved in informing the body of changes in its position. Senses that enable us to feel pain, temperature changes, touch, pressure, and the body's position in space are referred to as *somatic senses.* The receptors for pressure lie deeper in the skin and tissues than those for touch, although most of the same nerve endings serve both functions. Pressure is automatically considered a type of touch sensation.

Equilibrium. The nature of body balance and equilibrium has already been discussed from both physiological and psychological viewpoints. It should be sufficient merely to reiterate the role this sense plays as a basis for voluntary movement and control. Although posture and locomotion impulses can be distributed by the spinal cord alone, refinement of these impulses under changing body and environmental conditions is the responsibility of the higher nerve centers. Equilibrium must be extremely well developed in such performers as divers, trampolinists, and gymnasts, although it should be obvious that every activity requires a certain degree of body equilibrium.

Sense Restriction. As the athlete desires to be physically fit and to maintain his motor-skill proficiency his concern for sensory acuity is justified. A quick response to the starting command may determine the difference between winning and losing the 100-yard dash. To have the touch in bowling may produce a 200-plus game. To be visually alert may mean catching a ball thought to be uncatchable. And to feel the tennis serve can make the difference between an ace and just another serve.

In order to maintain the senses in a state of alertness (at least those involved in a particular motor activity), the individual must not restrict these senses preceding the time of performance. Sense restriction or deprivation study has been increasing, with evidence leading to the conviction that "man needs varying sensory stimulation in order to function adaptively" (Neff, 1965). Although research is still not sufficient in this area, at least in practical situations, one investigation is presented here to indicate the negative results of a nonvariable sensory environment.

Bexton, Heron, and Scott (1956) studied twenty-two male subjects during a three-day isolation period. The subjects were confined to cubicles where they were restricted in their daily activities and therefore experienced decreased variations in their sensory environments. They were subjected at different periods to cognitive tests, e.g., multiplying, completing series of numbers, and making words from jumbled letters. The subjects were found to suffer from an increasingly impaired intellectual ability and even suffered from visual hallucinations the longer they were under the experimental conditions.

This study emphasizes the need for varying stimuli to keep us aroused and mentally active. Although cognitive tasks were employed in the study described above, we might very well expect similar findings in motor tasks. When one is restricted to a bed for several days due to illness or injury, he commonly discovers acuity impariment in attempting skills he performed prior to the situation.

The role of activity and exercise in counteracting perceptual loss has been studied by Zubek (1963). In comparing groups of subjects confined to a chamber for a period of one week, he determined that even a few exercise periods a day seemed to eliminate many of the impairments produced by perceptual deprivation. Other research findings on the effects of sense restriction on perceptual and motor activities have been conflicting due to varying methods of experimentation. As a point of interest, other studies since the pioneer one of Bexton, reported earlier, have not usually found such pronounced detrimental effects of sense restriction. Some results even indicate an improvement in certain functions as a result of sensory deprivation. However, it would appear that a variety of perceptual and motor functions are susceptible to impairment as a function of sensory restriction, but the range of effects does not seem to be as great as was first believed.

It has also been found that impairment effects are temporary in nature. The study of attention and alertness, called *vigilance,* has indicated that as a subject views the same stimuli, his attentiveness decreases. Vigilance studies have been performed under a wide range of experimental conditions, mainly in order to determine pilot and military effectiveness during those times when concentration is important for long periods in which a specific, unsuspecting stimulus may suddenly appear. Even a novel stimulus will improve the subject's alertness. The baseball outfielder who rarely has a ball hit to him may be less alert than the third-baseman who has been frequently bombarded with shots directed toward him.

It is important to keep the senses in a state of alertness, for the information derived from sensory involvement in a given task is necessary for skilled movement patterns as well. The information, termed feedback, refers to the sensory information gained from a motor performance that helps to regulate present and future movements in terms of immediate and past experiences. Chase and others (1961) investigated delayed sensory feedback on two tapping tasks. One task involved simple regularity movements while the other required rhythmically patterned responses. Delayed sensory feedback did not appear to affect the regularity task negatively but there was a significantly impaired performance on the patterned task. Most motor skills are of the complex type, and it would seem that sensory involvement and feedback permit greater skill success.

Perceptual Mechanism

Limited knowledge of the structures involved in perception and in the nature of the perceptual process has proved to be a difficult obstacle in the past for psychologists to overcome in explaining the learning process. Perhaps this has been one of the reasons why traditional S-R (stimulus-response) theory, association theory, and reflex-arc models have been widely accepted in years gone by. After Gestalt theory, in opposition to S-R theory, made its mark in psychology in the 1920's and 1930's, its impact gradually weakened. In recent years, new research and theories have emerged from social psychologists, experimental psychologists, clinical psychologists, and physiological psychologists, once again emphasizing the role of perception as a factor in learning, adjustment, and personality.

This area of perception and perceptual learning is an exciting one which psychologists are no longer avoiding, but rather meeting directly. Because the latest trend of theories stress input, or the sensory apparatus, perception, as well as the other cognitive processes, is treated as an important facet of the learning process. Difficulties still arise in definition and clarification of terminology as may be expected in an area where scientific knowledge is relatively recent.

Description and Definitions. There is no doubt that the senses underlie perception and that several senses probably interact simultaneously during the perceptive process. The old idea that perception is a passive process has met with disfavor, but it is now accepted that perception, as well as learning, is an active process. It is also evident that perception depends on psychological and physiological characteristics of the perceiver in addition to the stimulus itself.

The structure of the sense organs has much to do with what is perceived, a fact which perhaps leads to confusion in distinguishing sensation from perception. In a manner of speaking, sense receptors are analyzers, as they transmit specific messages to the higher centers of the nervous system. There are, however, no special lines to the central nervous system. Instead, the resulting perception of each sensation is initiated and determined by a complex interaction of many passageways.

The elementary process of sensation underlies the more complex perceptual process. The senses involved will depend on the object(s) to be perceived. Perception depends on differences between stimuli and perceptibility, or ease of discrimination, and is closely related to the magnitude of the difference between stimuli.

One's viewpoint of psychology might well determine his definition of perception as well as his definition of learning. However, it does appear that the older concept of perception being merely more complex than sensation is unacceptable today. Perception is dependent on learning and is influenced by such individual factors as personality, attitudes, emotional factors, experience, and expectations, in addition to environmental variables.

Perception is usually distinguished from other processes involving thought, consciousness, and judgment. According to Bartley (1958) it is a form of discriminating behavior involving the overall activitiy of the person *immediately* following or accompanying stimulation of the sense organs. It may assume overt or introspective characteristics, e.g., viewing a painting is experiential, whereas reacting to a choice reaction-time apparatus produces observable motor activity. *Perception may be defined as knowledge through the senses of the existence and properties of matter and the external world.* It causes actions which in turn change it and is a continuous process. Friedman (1961) offers a clear distinction between sensation and perception, that helps us to understand these terms better. A sensation involves "...the presence of apparatus and means for *reception* of stimuli." Perception, on the other hand, involves "...the presence of apparatus and means for the *interpretation* of stimuli."

Some scholars have found fault with the application of the same term, *perception,* to describe an act, an event, a process, and learning. Solley and Murphy (1960) in their book *Development of the Perceptual World* attempt to clarify the generalized application of perception. These authors would define an event experienced as a *percept. Perceptual learning* is "...a change in the status of the logically-inferred perceptual state or process of an individual as a result of successive applications of the operations of a learning paradigm." The *perceptual act,* as they theorize it to be, involves five steps: expectancy, attending, reception and sensory reactions, trial and check, and conscious perception, or organization.

The critical student can thus observe that perception may be a process or a product. The process is stimulation structured and is referred to as perceiving. The product of the structural process is a percept. And finally, perception, along with such processes as memory, thinking, and imagination composes the *cognitive process.* So far, perception has been discussed in a general and somewhat theoretical manner. Some specific references may help to clarify this area; therefore, the personal variables affecting perception are discussed at this point.

Personal Factors in Perception. How and what man perceives in a given situation has been shown to be affected by many personal factors. His ability to attend, or to disregard extraneous and irrelevant information, contributes to perceptibility. Selectivity in perception reduces the number of stimuli surrounding the object, allowing it to be perceived more easily and quickly. *Selective attention* of stimuli is a process associated with highly skilled performance. The batter concentrates on the ball and disregards irrelevant cues. Similarly, the successful shooting of a foul shot requires attention to the feel of the ball and concentration on the rim of the basket. Possibly any awareness of the fans and their comments, of the other players, or any feelings of nervousness, will contribute to the player's ineffective performance. The athlete is faced with situation after situation where he must be able to discriminate, detect, and exclude stimuli, many times at the spur of the moment.

Actually, the amount of sensory information yielded in any situation is more than any one person can perceive. Since there are many sensory channels—auditory, visual, tactual, kinesthetic, and the like—much data is presented to the individual and duplicated at one time through the medium of the senses. The athlete must be *set*, to know what to look for. This factor of set, the ability to single out objects, is necessary in all motor activity. Skill is demonstrated when there is a minimal involvement of the senses; just those needed for the distinction of cues in order that the perceptual process will work quickly and accurately. There is no doubt that learning and performing motor skills certainly depend, to a great extent, on perceptual abilities.

Another factor that influences perception is *motivation*. A person must have the will to perceive if he is to attend to the necessary cues influencing discrimination. Need, drive, or other motivation prepares the individual; he develops a set or hypothesis as to what to expect. This anticipation, or expectancy, permits him to attend to the meaningful stimuli. In fact, sometimes we perceive what we wish to perceive with needs and wishes channeling the direction.

Previous experiences in the same situation with the same objects help in facilitating the perceptual process. These past experiences also promote a sense of expectancy, which in turn leads to better perception. Familiarity with stimuli in similar situations not only affects perceptual learning but learning in general, and it might be deduced at this stage of the discussion that many similarities exist between perceptual learning and motor learning.

Even as motor learning is altered favorably by motivated practice, so is perceptual learning. However, if there is no reinforcement or knowledge of results, there is little or no learning of motor skills. Knowledge of results cannot be withheld in perceptual learning, for the person always perceives something through his own efforts. This information reinforces the perceptual act even though it may not be accurate. Whereas in motor learning an outsider may provide the knowledge of results, for example, whether the tennis serve was executed in good form, an individual himself achieves the percept. But perhaps we can leave this issue to the theorists.

Theories of Perception. Gestalt theory, with the work of Wertheimer, Koffka, Kohler, and others, popularized the perceptual aspect of learning. Unfortunately, many of their principles were broadly stated, and these generalizations did not attract much research in this area. Because of the oversimplification of complex problems, it was difficult to analyze the theory experimentally. Basically, Gestaltists claimed that when dealing with things we acquire experiences with them, and this affects perception. The individual sees patterns or configurations in a particular field, which leads to the so-called *insight* he gains in problem solving. Gestaltists assumed that all people perceive the same way and that perception is influenced by the surrounding stimuli rather than by one's physiological and psychological structures.

In contemporary times since the formal presentation of Gestalt theory perceptual theories have taken different directions. Some psychologists exemplified by Witkin (1954) emphasize the role of perception in personality development. Other theories stress that (1) the nature of what is perceived is determined by the environment and not influenced by the perceiver's needs, emotions, or other personality factors; or (2) the emphasis should be on the nature of the stimuli influencing perception and the sense organs involved; whereas Witkin (3) believes primarily that perception is affected by personal factors. Perception is related to personality and contributes to adjustment. The perceptual capacities are part of the individual's resources in adjusting to life's problems and situations. Finally, we can examine perception by both the structure of the stimuli field and the personal characteristics of the perceiver.

Allport and Pettigrew (1957) designed a study hopefully to answer the old problem of whether visual perception is *nativistic* or *empiricistic* in nature. The nativistic theory holds that the role of a specific sense organ is unaffected by learning, whereas the empiricist upholds the importance of experience and learning in perception. In other words, the nativist believes that despite the individual's past experience he will still perceive as other people. This particular study, although indicating that primitive Zulus report a trapezoidal illusion about as often as urban Zulus and Europeans, was submitted by the authors as supporting either theory, depending on the interpretation of the results.

The approach Solley and Murphy (1960) take is to compare perceptual learning to learning in general. A five-step description of perception (see Figure 3–11) is offered: (1) first stage—preparatory, whatever exists prior to stimulation affects perception; (2) second stage—moment before stimulation, attention to significant stimuli; (3) third stage—reception, neural mechanism action; (4) fourth stage—trial and check, inferences; and (5) fifth stage—meaning, consolidation of stimulus traces.

In their minds there is no doubt that "Perceptual learning is dependent

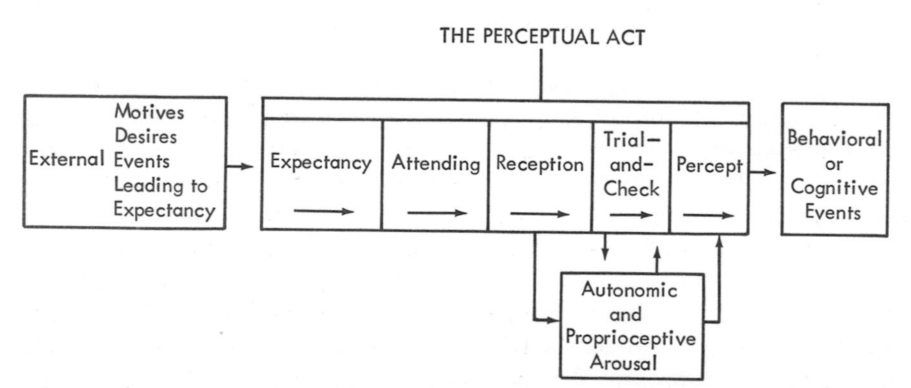

Figure 3–11. Solley and Murphy schematization of the perceptual act. The arrows indicate the major transitions between expectancy, attending, reception, trial-and-check, autonomic and proprioceptive arousal, and the final stuctured percept. (From Solley, Charles M., and Murphy, G. *Development of the Perceptual World,* New York: Basic Books, Inc., 1960.)

upon the level of maturation achieved by a child and, conversely, the full achievement of maturational potentials can be facilitated by the occurrence or nonoccurrence of specific learning experiences. Neither maturation nor learning can fully unfold independently."

Held (1965) describes a new theory stressing the importance of movement and sensory feedback in perceptual adaptation. There is a close relationship between signals from the motor nervous system, producing active movement, and the consequent sensory feedback. He cites evidence to show that when one lives in isolation or monotony, performance of perceptual and motor tasks declines. Other research shows that the young of higher mammals do not develop normal behavior if they are deprived of sensory and motor experiences. Held believes that the motor-sensory feedback loop helps newborn babies to develop motor coordination and also accounts for the changed relation between sensory and motor signals resulting from growth.

Piaget (1950) is noted for his developmental approach toward perception, whereas Helson (1951) offered an adaptation level theory of perception. As the reader can deduce, there is an abundance of present-day theories that have been formulated to explain the perceptual process. Further modifications of these theories and perhaps closer agreement will occur with the passage of time and accumulation of more substantial evidence.

Psychophysics. The study of the sensations, their relationships within a given sense modality, and the stimuli that cause them, is called *psychophysics*. Some authorities feel that the most precise knowledge of perceptions comes from the psychophysical field. Certain aspects of the sensations have been studied more than others in their role in perception, notably, size, color, pitch, space, depth, and distance. Unfortunately, these as well as other information-offering processes are still not completely understood.

Certain laws concerning the sense modalities have been formulated through the years. One of the most famous is the Fechner and Weber law, describing a person's ability to distinguish between two stimuli. Weber's original law, written in 1834, stated that in order for a second stimulus to be discriminated from the first, there must be a noticeable difference. Increments must be in constant fractions of the original stimulus. For instance, perhaps we would have to add one gram weight to ten grams in order barely to observe the difference between two weights. If this is the case, a twenty-gram weight would require two additional grams to the second stimulus in order for it to be perceived as different from the first. Consequently, a forty-gram weight necessitates the addition of four grams to the second stimulus; eighty grams would require eight, and so on. Fechner's law was a mathematical transposition of Weber's law. The Fechner-Weber law, which can be applied to the heavier of two weights, the longer of two lines, and the louder of two noises, has not always proved to be accurate but it is a generally accepted law.

Johannes Müller developed a doctrine of specific nerve energies. According to this doctrine, the sensation is determined by the fibers stimulated. However, the interrelatedness of the sense modalities and the respective functions within them, such as the determination of brightness, color, space perception, as well as visual acuity in the sense of vision requires us to realize the complexity of any given act or process. Because sensations are the basic underlying factors in perception, the study of the sense organs and the receptors certainly aids in describing one phase of the perceptual process: the role of the senses.

Figural After Effects. A commonly-occurring phenomenon in perception is the effect that an extended experience with a particular stimulus or situation has on the individual, once it has been discontinued. When a person continually observes curved lines and then straight ones, these straight lines appear to be curved in the opposite direction. Figure reversals can and have been demonstrated under a wide range of experimental conditions.

Every child has had the experience of turning in a circle a number of times, and then noticing, upon stopping, a feeling that the body is now turning in the opposite direction. The problem of maintaining balance after continued circular rotating confronts the ice skater attempting to master this skill. Other types of kinesthetic aftereffects are observed in sports situations. The baseball batter swings the weighted bat in the on-deck circle in order that his regular bat will appear lighter to him. Thus, he thinks he will be able to whip the bat around faster. The track man may practice with weighted boots in order to experience the feeling of lightness and speed once they are removed and his track shoes replaced during actual competition.

Figural aftereffects have been of particular interest to only a few physical educators, notably Cratty (1964). He defines a *figural effect* as "*...a perceptual distortion produced by prolonged...satiation of visual, auditory, tactual-kinesthetic stimuli, or some combination of these or of other stimuli....*" The most pronounced effect is experienced immediately following the satiation. A kinesthetic aftereffect would be the effect of a movement experience, contrasted with, say, the visual inspection of a straight line after viewing curved lines.

Although some investigations have obtained results favoring an overload prior to actual performance, such as throwing a heavier baseball before throwing a regulation baseball or warming up with a weighted bat, the bulk of the research indicates that little is to be gained by this practice. Interestingly enough, subjects invariably *feel* they perform better following an overload routine even though their performance does not improve more than the preoverload performance. Nelson has noted this phenomenon in a series of experiments. In one experiment (Nelson and Nofsinger, 1965) male students were tested for elbow-flexion speed prior to and following the application of selected levels of overload. The subjects all stated that they felt faster on the postoverload test, but in actuality, no significant differences were realized between pre- and post-overload tests. In other words, a kinesthetic illusion was created.

Perceived differences or distortions are generally temporary in nature, and the actual benefit to athletic performance has yet to be objectively substantiated through experimental research. However, the reported better feeling derived from practicing with weighted objects on subsequent speed and strength performances certainly necessitates a more thorough examination of this area.

Perception and Motor Learning. The role of perception and its importance in motor learning and performance should now be evident. Although perceptual learning has been studied separately from learning in general, there is no doubt that although one refers to the learning of athletic skills as motor learning, perceptual mechanisms operate in precluding any skilled motor act or subsequent to them. A person's ability to receive and distinguish among available cues in a given situation enables him to perform more skillfully. The batter may have the smoothest, ideal practice swing. If he cannot concentrate and attend to the important cues when he is up at bat in a game, if he cannot follow the ball as it comes to the plate and perceive a fastball or curve, a ball or a strike, his performance will be handicapped.

Cognitive Processes

Cognition consists of such higher mental processes as concept formation, problem solving, imagination, perception, and intelligence. Cognitive processes are extremely difficult to study objectively, and much of our knowledge of them has been inferred from behavior. This was shown to be the case with perception. Although we rely on the senses for environmental information, the object ultimately perceived results from the complex involvement of many neural mechanisms and the state of the organism. Even learning, whether simple or more involved, must be measured through performance.

Most writings and research in the area of cognition have dealt with perception and intelligence. The other cognitive processes have usually been somewhat neglected although there are certainly many questions, which, if answered, would be of interest to a number of people. For instance, are thinking and reasoning interchangeable terms? Is thinking a form of learning? George (1962) sees no distinction between learning and thinking and views thinking as a high-level form of skilled behavior, related to previous experience. In fact, thinking may be referred to as a form of problem solving and an integration of events in time and space. Although George describes imagination and creative thinking as occurring from the direct stimulation of the sensory storage system instead of through an external stimulation, a specific description of the process is lacking.

Cognitive psychologists are interested in thinking, concept formation, and in general, the acquisition of knowledge. Similarities and differences between the viewpoints of cognitive psychologists and neobehaviorist psychologists have been presented by Anderson and Ausubel (1965). Neobehaviorists are concerned primarily with conditioning, rote-verbal learning, and discrimination learning. Both groups of psychologists have attempted to explain all of learning and psychology through research completed in their respective areas. The behaviorists are interested in observed responses, and they manipulate environmental variables in order to determine cause-and-effect factors. The consciousness or *mentalistic* concept is pursued by the cognitive psychologists. They believe it is not only possible to study knowing, perceiving, meaning, and understanding (behaviorists say these processes cannot be objectively observed), but that they also provide the most important data.

In many ways, the cognitive viewpoint is associated with Gestalt psychology. These psychologists were not interested in Stimulus-Response Association theory and a mechanistic viewpoint but were involved instead in thinking and perception. However, many differences do exist between cognitive theorists and Gestaltists as well as among cognitive theorists themselves.

Relationship of Intelligence to Motor Abilities and Physical Factors. Earlier in this chapter, it was reported how Guilford factor-analyzed physical performance to arrive at underlying psychomotor abilities. The same author has attempted to determine the component abilities comprising the intellect as well as their relationships (Guilford, 1959). Through the factor-analysis method, he examined data obtained from a series of intelligence tests and proposed the least common denominators, i.e., independent factors. From fifty intellectual factors, he derived five: cognitive abilities, memory, evaluative abilities, divergent thinking, and convergent thinking. He interpreted the process of cognition as including discovery and recognition abilities.

Evidently, interpretations and categorizations of the higher mental processes lack agreement among psychologists in many instances. Guilford's use of the word *intellect* might very well be used interchangeably with the term *cognition*, depending on one's viewpoint. However, this section of the chapter is particularly concerned with intelligence tests and what they measure, and the relationship of these scores to various physical characteristics, motor abilities, and athletic success. Much research has been completed that has attempted to determine the relationship of intellectual and physical factors.

Intelligence tests, which may measure various aspects of intelligence depending on the nature of the tests, and academic achievement scores have been utilized as means of measuring intelligence. The most often used and respected intelligence tests are the Revised Stanford-Binet Scales and the Wechsler Intelligence Scale, both of which yield IQ's that correlate fairly well with academic achievement. These scales have been used in investigations in order to distinguish intellectual groups or relate intelligence to some other variable. The mentally retarded and the superior have been compared in physical performance, athlete and nonathlete differences in intelligence have been tested, and the relationship of motor-skill success to academic achievement has been investigated.

Intelligence and Physical Status. Some researchers have been concerned with the relation of intelligence to such physical factors as height and weight and performances on strength tests. In a sense, they have attempted to partially resolve the issue of whether a sound body usually coincides with a sound mind. The theory of organismic unity, that physical and intellectual factors are interrelated, has been questioned. The work of Klausmeier in a series of studies (also referred to in Chapter 5) casts considerable doubt upon the relationship of academic achievement and intelligence test scores with physical status.

In one study, he observed that a low level of physical development was not related to low achievement in arithmetic and reading. In a second study high and low academic achievers in the third and fifth grades were allocated to two groups. No difference between the groups was noted on measures of height, weight, and grip strength. Another investigation of Klausmeier's utilized five physical measures presumably contributing to a child's organismic age, as proposed in 1949 by Olson. He found these data to contribute little to mental and reading scores in predicting arithmetic and language scores.

In an early study Cates (1924) tested his subjects on such physical factors as grip strength, lung capacity, chest girth, weight, and height. He concluded that no single physical trait correlated in any meaningful way with mental age, or mental, social, scholastic, and emotional maturity. The combined physical traits did offer much higher correlations, though. However, after summarizing research evidence up to 1930, Paterson (1930) made the general statement that nothing more than low, positive relationships exist between physical status and mental status. Much of the present research permits the same conclusion. Exception to this has been demonstrated when mentally retarded children are compared to average and superior children in physical characteristics and motor abilities.

It should be pointed out that some research suggests a relationship between the physical and intellectual. For example, Rarick and McKee (1949) compared ten third-grade children of high motor proficiency with ten of low proficiency. The high group was taller, stronger, heavier, had higher intelligence, and a better scholastic average. But generally speaking, the present view is that there is little justification in relating intelligence factors with the physical aspects of children, at least in the normal population of school children.

Intelligence and Ability to Learn Motor Skills. Some writers have argued for an MQ, a motor intelligence score depicting a child's ability to learn motor skills, in conjunction with his obtained IQ. Other writers feel there is a direct relationship between such variables since the organism reacts totally to all experiences. According to the latter group, if a student does well on intelligence tests, he should be expected to learn motor activities more quickly and proficiently than those students who obtain lower intelligence ratings.

Kulcinski (1945) tested 125 fifth and sixth grade boys and girls as to their ability to learn fundamental skills. He found a positive relationship between this ability and intelligence, with the superior intelligence group displaying a significant degree of learning over normal and subnormal groups. In an early study, Ragsdale and Breckenfeld (1934) obtained data on 155 junior high school boys. They concluded that general intelligence was unimportant in the team sport skills tested.

Two recent studies have been completed by Ryan (1963) and Start (1964). In Ryan's investigation, eighty college students were required to learn how to balance on a stabilometer. Academic achievement did not distinguish the subjects in their ability to learn and perform the task. Start had forty-four college students mentally practice a novel skill for five minutes on each of six days. Performance on the skill, a single leg upstart on the Olympic high bar, was then rated by four judges. When the ratings were compared to IQ scores, an *r* of .08 was obtained.

Generally, it appears that the research, although by no means in agreement, indicates little relationship between cognitive and motor abilities. It might be emphasized that most experiments comparing intelligence to motor factors have utilized college or high-school subjects where distinctions on intelligence tests and IQ's are slighter than when comparing an entire population. Research on preschool youngsters, elementary school children, and slightly older children tends to show greater interactions between physical, motor, and intellectual factors.

Another concern is the nature of the tests employed. For instance, Ismail and others (1963) distinguished high academic achievers from low ones on tests of coordination and static balance. Tests of speed, accuracy, and strength did not differentiate the groups. The authors were able to conclude that for boys and girls between the ages of ten and twelve, coordination items were fairly good predictors of IQ and Stanford Standard Achievement scores.

Thus far it appears that research investigating intellectual and motor relationships has indicated higher relationships among young school-aged children than among college students. Child psychologists and others interested in growth and development have recently uncovered much evidence to show the relationship of motor development to academic aptitude and achievement. The work of Kephart at Purdue University as well as that of Doman and Delacato at the Institutes for the Achievement of Human Potential in Philadelphia certainly exemplifies this effort. Their work and the research of others is presented in Chapter 5. Suffice to say here, the potential role of the physical educator in developing basic motor patterns in children as a means of promoting intellectual growth has gone virtually untapped.

Athlete Versus Nonathlete in Intelligence. For many years the popular conception of the big dumb athlete has plagued physical educators and the athletes themselves. It takes only a few examples to confirm a hypothesis, especially one that is quite entrenched in the mind of the believer. Fortunately, most of the literature dispels such thoughts.

Some isolated studies do show athletes to score lower on intelligence tests than nonathletes. However, the majority of investigations have found little difference between the two groups on intelligence tests and academic achievement tests. A number of studies have even produced results favoring the athletes. As far as grade-point averages are concerned, athletes do as well as, if not slightly better than, nonathletes.

Motor and Physical Characteristics of the Mentally Retarded. The "normal" population of children, from birth to college age, has been extensively investigated. For many years, the mentally retarded have been neglected. With federal encouragement and enthusiasm at the local level, much work has been recently undertaken by educators, physical educators, and psychologists in order to promote more effective learning situations for the mentally-deficient child.

Evidence has been quite consistent with respect to certain points. It generally indicates a direct relationship between motor and physical factors and intellectual achievement. Thurstone (1959) undertook a comprehensive project concerned with educating the mentally handicapped. Her subjects, 559 boys and girls ranging in age from seven to fifteen years, had IQs recorded from 50 to 79. One phase of the study had to do with the acquisition and performance of gross motor skills. All the subjects were tested on such skills as (1) volleyball or soccer ball punt for distance; (2) tennis ball or softball throw for distance; (3) grip strength; (4) 40-yard run; (5) standing broad jump; (6) tennis ball throw for accuracy; and (7) side stepping for fifteen seconds. The scores of the mentally retarded children were compared with those of the normal children at different ages. The scores of the normal children were consistently and significantly better on almost every test, at all age levels.

In another study Howe (1959) formed two groups of children from six and one half to twelve years of age, equated as to age, sex, and background. A number of physical skills were tested, including a jump test, grip strength, ball throw for distance, tapping speed, balancing ability, and others. The normal children were superior to the mentally deficient on these tests. An astonishing discovery made by the author was that forty-one of the forty-three retarded children *could not balance on one foot for one minute.* This information coincides with the data obtained by Ismail (1963) in his study, already reported. Ismail had found that motor-coordination and balance tasks were highly related to the intellectual achievement of normal children.

The retarded child is usually two to four years behind the normal child on performance measures. In fact, motor performance appears to be more evenly equated when comparing the mental ages of children. The pattern of learning skills, that is, developmentally, is basically the same for both normal and subnormal boys and girls. However, at a given chronological age, the retarded perform with lesser degree of skill than normal children.

Can physical educators assist the retarded in improving their mental processes? A few studies have reported remarkable contributions of physical education programs to the total growth of subnormal children. Oliver (1958) matched two groups of mentally-deficient boys, one group (the experimental group) had a ten-week course in conditioning, the other group (the control group) did not. For the experimental group, all academic subjects except arithmetic and English were replaced by physical education activities. The control group continued under their regular program. Both groups were given pre- and post-physical and mental tests. The experimental group improved significantly on both the physical and mental tests, and Oliver hypothesized that the change was because of the effect of achievement and success, improved adjustment, improved physical fitness, and the effect of feeling important. The experimental group improved significantly on many physical, motor, and intelligence measures, and their IQ significantly *improved 25 per cent*!

It might be concluded, then, that motor proficiency is directly related to intellectual ability, when groups of intellectually subnormal and normal children are compared. Children who range within the normal intelligence limits are not distinguished on motor skill measures. This point has been well brought out in an experiment by Asmussen and Heebøll-Nielson (1956). Out of 204 boys, three groups were formed, two within the normal IQ limits and one below them. They were tested on the vertical jump, strength of the leg extensors and finger flexors, and maximum expiration and inspiration force. These tests did not distinguish performers within the normal range, but did distinguish the low IQ group from the other two. The investigators concluded that there is no difference in performance as long as the IQ is above 95. Below this (their low group had an IQ average of 83) performance is lower than in normal boys.

Although it might seem reasonable to expect the intellectually gifted to do exceptionally well in motor skill performance since the retarded are below average efficiency, this is not the case. General findings indicate that a greater intellect and outstanding academic achievement are not related to physical performance.

Emotional Effects

The purpose of this entire chapter is to demonstrate the interaction of physical, motor, sensory, perceptual, cognitive, and now, emotional variables in any given situation. All these factors contribute to the learning situation, facilitating or inhibiting, with the degree of emphasis of each dependent on the performer, the skill, and the environment.

Rarely is a person not emotionally involved to some extent in any activity in which he performs. Emotions, like instincts and habits, are basically involuntary. They determine actions, and if strong enough, emotions will initiate activity before there is involvement of the higher nervous centers. Emotions or feelings represent a wide range of states in the human organism: joy and happiness, anxiety and fear, stress, and sorrow, to name only a few. Even an individual who is motivated to do something would have his attitude changed, if he proceeds in a different emotional state. Not only are there many forms of emotion, but as many if not more varied causes. The athlete may be anxious before the event, fear his competition, dread the consequences, and/or react poorly in front of spectators. Although these emotions may be considered to have a negative effect, other emotional states, e.g., the optimal degrees of stress and motivation for the individual participant, will promote better performance. Emotions are a part of any activity, whether caused by the environment, the activity itself, or initiated in the mind of the performer.

Physiologically speaking, the parts of the brain involved in emotion appear to be the reticular activating system and the limbic system (parts of the thalamus, hypothalamus, and inner cortex). Pleasure and pain areas associated with the autonomic nervous system are located within the limbic system. During various emotions, such as stress, glands are stimulated and hormones are secreted in an attempt to recover body homeostasis (internal body equilibrium).

The word *emotion* means agitation of the feelings (from the French word *émouvoir,* to stir up). Emotion may be referred to in two ways: (1) as a conscious experience or feeling, or (2) by the physiological changes that take place within the body as a result of it. Emotions are psychological and physiological responses and reactions resulting from perceived situations. Some authorities feel that emotions are a special class of motives, whereas others disagree. There is no doubt, though, that emotions, much like motivation, may have an organizing or disorganizing effect on performance.

Although we are born with certain basic emotional instincts, other factors later influence them. Maturation brings about the development of various emotions, although many of them can be learned and even conditioned. Both maturation and learning increase emotions in number and complexity.

A person's emotion, his reaction to a particular stimulus, can be observed in his everyday behavior or in the research laboratory under controlled conditions. Under the latter condition, it is possible directly or indirectly to measure physiological changes taking place in the organism. Some methods employed in research efforts include:

1. *Measuring respirations,* their depth and rate. An increase is associated with an emotional state.

2. *Measuring body temperature.* It may rise or fall, depending on the nature of the stimulus and its particular effect on the organism.
3. *Determining amount of sweating.* It increases with the onset of stronger emotions.
4. *Analyzing electrical potentials of the brain* (*EEG or electroencephalogram*). They become irregular during emotional conditions.

Other specific physiological alterations are associated with particular types of emotions, such as stress and anxiety. It would be impossible to discuss here the impact all the various types of emotions have on the individual and his performance of motor skills. However, the general categories of tension, anxiety, and stress are familiar to most people, and research provides some interesting thoughts concerning them.

Tension. Tension may imply nervous reactions to situations, i.e., a mental feeling of anguish and overall bodily unrest, or the state of certain muscles of the body acting against a resistance. Physical educators are concerned with both conditions. In the first, hopefully, participation in physical activities would relieve the symptoms and suppress their tendency to occur. The second situation is most necessary for the successful performance of certain skills, for varying degrees of strength provide the basis for making participation possible.

Muscular tension and its relationship to motor-skill performance has been investigated by a few researchers who were interested in discovering the facilitating or detrimental effects of muscular tension on performance. Tension provides a state of arousal and a level of activation in the individual, and as such, is an aspect of emotion and motivation. The results of the research have been conflicting. For instance, Freeman (1938) tested his subjects on finger oscillation, mirror drawing, mental arithmetic, touch threshold, and the eyelid reflex during conditions of changing pressures on the body. It was concluded that body tension adversely affected the more complex tasks.

On the other hand, Eason and White (1961) found that tension led to better performance in rotary-tracking tasks where the tension was the result of effort at the same task. The authors reported these results from a series of five experiments with highly skilled subjects. It might be noted that tension in the study by Freeman was induced by a stimulus other than the task itself, whereas in the Eason and White experiment beneficial tension results were obtained from the effort displayed for the experimental task itself. When effort (tension) was associated with a second task, poorer performances occurred on the first one.

A third investigation, by Bell (1959) required tension to be induced by a weight, a five or ten pound dumbbell held in the nonpreferred hand as the subjects were performing on the pursuit rotor. Other subjects were given motivational instructions as a means for inducing muscular tension. No significant differences in performance were noted when comparing the two methods of causing tension.

In these three studies, tension was induced by different means and the tasks varied. The results were not in agreement. Research is lacking on the direct effect of tension on the learning and performing of skills associated with physical education. Perhaps the nature of many motor skills is such as to provide enough tension in the performer without the necessity of additionally induced tension.

Anxiety. Anxiety can refer to a perfectly normal reaction to a given situation or to a type of neurosis. Anxiety states, which include symptoms of continuing unexplained fear, are the most common of personality disturbances. Anxiety and fear are terms used interchangeably in psychological research, as anxiety denotes a signal of danger to the organism leading to a protective defense. Ausubel and others (1953) defined anxiety as an "...acquired reaction-sensitivity in individuals suffering from impaired self-esteem to overreact with fear to any adjustive situation that contains a further threat to self-esteem."

Other theorists see anxiety not as a disrupter of effective action but rather as a main drive to action. Whether anxiety is to be considered as a neurosis or as a condition similar to stress, which might facilitate performance, depends on the context in which the term is used. Stress and anxiety have often been used as interchangeable terms and observable symptoms would tend to encourage this practice. However, physiologically and psychologically, differences do exist. Cattell (1963) points out that the basic physiological anxiety pattern is not the same as that associated with stress. For instance, anxiety affects metabolism and may cause a loss of weight. Stress symptoms, clarified so well by the efforts of Selye, are to be presented briefly. Cattell provides an interesting psychological example to distinguish stress from anxiety. When a difficult problem is tackled, stress symptoms are demonstrated. Anxiety is displayed when the person retreats or utilizes other escape mechanisms. Cattell even distinguishes anxiety from fear, showing basically different physiological response patterns.

Most research in the area of anxiety has been concerned with comparing the performance of anxious versus nonanxious subjects on motor-skill tasks and written tests. Some researchers claim that anxiety disrupts and disorganizes behavior through a lowering of attention, concentration, and intellectual control. Supposedly there is a reduction in perceptual efficiency under anxiety. However, low levels of anxiety provide a general alerting mechanism whereby the organism can distinguish environmental stimuli better.

The Manifest Anxiety Scale and other written tests have been used to determine the anxiety level of a person. When comparing anxious to nonanxious subjects on performance tasks, investigators have arrived at conflicting conclusions. This confliction may be explained partly by the method of determining the personality nature of the subjects and partly by the varying test procedures employed by these experimenters. Such investigations have attempted to discover the effect of anxiety, hence drive, in learning and performance situations.

Ausubel (1953) separated college students into high and low anxious groups, based on Rorschach Anxiety Test scores. No significant differences between the groups were observed on a mirror-tracing test and a blindfold stylus test. These tasks were not overly difficult. However, on more complex tasks, studies generally show that higher-anxiety people do more poorly than those low in anxiety. Also, those who score low on anxiety tests perform more effectively under stress (in complex tasks) than under normal conditions. This is not the case with high-anxiety individuals, who are less effective performers under stress.

This type of information is extremely pertinent to a better teacher-learner and coach-athlete situation. Understanding the personality nature of each of his students will enable the teacher to be more aware of possible problems. He may expect some students to learn certain tasks with ease and others to experience great difficulty with these same tasks.

Stress. *Stress* is another term which has meant different things to different people. However, through the earlier efforts of Cannon and other physiologists and recently, Hans Selye, the public has been greatly enlightened as to the nature of stress. Stress, which is unavoidable, results from psychological, physiological, and emotional origins.

Any situation or activity places the individual under stress, anything can cause it. Sometimes it is desirable, sometimes not; nevertheless, we are continually under stress. What may be stressful to one person may not be so to another, and one condition may promote or be detrimental to the performances of different people. A representative example of this paradox is the effect of spectators on athletic performance. Some athletes perform poorer in actual competition before an audience than in practice; thus, this circumstance is detrimentally stressful to them. Others perform about the same under both practice and game-like conditions and are relatively unaffected. Still other athletes put on a superior demonstration in front of spectators; it would appear that to them this stress is beneficial.

It is commonly observed that certain situations are stressful to some people. By the same token, some situations are generally stressful to everyone. Regardless of the cause, the general state of stress is apparently physiologically reacted to in a specific pattern of internal adjustments. Gross (1958), in interpreting Selye's work, offers the definition of stress as "...a state manifested by a specific syndrome which consists of all the nonspecifically induced changes within a biologic system." In other words, the stress symptoms are nonspecifically caused but result in a specific physiologic state involving specific physiologic processes. It is a state that disrupts the homeostasis (internal body equilibrium) of the body.

Selye (1956) felt that the average reader encountered difficulty in understanding the preceding definition of stress, and he modified it to read "... the rate of wear and tear on the body." Life is a process of adaptation, and Selye, through his numerous publications, has attempted to describe how the body specifically copes with stress. He postulates a *General Adaptation Syndrome* (G.A.S.) composed of three states:

1. *Alarm–reaction stage.* The body is prepared to defend and does; it is in a state of readiness.
2. *Stage of resistance.* The organism is able to do regular tasks as the body handles the stress.
3. *Stage of exhaustion.* The stress situation is too severe; death results.

Stress is most evident in the alarm-reaction stage and usually causes a total response of the body. It is minimized in the second stage as specific parts of the body are involved in handling a particular stress. Obviously, a typical stress does not go past this stage. The reaction of stress, then, affects the entire body first and specific body defenses later. Besides proposing the G.A.S., Selye also suggested the L.A.S., *the Local Adaptation Syndrome*, a local stress response, an example of which is inflammation.

Selye noted that all three types of stress caused certain physiological adjustments to occur. *The triad*, as he termed them, includes adrenal-cortex enlargement, shrinkage of the lymphatic structures, and the development of bleeding and ulcers in the stomach. During stress situations, the pituitary gland and adrenals react to return the body back to normal. Eosinophil (a type of white blood cell) count decreases considerably and respirations increase when a person is in a state of stress.

The prediction of performance under various stressful conditions is an important problem facing educators. Associated with this problem is the consideration of a general resistance factor to stress; more specifically, do individuals who react favorably to the effects of one stress do likewise to a second type of stress? To answer this question, Parsons, Phillips, and Lane (1954) had fifty-seven industrial workers perform on the Dunlap hand-steadiness apparatus. The task required the subjects to keep a stylus from touching the side of a hole one-eighth of an inch in diameter. Stress was introduced during performance either by distraction or by informing the subjects of failure through false results and comments. No significant relationship was obtained between the two stress performance scores, therefore not substantiating the concept of a general resistance factor to stress.

The physiological and psychological effects of stress have been tested. Michael (1957) reviewed the literature and concluded that adaptation to exercise (physical stress) provides a degree of protection against emotional stress. This statement would appear to indicate the transfer effects of stress resistance from one situation to another. Ulrich (1957) measured the physiological effects of psychological stress. She tested twenty-eight college women students (a) under normal conditions; (b) anticipating one of a number of events—such as a basketball game, a written test, and participation in the game—but then being deprived; and (c) after the stressor condition. Blood samples, particularly eosinophil counts, pulse rates, and respiration rates were determined under all three conditions. Ulrich found stress to be caused by anticipation as well as participation or denial after expectancy.

Research indicates that stress affects complex tasks in a different manner from simple tasks. Stress is usually more disruptive for the learning and performing of complex tasks, whereas simple task performance either is not affected or else is facilitated under stress. Other studies suggest that if a stress is introduced early in the learning of a skill, it will be more disruptive than if introduced later. Frequently, if the skill has been learned well enough, the effects of stress will be unnoticed. In some cases, stress will improve performance with increased learning.

There is great practical importance in understanding the effects of stress on the learning and performing of motor skills. Emotional disturbances, such as stress, may benefit, disrupt, or have no effect on a particular individual learning a specific skill. Because athletics present a stressor situation, and participants are faced with the problem of performing at a high level of skill under stressful conditions, it should be obvious that stress plays a vital role in achievement or the lack of it. Emotional factors in general, then, are interwoven in every learning situation. Their effects will depend on the nature of the organism and the stimulus situation, which includes the to-be-learned skill and its relative difficulty, the stage of learning, and the surrounding conditions.

Summary

It is necessary to have an understanding of the nature of the learner that precedes the application of teaching techniques designed to improve his learning of motor skills. He is totally involved in any learning experience, and his skill attainment may very well be related to such personal factors as (a) physical characteristics, (b) motor abilities, (c) sense acuity, (d) perceptual abilities, (e) cognition, and (f) emotional effects.

Specific body types do not generally determine skill success, but there is a suggestion that outstanding athletes in certain sports have unique constitutions. Strength, endurance, and flexibility are physical qualities necessary, in varying degrees, for successful motor performance. Coordination, balance, kinesthesis, and speed of reaction and movement are factors underlying learning and performance. These abilities do not have a generalizing effect from task to task but, rather, are developed in accord with the particular task.

The senses, especially equilibrium, vision, the tactile sense, and the kinesthetic sense, contribute to skill achievement. No physical act is strictly motor, but rather the result of cognitive and physical interactions. Intelligence in normal children is apparently not related to physical characteristics, motor learning abilities and performance; but mentally-retarded children perform poorly at motor skills and are behind normal children in physical development as well.

Emotions, such as stress, tension, and anxiety are present in all people in varying degrees. Daily situations are emotionally reacted to, the how and extent depending on the nature of the organism. These emotions may promote, depress, or not affect performance.

References

Basic Considerations in Learning

Adams, Eleanor, G. The Study of Age, Height, Weight, and Power as Classification Factors for Junior High School Girls, *Res. Quart.*, 5:95–100, 1934.

Adams, Jack A., and Creamer, Cyle R. Proprioception Variables as Determiners of Anticipatory Timing Behavior, *Human Factors*, 4:217–222, 1962.

Allport, Gordon W., and Pettigrew, T. F. Cultural Influence on the Perception of Movement: The Trapezoidal Illusion Among Zulus, *J. Abnorm. Soc. Psychol.*, 65:104–113, 1957.

Anderson, Richard C., and Ausubel, David P. *Readings in the Psychology of Cognition*, New York: Holt, Rinehart and Winston, Inc., 1965.

Asmussen, Erling, and Heebøll-Nielsen, K. Physical Performance and Growth in Children, Influence of Sex, Age and Intelligence, *J. Appl. Physiology*, 8:371–380, 1956.

Ausubel, David P.; Schiff, Herbert M.; and Goldman, Morton. Qualitative Characteristics in the Learning Process Associated with Anxiety, *J. Abnorm. Soc. Psychol.*, 48:537–547, 1953.

Bachman, John C. Specificity vs. Generality in Learning and Performing Two Large Muscle Motor Tasks, *Res. Quart.*, 32:3–11, 1961.

Bannister, H., and Blackburn, J. M. An Eye Factor Affecting Proficiency at Ball Games, *Brit. J. Psychol.*, 21–382–384, 1931.

Bartley, S. Howard. *Principles of Perception*, New York: Harper and Brothers, 1958.

Bell, Howard A. Effects of Experimentally-Induced Muscular Tension and Frequency of Motivational Instructions on Pursuit Rotor Performance, *Percept. Mot. Skills*, 9:111–115, 1959.

Bexton, W. Harold; Heron, Woodburn; and Scott, Thomas H. Effects of Decreased Variation in the Sensory Environment, *Canad. J. Psychol.*, 8:70–76, 1956.

Botwinick, J., and Thompson, C. W. Premotor and Motor Components of Reaction Time, *J. Exp. Psychol.*, 71:9–15, 1966.

Cattell, Raymond B. The Nature and Measurement of Anxiety, *Scientific American*, 208:96–104, 1963.

CHASE, RICHARD A.; RAPIN, ISABELLE; GILDEN, LLOYD; SUTTON, SAMUEL; and GUILFOYLE, GEORGE. Studies on Sensory Feedback: II. Sensory Feedback Influences on Keytapping Motor Tasks, *Quart. J. Exp. Psychol.*, 13:153–167, 1961.

COZENS, FREDERICK W.; CUBBERLY, HAZEL J.; and NEILSON, N. P. *Achievement Scales in Physical Education Activities for Secondary School Girls and College Women*, New York: A. S. Barnes and Co., Inc., 1937.

CRATTY, BRYANT J., and HUTTON, ROBERT S. Figural After-effects Resulting from Gross Action Patterns, *Res. Quart.*, 35:116–125, 1964.

CUMBEE, FRANCES Z. A Factor Analysis of Motor Co-ordination, *Res. Quart.*, 25:412–428, 1954.

CURETON, THOMAS K. Flexibility as an Aspect of Physical Fitness, *Res. Quart.*, 12:381–390, 1941.

CURETON, THOMAS K. *Physical Fitness of Champion Athletes*, Urbana: University of Illinois Press, 1951.

DEVALOIS, RUSSEL C. Behavioral and Electrophysiological Studies of Primate Vision, in NEFF, WILLIAM D. (ed.), *Contributions to Sensory Psychology*, New York: Academic Press, 1965.

EASON, ROBERT G., and WHITE, CARROLL T. Muscular Tension, Effort, and Tracking Difficulty: Studies of Parameters which Affect Tension Level and Performance Efficiency, *Percept. Mot. Skills*, 12:331–372, 1961.

ESPENSCHADE, ANNA S. Restudy of Relationships Between Physical Performance of School Children and Age, Height, and Weight, *Res. Quart.*, 34:144–153, 1963.

ESPENSCHADE, ANNA S.; DABLE, ROBERT R.; and SCHOENDUBE, ROBERT. Dynamic Balance in Adolescent Boys, *Res. Quart.*, 24:270–275, 1953.

FLEISHMAN, EDWIN A. An Analysis of Positioning Movements and Static Reactions, *J. Exp. Psychol.*, 55:13–24, 1958a.

FLEISHMAN, EDWIN A. A Comparative Study of Aptitude Patterns in Unskilled and Skilled Psychomotor Performers, *J. Appl. Psychol.*, 41:263–272, 1957.

FLEISHMAN, EDWIN A. A Dimensional Analysis of Motor Abilities, *J. Exp. Psychol.*, 48:437–454, 1954.

FLEISHMAN, EDWIN A. Dimensional Analysis of Movement Reactions, *J. Exp. Psychol.*, 55:438–453, 1958b.

FORBES, GILBERT. The Effect of Certain Variables on Visual and Auditory Reaction Times, *J. Exp. Psychol.*, 35:153–162, 1945.

FREEMAN, G. L. The Optimal Muscular Tensions for Various Performances, *Amer. J. Psychol.*, 51:146–150, 1938.

FRIEDMAN, MERTON H. Sensation, Perception, and Symptom Formation, *Percept. Mot. Skills*, 12:42, 1961.

GATES, ARTHUR I. The Nature and Educational Significance of Physical Status and of Mental, Physiological, Social and Emotional Maturity, *J. Educ. Psychol.*, 15:329–359, 1924.

GEORGE, F. H. *The Brain as a Computer*, London: Pergamon Press, 1962.

GROSS, ELMER A., and THOMPSON, HUGH L. Relationship of Dynamic Balance to Speed and to Ability in Swimming; *Res. Quart.*, 28:342–346, 1957.

GROSS, NANCY E. Living with Stress, New York: McGraw-Hill Book Co., 1958.

GUILFORD, J. P. A System of the Psychomotor Abilities, *Amer. J. Psychol.*, 71:164–174, 1958.

GUILFORD, J. P. Three Faces of Intellect, *Amer. Psychologist.*, 14:469–479, 1959.

HELD, RICHARD. Plasticity in Sensory-Motor Systems, *Scientific American*, 213:84–94, 1965.

HELSON, HARRY (ed.). *Theoretical Foundations of Psychology*, New York: D. Van Nostrand Co., Inc., 1951.

HENRY, FRANKLIN M. Dynamic Kinesthestic Perception and Adjustment, *Res. Quart.*, 24:176–187, 1953.

HENRY, FRANKLIN M. Reaction Time—Movement Time Correlation, *Percept. Mot. Skills*, 12:63–66, 1961.

HIRATA, KIN-ITSU. Physique and Age of Tokyo Olympic Champions, *J. Sports Medicine and Physical Fitness*, 6:207–222, 1966.

HOWE, CLIFFORD E. A Comparison of Motor Skills of Mentally Retarded and Normal Children, *Exceptional Children*, 25:352–354, 1959.

ISMAIL, A.; KEPHART, N.; and COWELL, C. C. *Utilization of Motor Aptitude Tests in Predicting Academic Achievement, Technical Report No. 1*, Purdue University Research Foundation, P. U. 879–64–838, 1963.

KULCINSKI, LOUIS E. The Relation of Intelligence to the Learning of Fundamental Muscular Skills, *Res. Quart.*, 16:266–276, 1945.

LASZLO, JUDITH I. The Performance of a Simple Motor Task with Kinesthetic Sense Loss, *Quart. J. Exp. Psychol.*, 18:1–8, 1966.

LAUTENBACH, RUTH, and TUTTLE, WILLIAM. The Relationship Between Reflex Time and Running Events in Track, *Res. Quart.*, 3:138–142, 1932.

MATHEWS, DONALD K.; SHAW, VIRGINIA; and BOHNEN, MERIA. Hip Flexibility of College Women as Related to Length of Body Segments, *Res. Quart.*, 28:352–356, 1957.

MICHAEL, ERNEST D. Stress Adaptation through Exercise, *Res. Quart.*, 28:50–54, 1957.

MILLER, KENNETH D. A Critique on the Use of Height-Weight Factors in the Performance Classification of College Men, *Res. Quart.*, 23:402–416, 1952.

NEFF, WILLIAM D. *Contributions to Sensory Psychology*, New York: Academic Press, 1965.

NELSON, RICHARD C., and NOFSINGER, MICHAEL R. Effect of Overload on Speed of Elbow Flexion and the Associated Aftereffects, *Res. Quart.*, 36:174–182, 1965.

OLIVER, JAMES N. The Effect of Physical Conditioning Exercises and Activities on the Mental Characteristics of Educationally Sub-Normal Boys, *Brit. J. Educ. Psychol.*, 28:155–165, 1958.

OLSON, EINAR A. Relationship Between Psychological Capacities and Success in College Athletics, *Res. Quart.*, 27:79–89, 1956.

PARSONS, OSCAR A.; PHILLIPS, LESLIE; and LANE, JOHN E. Performance on the Same Psychomotor Task Under Different Stressful Conditions, *J. Psychol.*, 38:457–466, 1954.

PATERSON, DONALD G. *Physique and Intellect*, New York: Appleton-Century-Crofts, 1930.

PIAGET, JEAN. *The Psychology of Intelligence*, New York: Harcourt, Brace and Co., Inc., 1950.

RAGSDALE, C. E., and BRECKENFELD, IRVING J. The Organization of Physical and Motor Traits in Junior High School Boys, *Res. Quart.*, 5:47–55, 1934.

RARICK, G. L., and MCKEE, R. A Study of Twenty Third-Grade Children Exhibiting Extreme Levels of Achievement on Tests of Motor Proficienty, *Res. Quart.*, 20:142–152, 1949.

ROLOFF, LOUISE L. Kinesthesis in Relation to the Learning of Selected Motor Skills, *Res. Quart.*, 24:210–217, 1953.

ROSE, JERZY E., and MOUNTCASTLE, VERNON B. Touch and Kinesthesis, in FIELD, JOHN. (ed.), *Handbook of Physiology: Neurophysiology*, Vol. 1., Washington, D.C.: American Physiological Society, 1959.

RYAN, E. DEAN. Relative Academic Achievement and Stabilometer Performance, *Res. Quart.*, 34:184–190, 1963.

SCOTT, M. GLADYS. Measurement of Kinesthesis, *Res. Quart.*, 26:324–341, 1955.

SEASHORE, C. E., and LING, T. L. The Comparative Sensitivity of Blind and Seeing Persons, *Psychol. Monogr.*, 25:148–155, 1918.

SELYE, HANS. *The Stress of Life*, New York: McGraw-Hill Book Co., 1956.

SHELDON, W. H.; STEVENS, S. S.; and TUCKER, W. R. *The Varieties of Human Physique*, New York: Harper & Brothers, 1940.

SINGER, ROBERT N. Effect of Spectators on Athletes and Non-Athletes Performing a Gross Motor Task, *Res. Quart.*, 36:473–482, 1965.

SLATER-HAMMEL, A. T. Measurement of Kinesthetic Perception of Muscular Force with Muscle Potential Changes, *Res. Quart.*, 28:153–159, 1957.

SOLLEY, CHARLES M., and MURPHY, GARDNER. *Development of the Perceptual World*, New York: Basic Books, Inc., 1960.

START, K. B. Intelligence and the Improvement in a Gross Motor Skill After Mental Practice, *Brit. J. Educ. Psychol.*, 34:85, 1964.

STIMPSON, W. G. *The Art of Golf*, 1887, cited by MRS. STEWART HANLEY in The Sense of Feel in Golf, *J. Health, Physical Educ. & Rec.*, 8:366, 1937.

TANNER, J. M. Physique, Body Composition and Growth, in JOKL, E., and SIMON E. (eds.), *International Research in Sport and Physical Education*, Springfield, Illinois: Charles C. Thomas, Publishers, 1964.

THURSTONE, THELMA GWINN. *An Evaluation of Educating Mentally Handicapped Children in Special Classes and in Regular Classes*, Cooperative Research Project Contract Number OE-SAE-6452 of the U.S. Office of Education, The School of Education, University of North Carolina, 1959.

TRAVIS, ROLAND C. An Experimental Analysis of Dynamic and Static Equilibrium, *J. Exp. Psychol.*, 35:216–234, 1945.

ULRICH, CELESTE. Measurement of Stress Evidenced by College Women in Situations Involving Competition, *Res. Quart.*, 28:160–172, 1957.

WIEBE, VERNON R. A Study of Tests of Kinesthesis, *Res. Quart.*, 25:222–230, 1954.

WITKIN, H. A.; LEWIS, H. B.; HERTZMAN, M.; MACHOVER, K.; MEISSNER, P.; and WAPNER, S. *Personality through Perception*, New York: Harper and Brothers, 1954.

ZUBEK, J. P. Counteracting Effects of Physical Exercises Performed During Prolonged Perceptual Deprivation, *Science*, 142:504–506, 1963.

Annotated Student References

PHYSICAL AND MOTOR FACTORS

CUMBEE, FRANCIS. A Factor Analysis of Motor Co-ordination, *Res. Quart.*, 25:412–428, 1954.

In an attempt to answer the question, "What do co-ordination tests really measure?," five specific factors are isolated and discussed.

CURETON, THOMAS K. *Physical Fitness of Champion Athletes*, Urbana: University of Illinois Press, 1951.

Interesting analysis of the physical components contributing to the success of the outstanding athlete.

FLEISHMAN, E. A. A Dimensional Analysis of Motor Abilities, *J. Exp. Psychol.*, 48:437–454, 1954.

Illustrations and descriptions of tests devised by this author to measure motor abilities and the results obtained from data analysis.

GUILFORD, J. P. A System of the Psychomotor Abilities, *Am. J. of Psychol.*, 71:164–174, 1958.

An attempt at determining, through the factor–analysis method, the underlying common psychomotor abilities.

MELTON, ARTHUR W. (ed.). *Apparatus Tests*, AAF Aviation Psychol. Program Research Report No. 4., Washington, D.C.: U.S. Gov't. Printing Office, 1947.

Summarizes apparatus tests to measure various psychomotor abilities used during World War II for the selection and classification of air crew personnel.

ROSE, JERZY E., and MOUNTCASTLE, VERNON B. Touch and Kinesthesis, in FIELD, JOHN (ed.), *Handbook of Physiology: Neurophysiology*, Vol. I., Washington, D.C.: American Physiological Society, 1959.

Excellent physiological explanation of kinesthesis.

SIMON, E. Morphological Development and Functional Efficiency, in JOKL, E., and SIMON, E. (eds.). *International Research in Sport and Physical Education*, Springfield, Ill.: Charles C. Thomas, Publishers, 1964.

Discusses older and present–day methods of body classification and constitutional typology.

TRAVIS, ROLAND C. An Experimental Analysis of Dynamic and Static Equilibrium, *J. Exp. Psychol.*, 35:216–234, 1945.

An analysis of the factors potentially influencing static and dynamic balance, e.g., weight, height, vision, and sex, and a comparison between the two types of balance.

WIEBE, VERNON R. A Study of Tests of Kinesthesis, *Res. Quart.*, 25:222–230, 1954.

Provides twenty-one tests of kinesthesis as well as an excellent bibliography in this area.

WOODWORTH, ROBERT S., and SCHLOSSBERG, HAROLD. *Experimental Psychology*, New York: Henry Holt & Co., 1954.

Good basic discussion on reaction time and typical experiments found on this topic in the psychological literature.

SENSES

FIELD, JOHN (ed.). *Handbook of Physiology: Neurophysiology*, Vol. 1; Washington, D.C.: American Physiological Society, 1959.

Detailed articles by outstanding physiologists and scientists on the senses, their structures, functions, and methods of processing sensations.

NEFF, WILLIAM D. *Contributions to Sensory Psychology*, N.Y.: Academic Press, 1965.

Contains current research findings on all of the sensory systems as well as theories on the physiological basis of sensation.

SCHULTZ, DUANE P. *Sensory Restriction: Effects on Behavior*, N.Y.: Academic Press, 1965.

Emphasis on recent research findings on sense restriction or impairment as a means of understanding sense function and effect on behavior.

PERCEPTUAL MECHANISM

BARTLEY, S. HOWARD. *Principles of Perception*, New York: Harper & Brothers, 1958.

Elementary, basic presentation of information on all aspects of perception.

BEARDSLEE, DAVID C., and WERTHEIMER, MICHAEL. *Readings in Perception*, Princeton, New Jersey: D. Van Nostrand Co., Inc., 1958.

A collection of papers on perception representing the fields of experimental, comparative, personality, and applied psychology.

DEMBER, WILLIAM N. *The Psychology of Perception*, N.Y.: Henry Holt and Co., 1960.

Presents generalizations from research on perception with the content material geared for a course in perception.

HELSON, HARRY (ed.). *Theoretical Foundations of Psychology*, New York: D. Van Nostrand Co., Inc., 1961.

Excellent historical review of perceptual theory development as well as the presentation of the author's own *adaption level* theory.

SOLLEY, CHARLES M., and MURPHY, GARDNER. *Development of the Perceptual World*, N.Y.: Basic Books, Inc., 1960.

An analysis of experimental work on perception and a theoretical view on the perceptual process and perceptual learning.

WOHLWILL, JOACHIM. Perceptual Learning, *Annual Rev. of Psychol.*, 17:201–232, 1966.

Analysis of recent research and trends in perceptual learning.

COGNITION

THE COLORADO SYMPOSIUM. *Contemporary Approaches to Cognition*, Cambridge, Mass.: Harvard University Press, 1957.

Articles by leading cognitive psychologists geared toward a better understand-standing of man's cognitive behavior.

KIRK, SAMUEL A., and WEINER, BLUMA B. *Behaviorial Research on Exceptional Children*, NEA: The Council for Exceptional Children, 1963.

Summarizes the leading research in such areas as the gifted, mentally retarded, sense retarded, and emotionally disturbed.

PURDUE UNIVERSITY. *Symposium on Integrated Development*, Lafayette, Indiana: Purdue University, 1964.

Contains a number of articles by leading physical educators and psychologists on the relationship between academic proficiency and physical performance.

STEIN, JULIAN U. Motor Function and Physical Fitness of the Mentally Retarded: A Critical Review, *Rehabilitation Literature*, 28:230–242, 1963.

Summarizes research on the mentally retarded on motor ability, learning simple versus complex skills, physical fitness, growth and development, and other factors.

EMOTIONAL EFFECTS

MURRAY, EDWARD J. *Motivation and Emotion*. Englewood Cliffs, N.J.: Prentice-Hall Inc., 1964.

Emotions analyzed physiologically and psychologically, written with simplicity for the uninitiated student.

SELYE, HANS. *The Stress of Life*. New York: McGraw-Hill Book Co., 1956.

Summarizes, in simple and understandable language, the scope and nature of stress, mainly emphasizing the author's outstanding work on this topic.

ULRICH, CELESTE. Stress and Sports, in JOHNSON, WARREN R. (ed.), *Science and Medicine of Exercise and Sports*, N.Y.: Harper & Brothers, 1960.

Discusses the theory and physiological foundations of stress, with implication of stress for sports.

4
Individual Differences in Skill

It does not take keen observation to realize that humans differ widely in their achievement in the various so-called academic endeavors as well as in athletic participation. Numerous factors dictate this situation. With regard to motor skills, many of the underlying variables contributing to successful performance are discussed in Chapter 3. Motor skill will, to a great extent, depend on these variables. The question arises: Do some individuals possess general abilities that allow them to succeed more easily in their undertakings whereas others are less favorably endowed?

On the academic side, tests have been devised to predict success in college. According to Sanford (1962) mental abilities are highly generalized, that is, there are only a few and these are basic to expected general academic achievement. Verbal and mathematical tests are significant predictors of a student's average grades in college. As far as intellectual factors are concerned, though, we know that these include reasoning, abstract thinking, memorization, creativeness, and problem solving, to name a few. IQ tests do not measure all these qualities.

Even as there are many intellectual abilities, there are varied athletic abilities. A general mental ability test, such as an IQ test, will predict achievements in the various academic subjects fairly well. Specific tests, of course, will predict better. The general test will tend to correlate more highly with those subjects that have their matter better represented on the test. A motor ability test that purports to measure general athletic ability resembles in nature the purpose and accomplishments of a general mental test. However, in recent years, the so-called motor ability tests and the concept of a general motor ability have been questioned.

Motor Ability, Fitness, Capacity, and Educability Tests

Terminology advanced by physical educators interested in skill-test construction in reality has confused the outsider and less sophisticated physical educator. Such terms as *motor fitness, motor ability, motor capacity,* and *motor educability,* though often used interchangeably in test titles, describe tests with different functions. Terminology, tests, and test value as supported by research evidence are presented now and criticallly analyzed.

Characteristics. Motor ability, motor fitness, motor capacity, and motor educability tests have numerous purposes and supposedly measure various aspects of human abilities and aptitudes. There are unique characteristics to tests of motor ability, motor fitness, motor capacity, and motor educability and in some instances a certain amount of overlap.

Motor ability indicates present athletic ability. It denotes the immediate state of the individual to perform in a wide range of motor skills. A number of motor ability tests have been developed for application to both sexes at different stages in life. These tests have been proposed for classification and achievement expectancy, with the purpose of predicting an individual's possible competency in physical activities. Whether one general test can serve this broad function is debatable.

At this point, it is wise to examine similarities and differences between the terms *ability* and *skill.* An *ability* is thought to be something that is rather general and enduring. It is a trait affected by both learning and heredity. A *skill,* on the other hand, is specific to given tasks and is attained with experience. Because it is task oriented, skill usually refers to a highly developed specific sequence of responses. As an example, balance is an ability, and a person may demonstrate skill in trampolining, a sport that requires balancing ability. Balancing skill is necessary for success in other sports as well. However, although each sport may call for expressions of balancing ability, the skill demonstrated is specific to the situation in which it is practiced. Reseachers have tried and currently are attempting to describe skills in terms of more basic abilities, with varying degrees of success.

A term that has become confused with motor ability and physical fitness is motor fitness. *Physical fitness* implies the ability to perform a given task, in other words, having those physical qualities developed to the extent demanded by the task. *Motor fitness* refers to many of the qualities assumed to be included in physical fitness and motor ability. It is perhaps a more general term than physical fitness and at the same time, one aspect of general motor ability. Clarke defines the relationships as depicted in Figure 4–1.

Physical educators do not necessarily agree with the elements included in each category. To many, there is very little difference, if any, between physical fitness tests and motor fitness tests. In fact, many authors of texts in measurement in physical education include the American Association of Health, Physical Education, and Recreation (AAHPER) Youth Physical

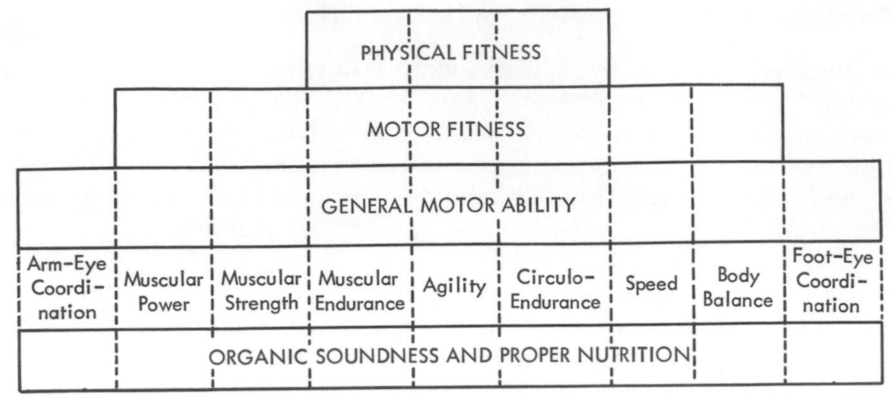

Figure 4–1. Relationship of physical fitness, motor fitness, and general motor ability items. (From Clarke, H. Harrison. *Application of Measurement*, Englewood Cliffs, N.J.: Prentice-Hall, Inc., 1959.)

Fitness Test in their motor fitness chapter. Motor fitness and physical fitness tests usually contain such items as a run, sit-ups, a jump, pull-ups, and the like. Motor ability tests may include these items as well as measures of coordination.

Motor capacity depicts the maximum potential of an individual to succeed in motor–skill performance. It is a person's innate ability, his motor aptitude. Whereas a motor ability test presumably measures present ability or developed capacity, a capacity test is designed to predict ultimate motor potential, a sort of motor intelligence test.

The last of the related terms, *motor educability*, refers to the ease with which one learns new athletic skills. Tests so classified must by necessity incorporate novel-type stunts, such that have not been previously practiced or learned by the performers.

Nature of Tests. Very few tests, designated as *motor capacity tests*, are found in the research literature. C. H. McCloy (1954), a leader in physical education for many years, reported a motor capacity test in the early 1930's. Generally, the test contains weighted measures for size and maturity, the Sargeant Jump, the Brace Motor Ability Test, and squat thrusts; and it can be used for different age levels.

Motor educability tests are also conspicuous by their absence in the literature. Brace (1927) provided impetus to this area of testing with his work in the late 1920's. Although he considered his test one of motor ability, it has been classified as a motor educability test by other researchers. McCloy revised this test, which included twenty stunts, e.g., the Iowa Brace Test includes the side kick, forward hand kick, one-knee balance, one foot-touch head, and stork stand, among others.

The nature of *motor fitness tests* has already been briefly described. There are numerous fitness tests, but this type of test is not of primary concern in this book. A number of *motor ability tests* have been constructed, beginning with the efforts of Oseretzsky (1925) and including the work of Cozens (1936), Humiston (1937), Scott (1939), McCloy (1934), Larson (1941), and finally Barrow (1954).

A few representative *motor ability* tests will serve to familiarize you with the general nature of *motor ability test* elements:

1. *Cozens' athletic ability test:* dodging run, football and basketball throw for distance, dips, standing broad jump, quarter-mile run, and a bar-snap for distance;
2. *Scott's motor ability test (short-form)*: obstacle race, standing broad jump, and basketball throw;
3. *Barrow's motor ability test (long-form)*: standing broad jump, softball throw, zigzag run, wall pass, medicine ball put, and sixty-yard dash.

Probably the most widely used test in psychology is the Sloan (1955) revision of the Oseretsky scale, entitled the Lincoln-Oseretsky Motor Development Scale. This test contains thirty-six items, mainly novel in nature, and is designed primarily for youngsters from six to fourteen years of age. It is a test that apparently has been disregarded by physical educators, in practice and in research.

Value of Tests. The worth of any test is determined by its validity, i.e., if the test measures what it purports to measure. Because of the dearth of motor capacity tests and investigations on this topic, we shall not attempt to discuss the value of those already in existence. This is not to deny the potential impact of developments in the area, but rather to wait for more elaborate research, which might provide more concrete answers. In passing, we may note that McCloy (1934) observed a correlation of .70 between his test and achievement in football and basketball. At the same time, Hoskins (1934) found low correlations between teacher-rated students in various activity classes and the McCloy Motor Capacity Test.

Tests of motor educability received greatest recognition in the 1930's. An examination of investigations concerned with motor educability tests reveals that this is but another area not well researched. Validity coefficients obtained with the Brace Test were not exceptionally high and the criteria used have been questioned. Little work has been done with the Iowa Brace Test, and its stated function has also been attacked by numerous researchers. The Johnson Test evidently is restricted in predictive value in that studies have found high validity only through the use of tumbling stunts and track and field events as criterion measures. This might be expected owing to the nature of the educability test. It contains stunts requiring body movements best represented by these activities.

One of the most damaging studies to the concept of motor educability was completed by Gross, Griesel, and Stull (1956). These authors tested their subjects, who were fifty-six beginners in a college-required physical educational wrestling class, on two motor educability tests and one strength test. The tests used were the Iowa Brace Test, the Metheny Revision of the Johnson Test, and McCloy's Strength Test. All were intercorrelated and correlated to wrestling success. The best predictor was McCloy's Strength Test, which yielded an *r* of .498 (only 14 per cent better than a guess). The Metheny Revision of the Johnson Test afforded a correlation of .33 with wrestling ability and a correlation of .46 was found with the Iowa Brace Test. Finally, the two intended tests of motor educability correlated only .402 with each other. In the words of the authors, "Evidently the two tests of motor educability were not measures of the same ability."

Gire and Espenschade (1942) found fault with other studies not attempting to relate ability to learn with motor educability tests (which is the stated objective of these tests). The authors obtained data on 193 high-school girls and their learning ability of specific skills in basketball, volleyball, and baseball. They noted that the Brace, Iowa Brace, and Johnson Tests of motor educability did not accurately measure the ease with which the subjects learned the skills. All these tests differentiated extreme ranges of skill, according to initial and final ability, but no test distinguished the girls who learned most from those who learned least. Interrelationships between the tests were also analyzed. The Brace and Iowa Brace correlated .77, which should be expected because of the similar elements in both tests. However, the Johnson and Brace Tests correlated only .20, whereas the data from the Iowa Brace and Johnson Tests yielded a coefficient of .48. Gire and Espenschade concluded that the tests did not measure the same ability to the same degree.

Motor ability tests and related research have been of greater interest to physical educators than tests of and research on motor educability and motor capacity. This statement is confirmed by the greater number of publications associated with motor ability. Whether motor ability tests measure immediate athletic ability can be verified only by an examination of research results.

Brace presents evidence to show that his own test, the Brace Motor Ability Test, does not correlate very well with achievement or ease in learning athletic skills. He reported correlations of .24 for basketball achievement and .56 for track and field with the Brace Motor Ability Test (Brace, 1937). Later, he found low correlations with his test and various activities and concluded that neither the Brace Motor Ability Test nor the Iowa Brace Test are effective predictors of the ability to learn skills (Brace, 1941). Di Giovanna (1937) using the Brace Motor Ability Test obtained a low, positive average correlation of .31 between this test and tests of athletic ability. These athletic tests administered to 295 male college students included the standing broad jump, javelin throw, push-ups, baseball throw for distance, 100- and 400-yard dashes, and other events.

Tests of motor ability have not consistently achieved their stated purposes, that of determining present athletic ability. For example, Roloff (1953) did not find a significant relationship between bowling achievement and the Scott Motor Ability Test, but between tennis achievement and the Scott Test an *r* of .44 was high enough to be significant.

On the other hand, McCloy's Motor Ability Test included track and field elements and a strength test, but the track and field scores, according to him, were sufficient in providing extremely high correlations of .92 with basketball and .84 with soccer-football achievement (1934). Humiston (1937), when validating her motor ability test for college women, found the test to distinguish significantly between athletes and nonathletes. Walters (1959) in one of the more recent studies (and recent research is sorely lacking) noted that better bowlers scored significantly higher than poorer bowlers on the Scott Motor Ability Test and the Johnson Educability Test. However, modest correlations were derived when comparing bowling ability with the motor ability test (.47) and the educability test (.32).

Wellman (1935) compared final grades in physical education activities to scores achieved on the Brace Test, the Burpee Test of Motor Agility and Coordination, the Physical Fitness Index, and her own tests of speed, agility, and balance. The best criterion to success in physical education activities as determined by final grades was the Physical Fitness Index (PFI = .53). The Brace Test correlated only .35. Brace himself offers some interesting findings relevant to his test, which he considers a test of motor ability. Validity for the Brace Motor Ability Test was merely .47 to .68 when judgment ratings of general motor ability were employed. Actual scores on athletic events correlated .70 to .80 with his test, not exceptionally high validity coefficients (Brace, 1927). In another investigation, Brace (1941) found that the Brace and Iowa Brace Tests were not good predictors of learning water skills and skills in tennis, volleyball, field hockey, rhythm, and stunts. Finally, he tested 100 junior high school girls on six learning tests. The McCloy, Brace, and Iowa Brace Tests, according to him, did not correlate well enough to be classified as tests of motor educability or motor capacity (Brace, 1946).

Implications of Research. What, then, does the research indicate as far as the physical educator is concerned? First, what about the research itself?

An interesting observation is that practically all the efforts in the respective areas of motor ability, motor educability, and motor capacity were put forth in the late 1920's, the 1930's, and the early 1940's. One may ask why this is so. Do physical educators feel that adequate tests for measuring skill have been constructed and well validated? Or is the trend away from viewing motor ability as something general, something that can be measured with one battery of tests? There are probably numerous individuals who fit either category. However, through improved field research and intensive laboratory research as well as sound reasoning, the emerging concept is that motor ability tests have limited value. Motor abilities in themselves are general measures, whereas task performance is specific to its peculiar nature and condition.

Many of these older studies employed research techniques that, although sound at that time, might be questioned in the light of present knowledge in research methodology. Appropriate experimental designs and statistics are of particular concern. Secondly, a number of the investigations lack clear and precise details on procedural operations. Finally, there have been consistent violations of terminology in the literature, with such terms as capacity, ability, fitness, and educability used interchangeably. The existence of these problems may account for many of the conflicting results obtained in the investigations. It certainly is difficult for one to arrive objectively at any definite conclusions with regard to the respective general motor tests.

Perhaps there is such a thing as general motor ability. Scott and French (1959) are of the opinion that a motor ability test has value in estimating an individual's expected level of ability in a new activity. They feel that when someone does better in a given sport than indicated on the motor ability test, it is because of extreme effort, motivation, and the like. If there is a general factor of motor ability, certainly more research is needed before doubters and disbelievers will be convinced. Much progress has been made since 1914, when Whipple (1914) wrote that many people were of the opinion that speed in tapping was the best test–index of motor capacity. Other means used then to determine motor ability were hand, arm, and body steadiness tests, and precision (tracing) and accuracy (aiming) tasks. There is still a long way to go.

Task Generality Versus Specificity

A number of outstanding psychologists, educators, and physical educators have asserted that cognitive factors and physical factors cannot be explained by general abilities. A proponent of motor-skill specificity is Franklin Henry. Perhaps one of the most vocal and literary physical educators in support of his beliefs on this topic, he has demonstrated, through research and proposed theory, the specificity nature of tasks. In other words, performance from one task to another is independent unless movement patterns are directly related.

Memory Drum Theory. Under the memory-drum theory, an analysis of motor-skill performance is offered by Henry (1960a, 1960b). The method by which a human functions in motor performance is likened to a computer. That is, the computer contains stored programs, ready to function in a desired fashion upon the appropriate signal. Humans also store specific well-learned motor acts in the form of neural patterns in the higher centers of the nervous system. This *unconscious motor memory* is retained as programmed movements on a so-called *memory drum.* Particular stimuli cause the arousal of a neuromotor center, resulting in the execution of an act.

A well-coordinated skill will be performed in an efficient manner because it has been stored on the drum. It can be initiated effortlessly at a point just above the unconscious level. A complicated less-learned or unlearned task is performed continuously at the conscious level in uncoordinated style. This is because of the lack of stored, organized information. An important concept of the theory is that *only* specific acts are stored, and even generally similar movement patterns will not correspond to the same program. Henry emphasizes this point through his research. One of his conclusions is: "Individual differences in speed of arm movement ability are predominantly specific to the type of movement that is made; there is only a relatively small amount of general ability to move the arm rapidly."

This statement summarizes an analysis of data obtained from subjects who performed three similar but distinct arm movements (Henry, 1960a). Low relationships from task to task were observed—individuals were not consistent on these tasks with regard to each other in their times to execute the prescribed movements. In other words, Henry did not find a general speed ability.

What these results indicate, in a practical situation, is that abilities to perform in the various sports are, perhaps, independent. Success in more than one skill is to be explained by means other than general abilities. Some plausible explanations are as follows. The person who is highly motivated to succeed, especially in sports, will put a greater effort into his undertakings. This general motivation may carry across many skill-learning situations. The athlete who has acquired skill and success in one sport may find himself struck with the urge to make a good showing of himself in other sports.

Secondly, past experiences are of tremendous import in determining present motor-performance status. When an individual performs a new skill well with little apparent practice, perhaps it is due to his previous experience in highly-related movement patterns. Motor ability tests reflect the ability to achieve well in whatever items are included on these tests. Sports demand certain skills, and initial ease in demonstrating success in some sports is dependent on these developed skills. According to Henry, past experiences contributing to proficient acts are stored on the memory drum, ready to be unlocked and put into action when the situation demands. And, of course, the situation must be specifically related to the situation in which the skills were learned. Much research has been completed on the specificity-generality problems of motor performance, directly or indirectly by psychologists and physical educators. Let us now turn to other representative investigations found in this area.

Research Favoring Task and Motor Specificity. It would appear as if much of the research indicates that excellence in one motor ability, sport, or skill provides no assurance of accomplishment in others. Positive but low intercorrelations obtained in many investigations between motor abilities as well as task accomplishments would support this statement.

Researchers have investigated relative success achieved when subjects perform in related movements as well as at dissimilar motor skills. The recently published research from the laboratory at the University of California at Berkeley under the direction of Franklin Henry (1961) indicates the uniqueness of apparently related tasks. For example, when comparing the reaction times and movement times of 120 subjects, he found a correlation of .02. Obviously, a person could not predict achievement in one movement very well from data on the other movement. Smith (1962) tested sixty male college subjects on speed of an adductive arm movement under resting muscle and pre-tensed muscle conditions. Timing stations were arranged at 15°, 53°, 90°, and 105°. Small and nonsignificant correlations were obtained between the conditions at each timing station.

Cooper (1940) also observed no relationship between reaction time and speed of a free arm movement. In a very recent experiment Considine (1966) compared the reflex times and reaction times within groups of athletes and nonathletes. The movement required was the same under both conditions: releasing a finger from a key upon presentation of the stimulus. However, an electric shock served as the stimulus for the reflex and a light was the stimulus for initiating the reaction. The coefficients obtained between the two movements were .38 for the athletes and .24 for the nonathletes, thus indicating low, positive, and insignificant relationships. Even though Youngen (1959) and Pierson and Rasch (1960) report significant relationships between reaction time and movement time, the obtained correlations are not high enough to warrant confidence. Pierson and Rasch determined a correlation of .33 and state on the basis of the findings that there is a general speed factor.

Lanier (1934) has stated that "...speed is not conditioned uniformly in all activities by some unitary factor or set of factors." Research findings in general would tend to substantiate this proposition. For instance, Lotter (1961) timed his subjects on their ability to turn a two-handled arm crank versus the speed of the arms individually versus comparable movements of the legs. Low intercorrelations further supported a theory of motor specificity.

After administering seventeen manipulative tests, six printed tests, and twenty-three physical-performance tests, Hempel and Fleishman (1955) concluded that the factors that contributed to successful gross physical task performance were not the same as those in fine manipulated tasks. Fleishman (1958) found a high degree of specificity among twenty-four position tasks. Singer (1966) attempted to determine the relationship of throwing and kicking skills. The subjects, thirty-eight college students enrolled in required physical education classes, threw a ball at a target and kicked a ball at a target, first using preferred limbs, then nonpreferred limbs. Correlations were obtained for all of the possible limb combinations. Five of the six correlations were low, positive, and significant. However, when statistically analyzed for generality and specificity factors, great specificity was noted in the limb relationships. Two balance tasks—a ladder climb and stabilometer performance—were administered to 320 subjects by Bachman (1961). Although both were balance tasks, no significant correlations were obtained. The balance ability required for each skill was evidently task specific.

Some investigators have been interested in the effect of practice upon motor-skill relationships. Buxton and Humphreys (1935) using four motor skills found the intercorrelations to range from .08 to .40 in the beginning of the experiment. After practice, they were − .02 to .39. Achievement in motor performances was related only slightly in the initial stages and remained that way throughout the investigation.

Tests of kinesthesis have also yielded low intercorrelations. Scott (1955) and Wiebe (1954) both concluded from their research findings that kinesthesis is composed of specific factors. Those subjects who performed well on one test did not necessarily do so on another test.

It can be observed, then, that the evidence from studies presented here (by no means exhausting all the available research) suggests a questioning of general motor ability. Task-to-task performance usually is related slightly, but not enough to justify predicting one's ability in many skills or sports from one test. From the material provided in this chapter and in Chapter 3, one may deduce that general learning ability does not exist. With the exception of the mentally retarded and young children, achievements in the cognitive domain are not meaningfully related to those in the motor area.

The following general statements concerning research findings on motor tasks would be valid arguments for the proponents of task specificity:

1. Low and nonsignificant relationships have been obtained when comparing reaction times to speed-of-movement times.
2. Low correlations are found between tasks, even when these tasks are somewhat related.

The ability to perform well in most motor activities is probably based on general factors, primarily a time element (speed), strength, and coordination. Many sports require abilities related to these variables. However, performance measures of each factor vary from activity to activity; hence speed in track is of a different nature from speed and quickness in a basketball game or on a tennis court. The balance demanded on gymnastic apparatus differs from body balance needed when striking a ball, shooting a jump-shot, or in wrestling skills. In other words, an athlete may demonstrate a highly refined example of balance in one sport but not in another. Evidently, one can exhibit strength, coordination, speed, and other qualities in dissimilar ways, and the relationship of tasks within a factor will depend on their degree of overlap and similarity.

The All-round Athlete. Coaches and physical educators might take caution in their interpretation and application of empirical evidence related to individual achievement in a number of sports. It is true that some people perform well in a variety of activities and have been termed *all-round athletes*. However these motor prodigies are the exception not the rule. Success in one sport does not imply that the same situation will occur in another sport, and only when certain factors are operating will this probability increase. These underlying factors are as follows:

1. Experience and intensive practice in a wide range of motor skills will result in apparent ease in skill acquisition. The person who has benefited from a childhood enriched with experiences in basic movement patterns and an assortment of activities, will be more favored in motor-learning situations. These past experiences and the resultant skills serve as a foundation for the learning of new skills.
2. Genetics determine the limitations an individual faces in motor-skill attainment. Even as heredity determines potential intelligence levels, hair color, and body size, it creates the boundaries of motor development. It should be stressed here that research, especially on intelligence, points to the tremendous influence of the environment and life's experiences on an individual's achievements. As a further point, it should be realized that one has to go a long way before he reaches his maximum potential, whether in intellectual or motor pursuits. Thus it may be seen that although hereditary factors contribute to limit potential proficiency in motor acts, many of these factors can be overcome with the presence of the necessary drive and ambition.
3. Motivation is necessary for success. It is hypothesized that the athlete who has achieved success in one sport transfers his high motivation and perseverance to other motor-skill endeavors. The all-round athlete may very well be a highly motivated performer in general who possesses the necessary personality characteristics for varied motor accomplishments.
4. Related sports offer a greater probability of accomplishment for the athlete. Therefore, if an athlete is proficient in a number of sports, there is a good chance that basic skills common to all of them have been mastered.

Other factors may also contribute to the relative ease a person shows in attaining success in various sports. However, there are also many reasons why an individual does not display proficiency in a number of activities. Of major concern is the unrealistic approach the coach takes in a situation involving a superior athlete in one sport attempting to progress in another activity in which he is not nearly so talented. Achievement and satisfaction may or may not come. Great success in one sport does not necessarily mean corresponding achievements in other sports. The ability to be an outstanding performer in a number of sports, even in only two, indicates an extraordinary human being, possessing remarkable talents and skills.

Form

Just as an individual differs in the nature and extent of his abilities, the manner in which he executes various motor patterns will probably be dissimilar to another's style. This method of expressing movement with a purpose, the way of doing something, is called *form.* The specific characteristics of one performer's act makes him different from others, sometimes worthy of emulation, other times best forgotten. Although form in executing skills is unique from person to person, generally accepted *good form* is usually associated with the outstanding athlete in a given sport. The desirability of molding a beginner in the style of the champion is open to question; certainly reasons may be provided for and against such a practice.

Individual Differences. Differences in form exist between performers. Sometimes these differences may be extremely slight so as to be almost unnoticed by the untrained eye, or they are obvious to all. The following factors are associated with form dissimilarities: (1) skill of the performer in the particular act or sport; (2) his personality; (3) his age; (4) the nature of the act or sport, e.g., its complexity; and (5) the physical characteristics of the performer.

Simple acts can be fulfilled in a similar manner from individual to individual. Form uniqueness becomes more observable when the act becomes more detailed, when there are a series of events that constitute a skill, or when gross motor movements are involved in the act. Most physical education skills are considered to be gross, as compared to the fine motor skills of tracing, typing, and tracking. Therefore, participants in gross skills are more apt to display observable form differences.

The nature of the performer, physically, mentally, and emotionally, will decide the method he employs to perform. Some people are more flamboyant or introverted, and their personality may be reflected in their actions. Secondly, skill already attained in the to-be-performed act(s) distinguishes success and form. If we assume that the outstanding athlete generally displays good form, it is apparent that a beginner will not be able to duplicate it until he has had more experience. Thirdly, physical attributes determine performance potential as to relative skill attainment and the form in displaying it. Height, weight, body build, strength, flexibility, and other physical and motor factors usually moderate the manner in which one performs. In other words, the available means often contribute to the style of expression.

Maturation, from infancy to adolescence, often facilitates motor skill performance. Children frequently have to approximate the way a skill should be ideally performed. Desired form in skill performance is assisted by mature minds and bodies, with knowing what to do and having the available resources with which to do it.

Relevance to Success in Skill Attainment. Successful performance may be displayed through a variety of forms and techniques, but it is rare when they violate established performance principles. In other words, for a given act or sequence of skills, there is a generally accepted good form, consistent with kinesiological, physical, and psychological evidence, with variations of the ideal form. This is not to deny the possibility of success in spite of form, but rather to emphasize the probability of success and form going together.

In actuality, in most sports, the outcome is more important than the means. Some sports, such as gymnastics and diving, are judged on skill and form. However, the baseball coach will not tamper with the batting style of a .300 hitter, even if he hits, as Mel Ott did, with his "foot in the bucket." The avid baseball spectator can readily picture the differences between the stances of Stan Musial and Ted Williams, yet both were great hitters. Evidently, at the point of ball contact with the bat both men had coordinated their body parts in a similar fashion, and both hit effectively for many years.

Some people have to adjust their style because of body build and other factors. Consistent conscientious practice can overcome many limitations. The displayed form may not be aesthetic, but effectiveness of the movement can be measured by the results. Perhaps one of the greatest problems the parent, physical educator, and coach is confronted with, is that of the youngster attempting to emulate a professional athlete, his particular idol. On the one hand, the practice is good, for the boy may gain great insight into the nature of the sport and the means of attaining success. However, progress may be impeded due to differences in physical characteristics, age, and so on.

It is usually poor practice, therefore, for a beginner or even an advanced learner, to attempt to copy every phase of an act or activity from someone else. The physical educator and coach should explain the reasons for executing a movement in a certain style and then expect and allow for individual variations. Robots do not make the best performers. Form, to a certain extent, provides direction for the learner and facilitates the learning process, but probably not to the degree imagined in years past. If it is possible to designate a performer as displaying such a thing, reasonable form is to be expected for probable success in skill attainment. A thought to remember is that the ideal form for a given act is continually remodeled as new evidence is accumulated. Therefore, open-mindedness and flexibility in style are necessary in order to take advantage of the research that points to more effective means of executing acts.

Aesthetic Appeal. One of the prime reasons for the demonstration of a certain form, other than that of scientific substantiation, is often merely to satisfy aesthetic appeal. Posture varies from person to person as does the concept of what good posture actually is, even so, form and ideal conceptual form for athletic performance also vary among individuals. Good posture implies either effective posture or pleasing-to-the-eye posture, or both, but these two conditions are not necessarily related. An individual can demonstrate physical efficiency with a scoliosis, lordosis, or kyphosis.

Good form can be likened to good posture. Is the reference to effectiveness, attractiveness, or both? Each type of good form can occur independently or in conjunction with the other. Whereas in the past the saying was, "Do it because it looks good," athletes now are more concerned with their own effectiveness in the performed skills, even if it means sacrificing aesthetic appeal.

For the same reasons that a pleasing posture impresses people and may promote an inner feeling of confidence, good form in skill execution can also be advocated. Professional and varsity athletes want to look good—aesthetically and skillfully—in front of spectators. A unique form, sometimes called showmanship when displayed at an extreme, helps to sell the player and sport to the fans. As long as skill is not worsened, this practice will serve its purpose. However, it is important for the individual to realize when he is performing primarily for aesthetic appeal and when he is performing for effectiveness. Ego involvement is the basis for one, whereas science is the foundation of the other.

Level of Aspiration

Before performing a skill, we typically formulate hypotheses about our chance for success. Success itself is relative and depends on what a person will accept for himself as achievement. Some people would consider themselves successful if they shot golf in the 90's; other people attain this feeling when they score in the 70's. The setting of a goal is termed *the level of aspiration*. Past experiences in similar situations, resulting in successes or failures, affect the aspiration level. In turn, the immediate aspiration level for a given task may very well determine its outcome, as will be noted a little later in this section of the chapter.

An individual's level of aspiration for a given task reflects his optimism or lack of it when faced with the challenge. It also indicates his level of reality —whether his goal is consistent with prior success, actual present achievement, and ability. Finally, it can be used to improve performance. If the level of aspiration is set high enough, it acts as an incentive, something for which to strive. Worell (1959) points out that for each person there may be different levels of aspiration, depending on interpretation of the term. It may mean a level hoped for, expected, or minimally satisfied with. In other words, a level of aspiration can indicate the discrepancy between previous performance and expected performance; between wished for and previous performance; or personally acceptable and previous performance.

It is unrealistic for a person to have a large discrepancy between his estimated performance and his actual performance. When the performance level is far below the aspiration level, the result is consistent personal failure. When the situation is reversed, there is a better chance of success. Therefore, it can be seen that success and failure may be determined in relation to the level of aspiration. An unhealthy situation occurs when too many successes or failures are experienced by an individual; hence it is desirable to have an approximate relationship between hoped-for and actual performance.

For example, Worell (1959) found that students whose aspirations were related to previous performances and who did not wish to achieve much more than they had already, received the highest college grades. They were considered to be realistic. There is not universal acceptance as to what the intended level of attainment should be. Atkinson (1957) found that the maximum level of performance was obtained when the probability of success was moderate (.50), and he predicted that it would be uniformly lower as the probability advanced in either direction. These findings have been contradicted by Locke's recent study. Locke (1966) observed a linear relationship between intentions and actual level of performance. The higher level of intended achievement resulted in high levels of performance.

Locke and Bryan (1966) verified these findings. These experimenters utilized the Complex Coordination Apparatus, where red and green lights are arranged to form an *H* on the display. The subject has to move controls (foot pedals and hand stick) to match lights with those illuminated. When the match is right, a new stimulus pattern occurs, and this continues until all thirteen patterns have been presented in sequence. It was found that performance goals influence the level of performance. The subjects with specific but high goals did better on the task than those who were told just to do their best (see Figure 4–2). Implications from these results may be applied to teaching methods. Having the students set precise high but attainable goals may be more effective as a learning technique than haphazard methods of motivation.

Certain statements concerning level of aspiration appear to be warranted. Research findings by Child and Whiting (1949) and other investigators are in agreement:

1. Success lends to a raising of the aspiration level whereas failure encourages a lowering of this level.
2. The greater the success, the greater the probability of a rise in the level.
3. The level of performance is influenced more by success than failure and the effect of success is more predictably stable (more upward shifts are noted after success than downward shift after failure).

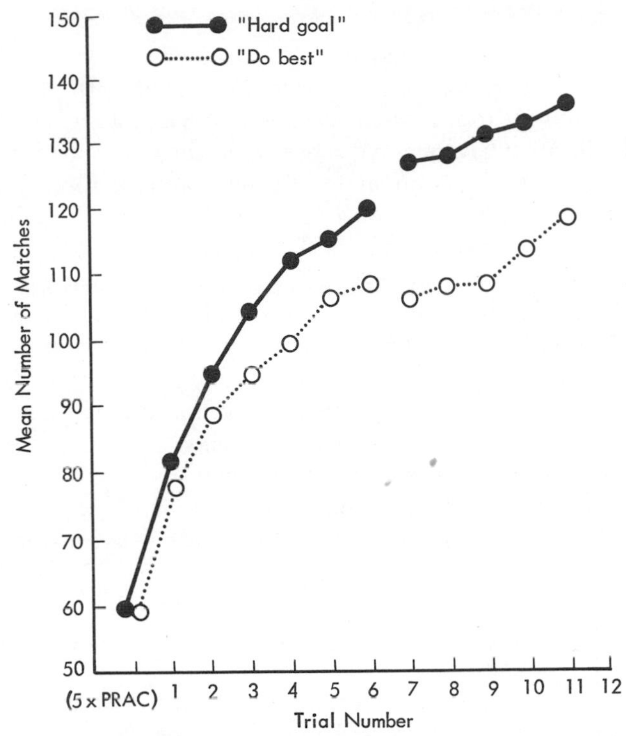

Figure 4–2. A comparison of two groups in performance on a complex motor task. One group had high standards and a difficult goal, the other group was merely told, "Do your best." The Hard-Goal group was significantly better than the Do-Best group. (From Locke, Edwin A., and Bryan, Judith F. Cognitive Aspects of Psychomotor Performance: The Effects of Performance Goals on Level of Performance, *J. Appl. Psychol.*, 50:286–291, 1966.)

The importance of success to level of aspiration and ultimate achievement is thus established. It would appear, then, that physical educators and coaches should place students in situations in which they can attain a reasonable amount of satisfaction. Unfortunately, this may not be the case in many athletic situations. Smith (1949) in his study discovered that college freshman football players usually demonstrated a large discrepancy between level of aspiration and actual performance. A considerable number of these football players experienced repeated failure. They had high aspiration levels of playing, but rarely played the amount of time they thought they would.

To conclude, aspiration levels continually change with repeated experience on a task and may be dissimilar from task to task. The skill level of the learner as well as his desire to improve, as demonstrated by high but attainable goals, describe but another aspect of the learning process. The psychological impact of a person's level of aspiration should be viewed as an important part of motor-skill learning.

Fatigue

Fatigue assumes many forms and may be localized or general. Physiologists have investigated the physiological factors associated with this state in an attempt to explain it from a scientific point of view. Perhaps psychologists and physical educators have ignored researching the effects of fatigue because of its more apparent effects on motor learning and performance. Logically one might expect fatigue to serve as a handicap to a person's undertakings.

The ill effect of mental and physical fatigue on directed activity was expressed early in this century by Ash (1914), who stated that fatigue tends to interfere with or inhibit activity. There is an interruption of the control one has in a given situation and a loss of efficiency. These general thoughts have been echoed through the years. Of course, individuals vary as to the degree of physical and/or mental work that would have a fatiguing effect on them. How limiting a factor fatigue would be depends on the condition of the performer and the nature of the skill to be learned.

An interesting problem is whether performance and learning are equally affected by fatigue. The similarities and differences between these terms are pointed out in Chapter 1. Latest research developments would appear to suggest that slight fatigue affects performance more than it does learning. Alderman (1965) required four groups of subjects to complete a speed test (the rho test) and an accuracy test (pursuit rotor). Two groups acted as controls (no exercise). Meanwhile the experimental groups were subjected to ten minutes of exercise between trials 4 and 5 on the rho test and exercised between trials 20 and 21 on the pursuit rotor. Alderman concluded that the conditions of his experiment caused poorer performance but not poorer learning.

Physical educators are concerned with the optimal period of time their students should spend learning skills before fatigue effects would make this time wasteful. Common sense is perhaps one of the best indicators as to when a person is too tired mentally or physically to receive any value from continued practice. However, Alderman's study serves as a warning that, although there are times when performance may suffer slightly under minor conditions of fatigue, ultimate learning does not. Under excessive fatigue, it is quite difficult for the learner to be attentive to new cues and new material. The returns of the practice of pushing the learner when he is too tired are of little value and, consequently, this practice is regarded as undesirable.

Level of Skill

In any given situation, a teacher finds himself facing students with a wide range of developed skills and potential abilities for achievement. The magnitude of the range will depend on whether the students are grouped at random or there is an attempt at homogeneity. It is often convenient to categorize students learning a physical education activity as beginners, intermediates, or advanced. This classification is arbitrary, for individuals fall in a continuum on the range of skill development. Recognizing differences in achieved level of skill allows the physical educator to proceed in a more effective manner, for each level requires special learning considerations.

Considerations at Different Levels. At the onset, it should be emphasized that certain learning principles apply to the acquisition of motor skills, regardless of skill level. One of the major purposes of this book is to relate the general considerations for all learners. However, the status of the individual in his skill achievement in a particular activity necessitates specific allowances and unique considerations. As might be expected, teaching techniques should be modified from the beginning to the advanced stages of an individual's motor-skill development.

The beginner, the person learning a sport or specific skill for the first time, poses problems to the teacher unlike those he confronts with a highly skilled performer. Although a naïve person might expect an easier time with beginners, the contrary is the case. In fact, it would appear that many young physical educators prefer working with the most highly skilled—the varsity athlete. The beginner is often neglected, for it is much more rewarding to direct the progress of individuals who are highly skilled, coordinated, and motivated. Each novice requires individual attention, although in many cases this might be impractical. What general procedures, then, may be followed to promote learning in a group of beginners?

First, beginners must *understand the goal* that they will be attempting to achieve. If it is to swim the side-stroke the length of the pool, they should observe a demonstration of this stroke in its entirety. They will then become aware of what is to be expected, of how the parts of the body are coordinated for this skill, and generally, what lies ahead of them. Second, beginners appear to *benefit most from activity,* thus verbal instruction should be kept to a minimum. Naturally, with increased age and maturity, there is less impatience and perhaps a greater mental capacity on the part of the students enabling them to benefit from verbal instruction. However, the generally accepted rule with beginners is to allow the actual physical activity to dominate the early lessons.

Third, this activity may be initiated by the performer or directed from *external sources,* such as the teacher manipulating a particular body area in order for the novice to get the feel of the desired movement. At the early stage of skill attainment, there is the unresolved question of introducing the mechanical and physiological principles related to the skill performance as well as the merit of using the problem-solving approach, of directing the students to attempt to determine the why's and the how's in their quest for skill mastery. Visual aides, in the form of movies, slides, and pictures are possible supplementary material. The methods and means of instruction to be utilized will depend on the background, nature, and ideas of the teacher.

There is no one set method of instruction. The point here, though, is that *physical activity should be emphasized in the early stages of motor learning.* This is especially true with younger children.

The physical experience allows additional methods of instruction to be more meaningful. Attention to detail can then be provided in verbal instruction. Specifics can only be attended to when the general aspects of an activity have been mastered. One of the greatest mistakes a teacher can make with beginners is to spend too much time on details and talking too much.

Although the effects of instruction on motor performance are dealt with in Chapter 7, the results of an investigation by Renshaw and Postle (1928) will serve to reinforce the concept of the importance of physical activity for beginners. These researchers formed three groups, all of whom learned a pursuit-rotor task. Group I received very brief demonstrations and instruction, Group II had additional instruction, and Group III observed a simple demonstration with detailed instructions. Groups I and II performed similarly on the task while Group III demonstrated the poorest performance. In this case, greater verbal instructions had the effect of impeding the acquisition of manipulatory skill. As Renshaw and Postle reason, progress in some motor skills may be inhibited where language (verbal habits) cannot substitute for direct sensory stimuli afforded by the task. The study is aptly and humorously concluded with the statement that the pursuit rotor is operated by the hands, not the voice box.

A learner will probably fare better in a sport new to him if the teacher attempts to build on skills familiar and already known to the learner. Resemblances of already-learned skills to those to be learned, if pointed out, promote faster learning. At least one leading tennis authority believes that it is quite difficult to teach anyone to hit the tennis serve if he cannot pitch a ball overhand. Similarly, if students cannot swing their arms freely at the shoulder, parallel to the ground, learning of the forehand and backhand groundstrokes will be impeded.

Simple motor skills of throwing, catching, pivoting, and the like must be accomplished before reasonable tennis proficiency can be expected. The tennis stroke is then likened to some familiar skill, as exemplified by swinging a baseball bat. The acquisition of new skills would be more fun and a faster process as well if these rules were followed.

Consideration should be given to the length of the practice sessions. For most beginners, *frequent, short, spaced, practice periods* are preferable to extended practice periods. Novice learners are more prone to a loss of interest and a lack of attention when they have to overcome the hurdles of learning something completely new. The acquisition of skill is usually a stubborn process.

The beginner demonstrates symptoms of tightness and wasted energy. As skill is acquired, efficiency in movement is observed. At first, it is as if the parts of the body are working independently, but later performance is characterized by minimal and only necessary coordinated movement patterns.

Neurologically, control of unlearned or poorly learned skills is at the cerebral level, but this area has less of a role in the performance of advanced learners. The cerebellum is more active in the latter situation. It is as if the beginner has to attend to so many cues (many unnecessary) that his performance suffers. With experience and instruction, he learns what he should respond to, how to respond effectively, and how to direct his thought processes during motor performance.

New skills should be taught in such a way that the *learner performs in practice the way he is expected to in the actual situation.* Slow-motion practice or emphasis on one factor when several are equally important to the successful performance of an act only makes for additional learning and relearning problems. If speed and accuracy are required, both should be simultaneously practiced. One can learn to shoot a stationary jump shot in basketball, but in actual practice the player is usually on the move before shooting. Simulating game-like skills in practice affords a better chance of success in the contest. An example of factor emphasis on the learning of a motor skill was demonstrated by Solley (1952). Three groups of subjects thrusted toward a target with their times and scores recorded. One group emphasized speed, the second accuracy, and the last group was directed to place equal emphasis on speed and accuracy. Among other conclusions, Solley found the following:

> In skills in which speed is the predominate factor for successful performance, the most efficient results are attained by early emphasis of speed.
>
> In skills in which both speed and accuracy are important to successful performance, emphasis on both speed and accuracy yields the most desirable results.

Many students have trouble learning motor skills because of a lack of experience with basic movement patterns in childhood. Ease in learning new skills will depend to a large extent on these many varied previous experiences. There are indications that even in later years familiarization with simple motor patterns facilitates the learning of more complex skills, e.g., those involved in sports. Salit (1944) found that her subjects, who initially scored low, significantly improved on the Scott Motor Ability Test through the teaching of basic skills. It is rare that new tasks require the learning of new motor skills. Basic, simple movements—those which are performed in childhood, including running, throwing, kicking, and jumping—underlie all sports. It is the means of organizing these patterns that differs from skill to skill and sport to sport. Therefore, learners who have not had the opportunity to play and develop the simple motor skills associated with childhood are handicapped in later, more complex undertakings.

Beginners should not be required to display the same ideal form for a specific skill. The important thing in the initial stages of learning is achievement and satisfaction, and casting a mold restricts the opportunity. Emphasis on particular desired styles can take place later as skill progresses.

The advanced learner, the one who displays a high level of achievement on a skill or group of skills, may be approached in a different manner from the beginner. More time can be spent with him on the critical details of his performance. Verbal instruction is more meaningful and, in general, the advanced are able to concentrate for a longer period of time on the task at hand. Practice sessions can be more intensive and extensive.

A highly skilled person usually achieves his status because of motivation, among other variables. Incentive will probably be less of a problem with this performer than the beginner, providing of course, his level of aspiration is high enough. As a standard rule, though, we all like to perform in activities in which we can demonstrate achievement. A beginner usually lacks confidence, the advanced typically does not.

All in all, teaching students who fall along the continuum of skill achievement presents general and special problems. Emphasis in instructional methods and considerations changes as skill progresses.

Early Versus Late Learners. Frequently, early progress in skill attainment is misleading in predicting ultimate success. Some individuals demonstrate better performance than others in the early stages of learning, almost as if they gain quicker insight into the problem at hand. Various factors may be attributed to individual differences in early skill achievement, but one conclusion appears justified: early success does not indicate later achievement.

Welch (1963) had her subjects perform a ladder-clmb test (to go as high as possible before toppling). They were tested on six different days, with each test consisting of ten trials. Welch concluded that general skill-attainment prediction is poor unless an estimation of learning ability extends over at least half of the practice days. Fleishman and Hempel (1954) demonstrated that different factors are emphasized with increased practice and learning. Hence, beginning success depends on certain factors and later achievement reflects the utilization of other factors. In other words, it would be quite difficult to predict end performance from beginning level of skill because variables vary in importance in each particular stage of learning.

Trussell (1965) required forty college women students to learn a ball-juggling task. She found that the learning scores were not significantly related to initial scores and that the best predictability of final performance was obtained during the first 60 per cent of practice. Implications from the evidence are that people learn at varying rates of speed and that some might be handicapped if a particular unit or skill to be learned is covered too quickly. Everyone has his own optimal learning rate, and unfortunately, in mass learning situations such as found in physical education classes, it is hard to consider individual differences. However, an awareness of this problem will at least allow the teacher to determine what is best for the group and where possible to adjust for extremes in fast and slow learners.

Summary

For many years, researchers have attempted to discover general motor abilities, to isolate a few which would predict or measure general athletic achievement or ease in learning motor skills. Although their investigations have been valuable, the abundance of research attempting to find relationships between achievement in motor skills has tended to indicate the specificity of task performance. A person who performs well in one sport or in one skill will not necessarily do so in other sports or in other skills. There are many motor abilities, each specific to the situation in which it is applied.

Just as abilities differ and are applicable to particular conditions, form in motor performance varies. One form is not appropriate for all performers. The level of aspiration is based on and determines personal success or failure and fluctuates within and between individuals. This intended level of achievement should be reasonably high if a better level of performance is to be reached.

Teaching techniques should be considered and adapted to the learner's level of achievement. Beginners require physical involvement and progress more efficiently when verbal instruction is minimized. Practice sessions should be shorter because of low spans of attention and a possible lack of student motivation. Advanced learners will receive more value from detailed explanations and analyses of their performances. There is a wide range of effective teaching methods, and the teacher should employ those techniques that are sound and which he can handle comfortably. As learning progresses, emphasis on certain teaching methods and procedures are more desirable than others. Finally, consideration must be given not only to the general skill status of groups but also to individuals and their learning rates.

References

Alderman, Richard B. Influence of Local Fatigue on Speed and Accuracy in Motor Learning, *Res. Quart.*, 36:131–140, 1965.

Ash, Issac E. Fatigue and Its Effects upon Control, *Archives of Psychol.*, 31, 1914.

Atkinson, J. W. Motivational Determinants of Risk-Taking Behavior, *Psychol. Rev.*, 64:359–372, 1957.

Bachman, John C. Specificity vs. Generality in Learning and Performing Two Large Muscle Motor Tasks, *Res. Quart.*, 32:3–11, 1961.

Barrow, Harold M. Test of Motor Ability for College Men, *Res. Quart.*, 25: 253–260, 1954.

Brace, David K. *Measuring Motor Ability*, New York: A. S. Barnes and Co., 1927.

Brace, David K. Studies in Motor Learning of Gross Bodily Motor Skills, *Res. Quart.*, 17:242–253, 1946.

Brace, David K. Studies in the Rate of Learning Gross Bodily Motor Skills, *Res. Quart.*, 12:181–185, 1941.

Buxton, C. E., and Humphreys, L. G. The Effect of Practice upon Intercorrelations of Motor Skills, *Science*, 81:441–442, 1935.

Child, Irvin L., and Whiting, John W. Determinants of Level of Aspiration: Evidence from Everyday Life, *J. Abnorm. Soc. Psychol.*, 44:303–314, 1949.

Considine, William. Reflex and Reaction Times Within and Between Athletes and Non-athletes, Unpub. master's thesis, Illinois State University, 1966.

Cooper, John H. An Investigation of the Relationship Between Reaction Time and Speed of Movement, Unpub. doct. dissertation, Indiana University, 1940.

Cozens, F. W. *Achievement Scales in Physical Education Activities for College Men*, Philadelphia: Lea & Febiger, 1936.

Di Giovanna, Vincent G. A Comparison of the Intelligence and Athletic Ability of College Men, *Res. Quart.*, 8:96–106, 1937.

Fleishman, Edwin A. An Analysis of Positioning Movements and Static Reactions, *J. Exp. Psychol.*, 55:13–24, 1958.

Fleishman, Edwin A., and Hempel, Walter E., Jr. Changes in Factor Structure of a Complex Psychomotor Test as a Function of Practice, *Psychometrika*, 19:239–252, 1954.

Gire, Eugenia, and Espenschade, Anna. The Relationship Between Measures of Motor Educability and Learning of Specific Motor Skills, *Res. Quart.*, 14: 43–56, 1942.

Gross, Elmer A.; Griesel, Donald C.; and Stull, Alan. Relationship Between Two Motor Educability Tests, a Strength Test, and Wrestling Ability After Eight-Weeks' Instruction, *Res. Quart.*, 27:395–402, 1956.

Hempel, Walter E., Jr., and Fleishman, Edwin A. A Factor Analysis of Physical Proficiency and Manipulative Skill, *J. Appl. Psychol.*, 39:12–16, 1955.

Henry, Franklin M. Increased Response Latency for Complicated Movements and a "Memory Drum" Theory of Neuromotor Reaction, *Res. Quart.*, 31:448–458, 1960 a.

Henry, Franklin M. Influence of Motor and Sensory Sets on Reaction Latency and Speed of Discrete Movements, *Res. Quart.*, 31:459–468, 1960 b.

Henry, Franklin M. Reaction Time—Movement Time Correlations, *Percept. Mot. Skills*, 12:63–66, 1961.

Henry, Franklin M. Specificity vs. Generality in Learning Motor Skills, *Coll. Phys. Educ. Assoc. Proc.*, Washington, D.C., 126–128, 1958.

Hoskins, Robert N. The Relationship of Measurements of General Motor Capacity to the Learning of Specific Psycho-Motor Skills, *Res. Quart.*, 5:63–72, 1934.

Humiston, Dorothy A. A Measurement of Motor Ability in College Women, *Res. Quart.*, 8:181–185, 1937.

Johnson, Granville B. Physical Skill Tests for Sectioning Classes into Homogenous Units, *Res. Quart.*, 3:128–136, 1932.

Lanier, Lyle H. The Intercorrelations of Speed of Reaction Measurements, *J. Exp. Psychol.*, 17:371–399, 1934.

Larson, Leonard A. A Factor Analysis of Motor Ability Variables and Tests, with Tests for College Men, *Res. Quart.*, 12:499–517, 1941.

Locke, Edwin A. The Relationship of Intentions to Level of Performance, *J. Appl. Psychol.*, 50:60–66, 1966.

Locke, Edwin A., and Bryan, Judith F. Cognitive Aspects of Psychomotor

Performance: The Effects of Performance Goals on Level of Performance, *J. Appl. Psychol.*, 50:286–291, 1966.

LOTTER, WILLARD S. Specificity or Generality of Speed of Systematically Related Movements, *Res. Quart.*, 32:55–62, 1961.

MCCLOY, C. H. The Measurement of General Motor Capacity and General Motor Ability, *Res. Quart. Suppl.*, 5:46–61, 1934.

MCCLOY, C. H., and YOUNG, NORMA D. *Tests and Measurements in Health and Physical Education*, New York: Appleton-Century-Crofts, Inc., 1954.

OSERETSKY, N. I. A Metric Scale for the Study of the Motor Ability of Children, *Zsch. of. Kinderforsch.*, 30:300–314, 1925.

PIERSON, WILLIAM R., and RASCH, PHILIP J. Generality of a Speed Factor in Simple Reaction and Movement Time, *Percept. Mot. Skills*, 11:123–128, 1960.

RENSHAW, S., and POSTLE, D. K. Pursuit Learning Under Three Types of Instruction, *J. Gen. Psychol.*, 1:360–367, 1928.

ROLOFF, LOUISE L. Kinesthesis in Relation to the Learning of Selected Motor Skills, *Res. Quart.*, 24:210–217, 1953.

SALIT, ELIZABETH P. The Development of Fundamental Sport Skills in College Women of Low Motor Ability, *Res. Quart.*, 15:330–339, 1944.

SANFORD, NEVITT. Higher Education as a Field of Study, in SANFORD, NEVITT (ed.), *The American College*, New York: John Wiley & Sons, Inc., 1962.

SCOTT, M. GLADYS. Assessment of Motor Ability of College Women Through Objective Tests, *Res. Quart.*, 10:63–83, 1939.

SCOTT, M. GLADYS. Measurement of Kinesthesis, *Res. Quart.*, 26:324–341, 1955.

SCOTT, M. GLADYS, and FRENCH, ESTHER. *Measurement and Evaluation in Physical Education*, Dubuque, Iowa: Wm. C. Brown Co., Pub., 1959.

SINGER, ROBERT N. Comparison of Inter-Limb Skill Achievement in Performing a Motor Skill, *Res. Quart.*, 27:406–410, 1966.

SLOAN, W. The Lincoln-Oseretsky Motor Development Scale, *Genet. Psychol. Monogr.*, 51:183–252, 1955.

SMITH, CARNIE H. The Influence of Athletic Success and Failure in the Level of Aspiration, *Res. Quart.*, 20:196–208, 1949.

SMITH, LEON E. Influence of Neuromotor Program Alteration on the Speed of a Standard Arm Movement, *Percept. Mot. Skills*, 15:327–330, 1962.

SOLLEY, WILLIAM H. The Effects of Verbal Instruction of Speed and Accuracy Upon the Learning of a Motor Skill, *Res. Quart.*, 23:231–240, 1952.

TRUSSELL, ELLA. Prediction of Success in a Motor Skill on the Basis of Early Learning Achievement, *Res. Quart.*, 39:342–347, 1965.

WALTERS, C. ETTA. Motor Ability and Educability Factors of High and Low Scoring Beginning Bowlers, *Res. Quart.*, 30:94–100, 1959.

WELCH, MARYA. Prediction of Motor Skill Attainment from Early Learning, *Percept. Mot. Skills*, 17:263–266, 1963.

WELLMAN, ELIZABETH. The Validity of Various Tests as Measures of Motor Ability, *Res. Quart. Suppl.*, 6:19–25, 1935.

WHIPPLE, GUY M. *Manual of Mental and Physical Tests*, Baltimore: Warwick and York, Inc., 1914.

WIEBE, VERNON R. A Study of Tests of Kinesthesis, *Res. Quart.*, 25:222–230, 1954.

WORELL, LEONARD. Level of Aspiration and Academic Success, *J. Educ. Psychol.*, 50:47–54, 1959.

YOUNGEN, LOIS. A Comparison of Reaction and Movement Times of Women Athletes and Non-athletes, *Res. Quart.*, 30:349–355, 1959.

Annotated Student References

MOTOR ABILITIES

BRACE, DAVID K. *Measuring Motor Ability*, N.Y.: A. S. Barnes and Co., 1927.

One of the pioneer efforts in motor-ability test construction.

HENRY, FRANKLIN M. Increased Response Latency for Complicated Movements and a "Memory Drum" Theory of Neuromotor Reaction, *Res. Quart.*, 31:448–558, 1960.

Research substantiating Henry's theory of motor learning, providing insight into the specificity of task learning.

LOTTER, WILLARD S. Specificity or Generality of Speed of Systematically Related Movements, *Res. Quart.*, 32:55–62, 1961.

Representative investigation upholding a theory of motor specificity.

SEASHORE, ROBERT H. Individual Differences in Motor Skill, *J. Gen. Psychol.*, 3:38–66, 1930.

Early summary of research on motor ability indicating the independence of skills.

LEVEL OF ASPIRATION

LEWIN, KURT, and others. Level of Aspiration, in HUNT, J. Mc V. (ed.), *Personality and the Behavior Disorders*, Vol. I., N.Y.: Ronald Press, 1944.

One of the most extensive treatments of the area, containing a review of the literature and theoretical implications.

SMITH, CARNIE H. The Influence of Athletic Success and Failure in the Level of Aspiration, *Res. Quart.*, 20:196–208, 1949.

One of the few studies relating athletic success to level of aspiration, providing ideas for further research.

FATIGUE

BARTLEY, S. HOWARD, and CHUTE, ELOISE. *Fatigue and Impairment in Man*, New York: McGraw-Hill Book Co., Inc., 1947.

The psychological and physiological effects of fatigue and the various causes of the state are discussed with special application to the industrial worker.

5

Developmental Factors and Influence on Skill Learning

Learning as is defined in Chapter 1 is demonstrated by overt behavior and is implemented by reinforced practice. In an experimental sense, learning is usually measured independently of maturation. Practically speaking, though, maturation is related to behavior, and the two are inextricably interwoven. Maturation determines human potential and sets the upper limits of learning and performance.

As the youngster grows, develops, and matures certain patterns of behavior unfold, mostly learned, but in some cases occurring in spite of a lack of experience. Researchers can measure the effects of maturation on learning and behavior when practice in or experience with certain skills are held to a minimum. Those interested in distinguishing learned acts from the natural instinctive behavior of a species have used this method. Some simple reflexes and more complicated acts of human babies have been identified as being independent of learning. However, it is generally conceded that the attainment of complex skills and most behavioral patterns as defined by adult standards are the result of maturation and experience.

Certain behavior is primarily influenced by learning whereas other behavior is affected most by maturation. Educators by necessity should expect unique behavior and abilities relevant to an individual's age and maturational level. They should also understand how to teach, when to teach, and what to teach children at each level. Oftentimes a mistake is made in assuming that body size represents development and readiness to learn. *Growth* implies an increase in stature, *development* denotes increasing complexity of structure and function, and *maturation* indicates that the organism is approaching a somewhat stable structure. Behavior is more purposeful when development and maturation take place. Age is another factor which is misconstrued as representing maturity. This is why psychologists distinguish the chronological age from the maturational age of a child.

Throughout life from birth to that inevitable day, experiences accumulate and the body grows and changes, and individual differences in abilities and achievements will be observable. Age differences, sex differences, innate abilities, personality factors, environmental experiences—all and more interact to determine human attainment. Developmental factors as they contribute to academic success and life's adjustment have been the concern of psychologists. The interest in this area has led to a course of study and field of research termed *developmental psychology*. It is unfortunate that physical educators, professionals who deal in physical activity, a product most cherished by young children regardless of race, color, or country, have contributed so little to fuller understanding of the learning process as affected by developmental factors.

When should children be taught certain basic skills or introduced to particular sports? When is this age of readiness? What is the relationship between the ability to perform simple motor patterns and intellectual potential? Does sports participation really change behavior for the better and modify personalities? What exactly is the role of sports participation in personality development? At what ages do individuals reach their peak in skill performance? Up until what age is it possible to demonstrate a reasonable amount of skill in a given activity satisfactorily? How much of a factor in skill attainment is sex—why do boys usually demonstrate a greater proficiency in motor skills than girls during adolescence and later? How different are they in childhood?

These are but a few problems that may be associated with developmental factors and motor development. The responsibility of the physical educator lies in attempting to seek the answers through available sources. This chapter attempts to provide some information on the developmental factors related to motor learning but succeeds more in raising questions than in answering them. A dearth of research in this area is responsible for this situation. However, this fact should be an even greater stimulation to physical educators to pursue those persistent problems that require satisfactory explanations.

Early Motor Development and Critical Learning Periods

One of the most fascinating concepts in psychology is that a certain period during a lifetime is optimal for affecting behavior and promoting learning. This phenomenon has been observed in a number of species, although it is more apparent in infrahumans. In fact, most research has been accumulated on animals and birds and indicates specific periods crucial for the development of certain behavior. Types of experiences and the periods in which they are experienced by the organism may have critical bearing on future behavior. *Critical periods*, as applied to human learning, *refer to the optimal periods for attempting to acquire fundamental and complex skills*. The *critical period* for any specific sort of learning is that time when the *maximum sensory, motor, motivational, and psychological capacities are present.*

A critical period for the learning of certain tasks or development of behavioral patterns may be determined by sense or experience deprivation, by introduction to the experience, or by environmental enrichment at a given time in life. Humans and animals have been subjected to all three conditions by researchers intent on discovering these periods. In order to discover the best time for learning, it is necessary first to examine the normal learning progress from birth to later childhood. In his earliest stage of development, the baby cannot walk, reach for objects, or perform relatively simple motor acts. These responses as well as more complicated ones are demonstrated with increased development of the nervous system. Earliest activity is primarily reflex in nature. Doctors can usually detect unusual neurological activity and disturbances if the baby exhibits certain involuntary movements or lacks others. Through examination of numerous babies doctors have come to expect the presence of specific types of activity with progressing age. After approximately six months of life many of the innate reflexes are replaced by purposeful responses.

Espenschade has undertaken much research in children's motor development, and in 1960 she presented an excellent summary of the research in this area. She pointed out that early behavior patterns are generally consistent from infant to infant, but developmental rates differ widely. This may be because of heredity and/or environmental deprivation or enrichment.

A baby should receive much opportunity to explore and practice—to reach for toys, to walk, to roll over, to pull himself up. Throughout life more complex skills will be built upon a foundation of simple movements. With experience and maturity, the child will learn how to perform gross motor patterns and eventually finer motor skills. Genetic factors will influence performance potential. Within limitations, preadolescent children are able to perform in a wide range of sports, especially those based on running, throwing, and jumping skills. These skills are developed to an adequate degree in most children by reason of frequent opportunities for participation in activities requiring these movements. It should be emphasized that movement mastery, the ability to coordinate motor patterns into a highly skilled act, *is learned.* Skilled movements do not occur as a result of the maturation process.

The natural questions that follow are (1) Will intensive and extensive training at a relatively early age result in superior athletic prowess later in life? (2) What is this critical age and is it unique for each sport? (3) Will deprivation of certain motor experiences never be compensated for and thus result in producing subpar performers?

The impact of early experiences on later behavior and development has been explained through the recently popularized and accepted *stage* approach. The traditional concept embraced periods of expectant transition that occurred because of increments in age. At present, many psychologists believe

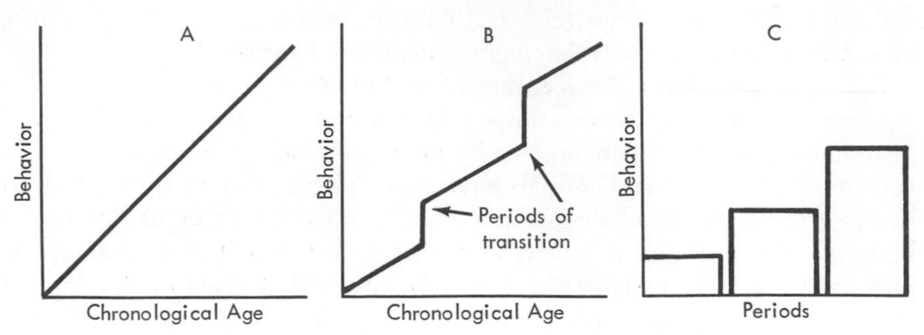

Figure 5–1. Illustrations **A** and **B** represent the traditional concept of behavior expectancies according to chronological age. Illustration **C** discounts the importance of age and emphasizes the stage approach: children progress from one stage of behavior to another, irrespective of age.

that children do not go through the same experiences according to their chronological age but, rather, according to critical periods or stages. When one stage has been achieved, the child progresses to the next stage. Figure 5–1 illustrates the dissimilarity between the chronological age approach and the stage approach.

The works of a few outstanding psychologists have helped to substantiate the stage approach in child development. Freud made child psychology an appealing area of study and emphasized the impact of early experiences on later behavior. He attempted to explain adult neuroses through inadequate resolutions of certain sensitive periods in childhood. Hebb depicted stage evolvement through a neuropsychological approach to learning and behavior. One of the most influential men on child development is Piaget, and he writes extensively on formal or specific stages that all children experience in a predictable manner. Finally, Scott has completed a considerable amount of work on critical learning periods in animals.

Supposedly, if an animal or human is exposed to a given experience at a particular critical period or stage, it has a greater effect on adult behavior than the same experience at a later period. Unfortunately because of the complexity of the problem, research on humans is lacking, thus permitting very few generalizations. However, as is the case in so many experimental areas, animal research has paved the way for implications in human behavior as well as for procedures that may be used in human research. King (1958) discusses seven variables which should be considered in critical-period research. Although meant for animal investigations, they certainly may be applied to human study. These factors are (1) the age of the subject during the experience, (2) the age when tested which is usually at maturity, (3) the type of experience, (4) the duration of the early experience, (5) the type of performance task, (6) the persistency of the test effects, and (7) genetic background of the subject.

Infrahuman research points to the fact that behavior development is not only dependent on heredity, maturation, and practice, but also is related to perceptual learning experiences in infancy. Beach and Jaynes (1954) have summarized animal-research investigations that were concerned with early experiences upon later behavior. The areas of study touched upon were

1. *Sensory discrimination and perception.* A lack of early visual stimulation results in an inability to respond to visual cues later in life. However, with the higher species, usually these defective responses are not permanent and disappear with experience. There are more pronounced effects with rabbits, pigeons, and fish. (More recent research by Dember (1960) indicates that when human youngsters undergo restricted environmental experiences, they later are deficient in form perception. Extra experience provides better later perception.)
2. *Touch and proprioception.* Studies on chimpanzees, who had their feet and hands bandaged in childhood, have demonstrated that these animals show abnormal behavior when the restrictions are removed.
3. *Feeding behavior.* In studying the pecking behavior of chicks, those who were spoon-fed in the dark for two weeks never did learn how to peck later.
4. *Hoarding.* If deprived of food in infancy (first fifteen days), afterwards there is tendency for rats to hoard. Also, these deprived rats eat faster in adulthood.
5. *Social behavior.* Birds and chicks raised in isolation have shown antisocial behavior.

Lorenz (1937) has demonstrated a phenomenon termed *imprinting.* Imprinting refers to that first stimulus which evokes an instinctive reaction and becomes the only stimulus that will cause this reaction. It takes place in a critical stage of life and is irreversible throughout life. In a sense, it is a primitive form of learning. Geese that have been exposed to humans in childhood but never to adult geese tend later to stay near humans rather than geese. Certain species, after being brought up with humans, never can react normally to their own kind. Sluckin and Salzen (1961) report that the most optimal period for duckling and chick imprinting is one or two days after hatching. They will follow almost any moving object at this time. This would not occur though, if the experience is delayed more than two days.

Social behavior, as explained through critical periods, has been of particular interest to Scott (1962). He presents further evidence on the effects of early experience on later behavior. Young rats that have been stimulated (handled) learn quicker, are less timorous, and more vigorous. When rats are brought up surrounded by many playthings as compared to a barren environment, their performance on learning tasks is better. Ravizza and Herschberger (1966) raised rats in an inhibited environment while another group of rats were allowed to climb. As adults the rats allowed freedom of exploration were more active in exploration tasks, showed superior performance on an intelligence test, and were less emotional in a novel situation. Mice reared in groups have a tendency to fight more than mice raised in isolation.

According to Scott, there are three kinds of critical-learning periods: (1) optimal periods for learning; (2) infantile stimulation; and (3) the formation of basic social relationships. Infantile (human or otherwise) stimulation, in the form of large amounts of perceptual experience leads to better learners later on than if these organisms are deprived of such experience. As development occurs, learning capacities change. When dealing with young children, we are obviously not concerned with complex sport and skill learning. Rather, we are concerned with basic movements and patterns which are performed as if by habit. Habits formed early in life persist in adult life and are resistant to change. It is therefore necessary that these learned movements be desirable, for the acquisition of one habit may prevent the learning of others. What is learned at a particular time may interfere with later learning. In the words of Scott, "organization hampers reorganization."

Not only is there need to be concerned with what the child does experience but also with what he does not. Johnson (1964) indicates that Luria stated at the 1959 World Health Organization seminar in Milan, Italy, "Sometimes, if a single link of training is missed, if a certain stage in the development of the necessary operation is not properly worked up, the entire process of further development becomes retarded...."

What motor skills, then, should be taught to children, and when? McGraw's (1935) famous twin study indicated that learning varies for each motor activitiy; each activity has its own optimum period for rapid and skillful learning. Jimmy was the control twin and was raised in typical fashion. Johnny was the experimental twin and received special training to increase his neuromuscular development and demonstrated an ability to acquire many skills at an early age. This study refuted the concept that an infant is unresponsive to practice because of an immature nervous system, a concept espoused by leading child psychologists such as Gesell.

McGraw attempted to discover the period when a child would profit by a particular experience or practice. Johnny was stimulated daily while Jimmy was provided with a few toys and experienced a routine environment. At about one year of age, Johnny was directed in various motor activities usually experienced by children later in life, e.g., riding a tricycle, swimming and diving, roller skating, jumping from heights, and sliding. Jimmy received intensive practice and instruction in the same activities for two and a half months when he was twenty-two months old. When Johnny was less than a year old, he could swim the length of a seven-foot tank while supported by a strap. He swam the distance without support at 411 days, performed a dive into the tank at 422 days, and when 467 days old, dove off a five-foot board into a lake.

After Jimmy's training period, the two boys were compared in performance. In swimming and diving behavior, Johnny demonstrated superior talents and better attitudes, which were attributed to his extensive swimming experience. As to skating, Johnny had the advantage because of his earlier training. He was adjusted to falling, a problem that Jimmy had difficulty in overcoming. It would seem that the best time to learn skating occurs when the baby is learning to walk, for he is gaining control of equilibrium factors. Johnny also demonstrated a more coordinated jump from heights, having overcome fear at the early age at which he had had related experiences. These activities were learned better because of their earlier introduction. Some activities were not facilitated by earlier practice—for example, walking. Both boys demonstrated approximately similar patterns despite the extra practice Johnny received. Other activities appeared to be disrupted because unskillful habits were formed. McGraw suggests that not only was Johnny not benefited by his earlier experience with the tricycle, but, in fact, these experiences actually hindered him. Jimmy practiced less on this skill, and the delay in his exposure to the tricycle proved to be more economical to learning.

McGraw (1939) retested the boys at school age. The skills were demonstrated in varying patterns in their tendency to be retained or forgotten. For example, Johnny and Jimmy were about equal in tricycling and in roller skating. However, whereas both boys demonstrated no loss of skill in tricycling after the long layoff, it appeared as if skating skill underwent deterioration. Nevertheless, *Johnny generally displayed greater motor coordination and daring in physical performance.* The retention of specific skills, according to McGraw, depends on whether performance was composed of well-integrated movements. Poorly developed skills are not retained to a high degree.

The McGraw investigation allows other general assumptions. There is no one critical period, no one chronological age for all skills, as periods differ for each behavior pattern. In fact, the critical period is not determined by chronological age but, rather, is based on the maturational status of the nervous system for a given activity and evidently may extend for quite a long period for the acquisition of many skills. As long as the organism grows, so do the powers of restoration and compensation. Unless there is an unduly long deprivation period (a time when the child does not have any experience with the skill in question), he can usually be brought to approximate the achievement level of another child who has begun practice earlier than he did. (Jimmy did approximately match Johnny's skill level in the various activities after the intensive training period, but it should be remembered that Johnny demonstrated better overall motor coordination.) Finally, because the twins were normal and about equal in intelligence-test scores, exercise in special motor activities did not appear to accelerate intellectual functions. The important role that perceptual-motor experiences have in contributing to potential intellectual achievements is not to be denied, though. This particular study merely indicates that additional motor activity will not improve upon the normal intelligence.

Empirical evidence indicates that young children can learn much more than they are given credit for. Investigations on outstanding athletes show that usually they began learning their specialties at early ages, and have undergone continuous intensive training. In McGraw's study, Johnny could swim seven feet (with one breath) at one year of age. Children in general are learning sports associated with adulthood such as golf, bowling, and tennis earlier in their lifetimes than was the case with preceding generations. If, as Bruner (1963) says, *any subject can be taught in a legitimate way so as to be of value to the child at any stage of development*, the implications are great for physical educators. Although Bruner's thoughts in general lie more in the cognitive domain with great issues, principles, and values of society, his concept also may be applied to the learning of motor skills. Certainly, physical education offers experiences that most children are receptive to, i.e., a child usually does not have to be forced into participating in games and play. It is up to the creative teacher to present the material in a meaningful way, by understanding the development stages of childhood.

Motor skills can be taught in a modified way to the child once he has reasonable control of his body. However, the desirability of encroaching on the maturing process, of teaching particular activities to children who are too young to comprehend and respond to them adequately, is questionable, after considering some experimental results. For instance, Hilgard (1933) tested one pair of twins, four-and-a-half years of age, on tests involving walking boards, cutting, digit memory, a ringtoss, and object memory. Each twin served both as the practice and control subject throughout the study. After eight weeks of practice, the practiced twin was superior to the control twin on all test measures except the largest walking-board time score. However, after three and six months of no practice for either twin, performances compared between them were as similar to each other as at the beginning of the experiment.

Instruction does not always improve performance. Miller (1957) tested first-grade children on the overhand throw. After 26 twenty-minute periods of practice, an experimental group, provided with throwing instruction did not end up significantly better in throwing accuracy than the control group (non-instruction). The author did hypothesize that possibly a longer practice would have provided a significant difference in favor of the instruction group.

In another study, Brown (1936) attempted to determine the optimal age for learning to play the piano. She found a .60 correlation between chronological age and the rate of learning but only .23 between mental age and the rate of learning. The critical age for initiating piano practice was determined to be about seven, and Brown stated that little is to be gained by starting a piano student too early. No doubt this statement holds true for the learning of athletic skills. *Successful skill attainment at maturity is not dependent on the earliness of instruction but rather on its timeliness.*

Research on critical-learning periods permits only generalizations from animal research to human behavior. It does not, at this time, tell us the optimal time in life in which to learn, say, basketball, golf, or archery. It does call attention to the theoretical impact of the proposition that there are critical periods in life for the learning of everything. It remains for researchers to investigate this area further, to determine the stage of approximate age of readiness for specific motor-skill experience.

Relationship of Physical, Neurological, and Cognitive Processes

A child begins elementary school and displays poor readiness skills. It may appear that he has low intellectual potential, brain damage, or indications of mental retardation. Can anything be done to remedy the situation?

Obvious solutions include reading therapy, special training in intellectual skills, or allowing nature to take its course. A more practical approach would be to determine the cause of the child's problems and to proceed from there. Causes of problems associated with a low level of readiness for achievement in school may be genetic factors, brain injury, or inadequate environmental experiences. Barring extreme cases in the first two categories, dramatic research evidence indicates all three limiting factors can be overcome reasonably through a corrective program. Basically this program includes introduction to and practice in certain basic motor patterns.

Evidence for the low correlation between motor-skill achievement and intelligence in adults and older school-aged children is presented in Chapter 3. What of the relationship in infancy and early childhood? Statements by pioneer researchers, educators, and psychologists concur on the concept of a general maturational trend early in life. However, it has remained for present-day leaders, through their energies, writings, and practices, to bring a practical solution to the child's readiness problems to the attention of an interested public. Two outstanding workers in this area are Newell C. Kephart of Purdue University and Carl H. Delacato, Associate Director of the Institutes for the Achievement of Human Potential, Philadelphia, Pennsylvania.

Successful results have brought these men many admirers and followers. Their philosophies and practices as to overcoming readiness limitations are generally the same: Intellectual growth can be stimulated through the achievement of simple motor patterns.

In their book, *Success through Play*, Radler and Kephart (1960) emphasize the importance of visual development in intellectual development, which in turn is dependent on simple motor skills. Poor motor coordination results in decelerated intellectual growth. According to Kephart, coordination is composed of (1) *laterality*—the sense of one's symmetry, of leftness and rightness and (2) *directionality*—laterality projected into space, which is obtained through and experienced in motor skills. An inability to perform or realize laterality and directionality must be overcome if the child is to be successful in school. And, indeed, Kephart recommends various movement patterns that may be learned and practiced by youngsters needing a corrective program.

Kephart (1966) clarified his thoughts at the annual convention of the

American Association for Health, Physical Education, and Recreation, held in Chicago. He offered the proposition that systematic motor exploration is the basis for all learning, since motor activity is information gathering. Ultimately, we may be teaching motor activity through physical education in order to promote reading. Kephart stated that 15 to 20 per cent of all children suffer from learning disorders; they have difficulty in learning. Children need generalized motor experiences; they need to explore, in order to have the background necessary for later success in school work. These motor generalizations include

1. *Balance and posture.* The child must know where gravity is as well as comprehend direction.
2. *Propulsion and receipt.* He should be able to move himself and objects away and toward something.
3. *Locomotion.* This refers to body movement through space, overcoming obstacles, and changing pace. Locomotive generalizations go on unconsciously so the child may explore.
4. *Contact and manipulation.* The child's relationship with objects is determined by such abilities as reaching, grasping, and releasing.

Because of the importance attached to motor generalizations in intellectual development, natural questions arise. Are professional athletes more highly intelligent individuals? Kephart states that this is not necessarily so, as they may have dropped out at one of the developmental levels above motor-skill accomplishment. Athletes have the potential for high intellectual attainment, but only if they have successfully gone through all the development levels during childhood. He calls for more emphasis on the developmental aspects of sports and less on the competitive and social aspects. What about high degrees of skills in many motor performances? This is not necessary, but instead what is desired is a minimum ability in a wide range of activities. Overconcentration on one skill is not as effective as varied motor experiences in contributing to the cognitive processes.

Just as Kephart suggests that low achievers in school lack basic readiness (motor) skills which can be made up if they are taught, Delacato (1966) expresses similar thoughts. In a series of articles and books, culminating in *Neurological Organization and Reading,* Delacato favors a concept of neurological organization. It is used to explain deficits in readiness and to show how a child develops physically and neurologically in his early years and ultimately intellectually. Neurological Organization describes the process of activities control that begins at the level of the spinal cord and medulla at birth, then goes to the pons, to the midbrain, and finally to the cortex. This organization terminates when the child is approximately six to eight years of age. In other words, the neurological development process is complete at this time.

Delacato has tested children on various tasks to see whether they have progressed normally from one stage to the next stage. For example, cortical-level control is measured by the child's ability to perform cross-pattern walking and visual pursuit. A failure on a test at any control level indicates that the neurological organization is incomplete, with potential detrimental effects in reading ability. Reading problems are thus created before a child enters the school; the school merely points them out. The most important element for successful reading endeavors is cortical hemispheric dominance, or one-sidedness. Lack of complete and constant laterality results in reading and language problems. (Compare with Kephart's views.) From his observations, Delacato states that 60–80 per cent of the superior readers are completely one-sided. Preventive or corrective measures include mastering general motor patterns, such as homolateral crawling at the lowest stage, and creeping, walking, and walking in cross patterns at later stages.

A number of recent studies, on the other hand, have not found any difference in reading ability between established and nonestablished laterality groups. Capobianco (1967), for example, administered five tests of handedness and four tests of eyedness to subjects with special learning disabilities. These test scores were correlated with reading-ability measures. Results indicated that lateral dominance did not facilitate reading achievement; in fact, incomplete dominance, in certain cases, resulted in better reading performance.

The relationship of motor abilities to other motor abilities as well as to the cognitive processes has been determined by other researchers. Bayley (1935), a prominent figure in the area of child growth and development, tested sixty-one infants, from birth to thirty-six months of age, on the California Infant Scale of Motor Development. She noted that motor abilities were more closely related in infants than in adults. She obtained a correlation of .50 between the motor and mental tests and one of .39 between the age of walking and age of talking. Cunningham (1927) administered motor tests to over 100 children from twelve to forty months of age. Moderately high positive correlations were obtained between motor-test scores and Binet Intelligence Test scores.

The extent of the interrelationship of growth and development variables has been open to conjecture. At one extreme are those persons who favor a minimum interdependence, while at the other end of the continuum are the proponents of the *whole* child. The latter position can best be represented by Olson's (1959) concept of an organismic age. The organismic age, as proposed by Olson, consists of the average of seven ages, including such physical characteristics as height, weight, and grip strength, as well as mental, dental, reading, and carpal factors. He believes that achievement in school is a function of the child's total growth, and therefore there is a strong relationship between physical measures and academic achievement.

Tyler (1953) has raised some serious questions relative to the concept of the organismic age as well as to the validity of the data used to support it. He feels that Olson stresses maturational factors, whereas in actuality genetic and environmental factors must also be considered. A series of experiments by Klausmeier (1958a, 1958b, 1958c, 1959) also casts doubt on the acceptance of the organismic-age concept. He has generally found little relationship between physical development and achievement in school. Perhaps the difficulty lies in the attempt to relate purely physical characteristics, e.g., height, weight, and strength to intellectual success, for evidently motor-coordination items are more highly related to academic achievement.

Recent efforts by Ismail (1965) support this contention. He has obtained success in utilizing coordination tasks and balance tasks as predictors of intellectual achievement, and interestingly enough, the subjects have been as old as preadolescents. Perhaps the nature of these tasks requires greater perceptual and cognitive involvement than is needed for such simple tasks as exhibiting hand-grip strength. High neural centers are thus influencing intellectual attainment as well as complex motor-skill success, at least in the beginning of practice. Much more work in this area, especially as it pertains to school-aged children and adults, is necessary before any definite conclusions may be reached. So far, the organismic approach appears to be somewhat limited in application. The best evidence for this concept is in infancy. With age, performances in certain motor skills are probably more interrelated with intellectual factors than are physical characteristics.

Age

Chronological Versus Maturational Age. In this chapter we have seen that chronological age often misrepresents readiness skills and expectant behavior. All children go through the same sequence of developmental stages, but vary in their rate of progress. To post norms based on age is often a matter of convenience and practicality, and deviations should be weighed accordingly. It would be better to understand the child and his stage of maturational development, since early and late maturers do not display similar characteristics at the same chronological age.

Mental age, as represented by the IQ test, is, in a sense, independent of chronological age. The intelligence quotient is a ratio of the child's mental age as determined by an intelligence test over his chronological age. It is possible, indeed probable, that students in a given class composed of children of the same chronological age will be widely distributed according to mental age. By the same token, children making the transition from childhood to adulthood demonstrate physical development according to their rate of maturation rather than age. Such a factor as strength is an important determiner of potential success in many motor activities, and obviously early maturers may be expected to perform more ably in sports because their physical development has accelerated.

Numerous investigations have been completed relating motor achievements to chronological age. Reservations should be present in any application of norms to one person's scores, but there is value in comparing age and motor-performance variables. The data may be used in order to compare a child's performance with similarly aged classmates for motivating purposes or for clinical reasons.

Age and Motor Performance. Motor behavior in infancy and early childhood has been discussed already and need not be treated here. School-age children display characteristics of skilled movements in their play and the nature of their play is such that, with increasing age, more complex skills and diverse sports are mastered and demonstrated. Two widely used methods for obtaining performance data relevant to age are the *longitudinal* and *cross-sectional* approaches. Subjects at each age are sampled under the *cross-sectional* approach, whereas the same individuals are followed for a length of time with the longitudinal method. Both research methods contribute to our knowledge of growth and development, although the longitudinal technique usually is more time consuming and contains more administrative problems than the cross–sectional method. However, the longitudinal study more accurately describes the changes that take place within individuals in succeeding years. Famous longitudinal studies include Terman's follow-up of genius youngsters to adulthood and Jones' observation of strength changes during the adolescent period. The longitudinal study permits an analysis of the growth process and does not conceal unusual occurrences, such as growth spurts.

When dealing with youngsters, there is always a question as to the effects of instruction on the learning of motor skills versus the effects of maturation. Research results have been conflicting as to the relative benefits of instruction. For instance, Hicks (1930) administered four motor-skill tests to children from ages three to six. The tests included a perforation test (punching out circles on a piece of paper), strength test, tracing test, and an accuracy test (throwing at a moving target). With no instruction, significant gains were found on three of the four tests when the subjects were retested, and Hicks concluded that skill improvement at these ages and on these tests is attributed mainly to maturation and general practice. Wild (1938) studied the overhand throw, through motion pictures, of children ranging in age from two to seven. She felt that maturational factors were important in motor learning until the age of six, and that learning was more beneficial afterwards.

On the other hand, Humphries and Shephard (1959) trained their subjects, from four to ten years of age, in a reversed task of the Toronto Complex Coordinator. These investigators noted that the level of performance was positively related to age and that all age levels constantly improved with training. Many studies, because of contradictory results, confuse the issue as to whether to provide training in motor tasks to youngsters at an earlier time in life than traditionally expected. It is usually found that training in specific skills improves performance, but it is better to wait a little longer—

until the children are at that period of obvious readiness. This information would appear to imply that maturation is more important than experience.

However, Fowler (1962) is critical of this assumption and supports the concept and practice of early training, especially in complex motor skills. In those studies which demonstrated the importance of maturation over experience and training, he offers the following explanations. First, because of the simplicity of skills to be learned high levels are achieved too quickly. Secondly, the related experiences of the control group (a group not receiving benefit of experience and/or instruction) have not been well controlled. And finally, pre-experimental experience information often is lacking.

As to motor skills themselves, certain trends are apparent. As a general rule, performance increases with age throughout childhood. Running, throwing, jumping, balance, agility, stroking, and catching skills in 510 primary grade children were investigated by Seils (1951). Mean performances were found to be greater at each age level. Extending the analysis of age to performance in later ages, improvement increments are noticed to a certain time in life, depending on the skill. It should go without saying that individuals learn and improve in performance up to varying ages, and any evidence presented here is based on average performance.

Goodenough (1935) tested the reaction times of 246 children from two-and-a-half to eleven-and-a-half years of age. She observed a decrease in reaction time with age. Four-hundred and eighty female subjects with ages ranging from six to eighty-four had their reaction times taken by Hodgkins (1962). It was discovered that reactions improved from childhood to nineteen years, remained constant from nineteen to twenty-six, and decreased afterwards. Similar results were obtained in another study by Hodgkins in which she tested both the reaction time and movement time of males and females. Figure 5–2 illustrates her findings.

Slowness of behavior is characteristic of older age and may be caused by many factors. At least one writer suggests the process of aging in the nervous system as being a leading cause. Some studies show a 10 to 20 per cent slowing of reaction times between twenty and sixty-year olds. However, the actual time difference may be as little as .02 of a second, which, practically speaking, is not much.

Some writers have found conflicting results using different tasks to measure a similar variable. For instance, Cron and Pronko (1957) tested balance by having their subjects walk on a balance board, whereas Bachman (1961, 1966) used the stabilometer and vertical ladder climb. In the former study, 501 children were represented, spanning in age from four to fifteen. Balance ability improved with age, then leveled off, and declined in the twelve to fifteen-year old group. The girls were superior in the four to eight year bracket, but the boys exceeded the girls in the eight to fifteen-year range. In the first study by Bachman, the subjects were from six to twenty-six years of age, and in the second investigation, they aged from twenty-six to fifty.

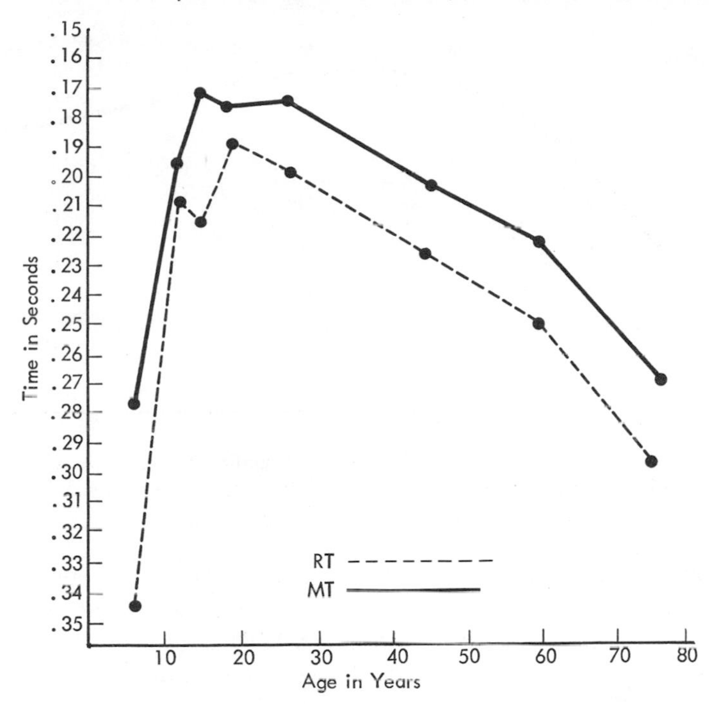

Figure 5–2. Reaction time (RT) and movement time (MT) changes as a function of age. (From Hodgkins, Jean. Reaction Time and Speed of Movement in Males and Females at Various Ages, *Res. Quart.*, 34:335–343, 1963.)

In both tasks and in both studies, it was generally found that learning was not related to sex or age.

Talland (1962) tested three groups of men; members of group one were in their early twenties; of group two, between forty and sixty-three; and of group three, between seventy-seven and eighty-nine. There were eighteen subjects in each group. The tasks they performed were (1) continuous working of a manual counter, (2) moving beads with a tweezer, and (3) selecting beads of one hue from a mixed stock and moving them with a tweezer. Significant differences were found between each group in favor of each preceding younger group. The results suggest that even the simplest motor skill declines in speed with age, even though it involves little exertion or coordination of movement.

With regard to athletic skills, it appears that they are continually developed to a high degree of proficiency, especially in the first two decades of life. Brace (1930) administered twenty motor-skill tests to several hundred boys and girls between the age of nine and sixteen. With increasing age, the number of tests passed also increased. Brace singled out the nine to twelve year old bracket as the time when there was an emergence of abilities to perform complex motor acts. Individuals may continue to improve in skill attainment throughout a good portion of life, depending on the nature of

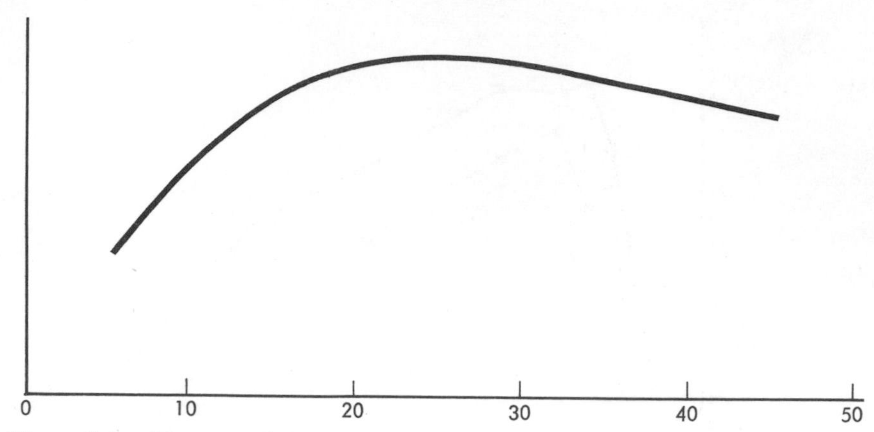

Figure 5–3. The general form of the curve of ability to learn in relation to age. (From Thorndike, Edward L.; Bregman, Elsie.; Tilton, J. Warren; and Woodyard, Ella. *Adult Learning,* New York: The Macmillan Co., 1928.)

the skill and the training habits and personality of the performer. Empirical evidence indicates the late twenties as the period before performance worsens. Many top athletes in baseball, football, and a host of other sports appear to reach their prime in the middle and late twenties.

Thorndike and his coresearchers investigated the changes in learning different types of materials that take place from early ages to age forty-five. Figure 5–3 depicts the generalized learning curve for varied sorts of learning matter. Peak performance years appear to be in the late twenties. The process of maturation, which occurs up to about age twenty, increases one's ability to learn and perform. Later in life, the psychological and physiological degenerative effects of age cause a decline in learning ability.

A picture of Olympic champions raises serious questions as to whether we can indicate a given age for optimal athletic performance justifiably. Jokl (1964a) presents age and sport data from the 1952 Olympic Games in Helsinki. The swimming participants had the lowest mean age, twenty-one and a half. Boxers, cyclists, short-distance runners, hurdlers, and jumpers were on the average under twenty-five. As to the running events of over 1500 meters, an average increase in age was noted as the distance increased. Those who participated in the decathalon, free-style wrestling, long-distance running events, and weight lifting were between twenty-five and thirty, on the average. The ages of the male Olympians were from thirteen to sixty-six, and a number of middle-aged men were observed to give excellent performances.

Data from the 1964 Olympics substantiated Jokl's earlier findings. Hirata (1966) categorized Olympic athletes by age and event. Much of his data indicates that those events in which a performer relies primarily on muscular strength are represented by more youthful athletes. Those events requiring more refined skill and technique are accomplished later in life. Swimming, for example, which does not demand so much technical ability, was represented by the youngest athletes. Male swimmers averaged approximately twenty years of age, whereas performers in such technical sports as gymnastics and wrestling were in the middle and late twenties. Some other mean ages, representing the male Olympians of various sports, were found to be as follows:

Sport	Age
Volleyball	26.2
Basketball	25.3
Foil Fencing	27.5
Track: 100–meter	24.5
Marathon	28.3
Cycling	24.0
Weight Lifting	27.2
Soccer	24.9

Although it would appear as if certain ages are more desirable for successful sports participation, there was a wide range of ages for the Olympic champions, as was the case in the 1952 Olympics. The male Olympians ranged from fifteen to fifty-four years in age, while the ages of the female Olympians went from thirteen to thirty-five years.

It is evident, then, that through ability and hard training, man can demonstrate superior skills at earlier and later ages than ever before. Perhaps one of the reasons why drop-offs in performance are noted in early adulthood is because of incentive loss. Additional responsibilities, new values, and even boredom from practice repetition may contribute to a decline in performance with age. High levels of skill, once attained, are not easily forgotten. Most highly skilled activities demand a well conditioned body, but once strength, endurance, and speed deteriorate, coordination also falls. Certain sports, with constant practice and the maintenance of good body condition, allow successful participation until a person is in his fifties and even sixties.

Birrens (1964) writes that industrial studies indicate that there is little change in worker performance up to the ages of sixty and sixty-five. Performance in typical industrial tasks should be little influenced by physiological changes except where time limitations are present, i.e., when a task must be performed in some time context. An older person may be limited in performing a number of tasks in a short period of time or over a long period where fatigue sets in.

Athletic competition is usually more demanding. Reductions in such capacities as strength, sense acuity, and reaction time are more apparent in their relative effects. In those sports where the response is self-pacing, e.g., archery, bowling, and golf, high skill achievement can be more easily attained.

Also, when the older person has a long time to anticipate or preview the stimulus conditions, he has a better chance for success. Certainly this is the case in noncompetitive sports. Finally, the quality and quantity of the cues present in the situation will determine task performance.

Learning is not only associated with growth, for it can continue throughout life. Changes with age in ability to learn are usually small up to sixty. Learning difficulty may be attributed to perception, motivation, set, attention, and the physiological state of the organism. Nevertheless, it is harder to teach an adult because of the complexity and maturity of the organism. A structured past and movements that have to be unlearned lead to learning difficulty. Motor abilities are more general in childhood, and with advancing age and varied experiences they become more specific. Differences in age and learning methods have been examined by Henry and Nelson (1956). Ten-year olds were characterized by their ability to learn with less task specificity than fifteen-year olds. The initial level of skill rather than ability to learn was important in the older group in ultimate task performance.

Thus, it can be seen that age groups may be characterized by unique learning abilities, developed capacities, attitudes and interests, maturational levels, and physiological development. Specific sports and tasks differ in the optimal age a human should have for highest skill attainment. Even within a given activity, a wide range of age levels may be represented by successful performers. Increased sports knowledge, nutrition, health, training, and motivation interact to provide levels of skill attainable to young and old alike.

Sex

Sex differences in motor performance become more apparent with increasing age. Young boys and girls can compete in similar activities with satisfaction until they approach adolescence. During this period, motor skills related to the dominant form of play of each sex distinguishes the two sexes. From adolescence to adulthood, boys continually advance in motor performance, girls improve very slightly or even worsen, and the gap in performance between the sexes widens. Why this occurs and indeed, if it actually should, is open to conjecture.

Numerous researchers have investigated and compared the motor performances of boys and girls from youth to adulthood. Witte (1962) tested boys and girls in the seven to nine-year range and found the boys to be significantly better than the girls in a ball-rolling skill. No difference in kinesthesis, as measured by the author, was observed. Three-hundred children aging from five to seven were utilized in an investigation by Jenkins (1930). The boys were superior to the girls at each age level on the 35-yard dash, baseball throw, and soccer kick for distance (in fact, the five-year old boys were about the same as the seven-year old girls), and the broad jump. The girls demonstrated better skill in only one event, the 50-foot hop.

Latchaw (1954) designed a battery of seven tests to measure the skill of fourth, fifth, and sixth grade children in running, jumping, catching, striking, and kicking. The boys performed higher in the tests at each grade level. Cowan and Pratt (1934) diagnostically analyzed the coordination of children three to twelve years of age from hurdle jump scores. Among other findings, there was inconclusive evidence that the girls were better than the boys below the age of seven, but the boys were superior above the age of seven.

One of the more complete research projects having to do with the interaction of age and sex on performance was completed by Noble, Baker, and Jones (1964). A Discrimination Reaction Time apparatus was used (see Figure 5–4A) that required the subject to snap one of four toggle switches in response to changing light-stimulus patterns. A total of 600 subjects took part in the study, ranging in age from eight to eighty-seven. Twenty males and twenty females were placed in each of fifteen experimental groups according to age. It can be observed in Figure 5–4B that the expected performance curves were obtained, i.e., peak performance for both groups was attained at approximately the late teens and early twenties and worsened with advancing age. These data coincide very nicely with that reported by Hodgkins (see Figure 5–2).

It is interesting to compare performance differences at the various ages. With the exception of the ten to thirteen-year age bracket and the seventy-one to eighty-seven-year age bracket, males displayed a general superiority over the females in response speed. Generally speaking, the two sexes perform similarly until the age of sixteen, when the females level off in performance and show decrements with increasing age. Males continue to improve until the early twenties, and then they too undergo declining performance.

In most physical and motor measures, both boys and girls compare favorably, with boys holding a slight edge until approximately the age of twelve or thirteen. Body size and strength has much to do with althletic accomplishments. During adolescence, boys generally grow larger and demonstrate a greater magnitude of strength, and as these differences between sexes become more apparent, so do motor performances. Jones followed the strength develpoment of boys and girls over a period of time. Figure 5–5 presents a comparison between boys and girls, from age eleven through seventeen, in right and left hand-grip strengths. The girls begin trailing off at about fifteen years of age, whereas the boys are still increasing with great rapidity at the age of seventeen. Differences in strength, although in favor of the boys at eleven, become more noticeable at thirteen, and continue to widen at each succeeding age.

The same trend is noticeable with most motor skills. Espenschade, after accumulating much data on the subject, has organized the material as it appears in Table 5–1. The four skills, running, standing broad jump, jump and

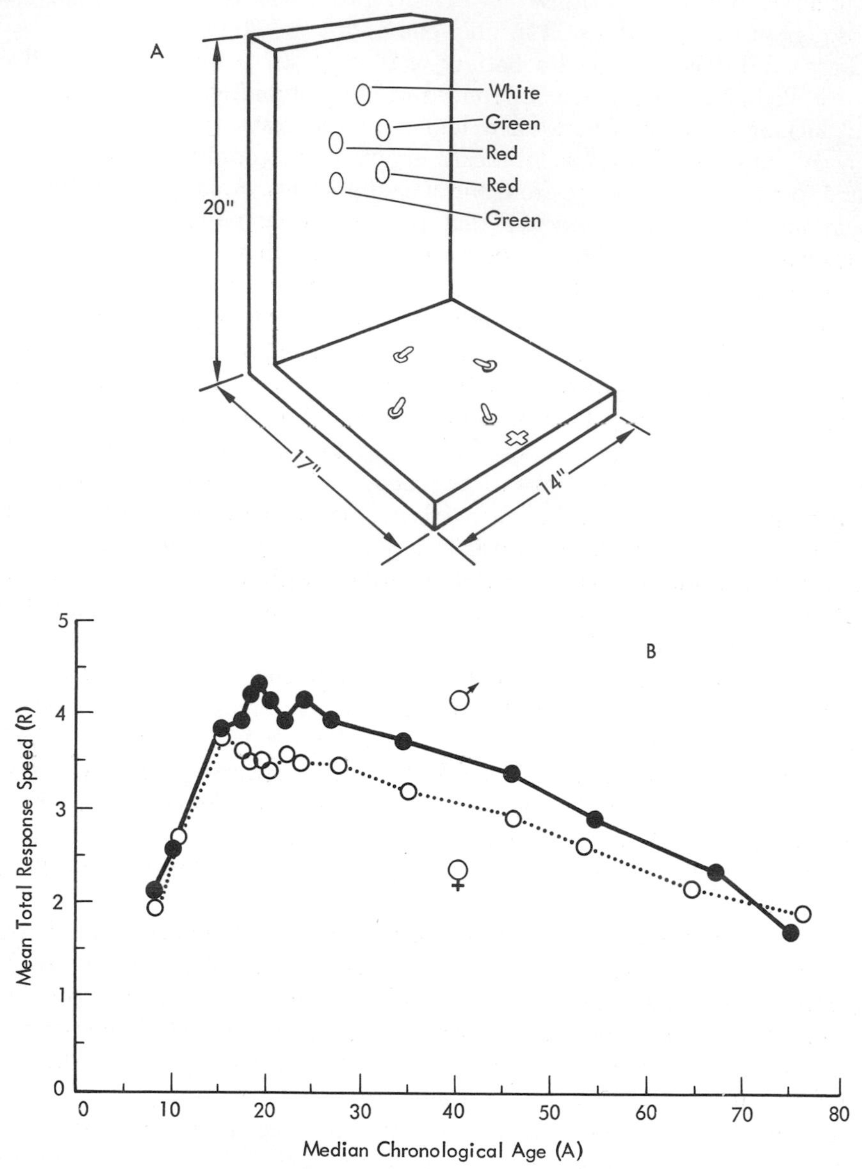

Figure 5–4. **A** Discrimination Reaction Time Apparatus; **B** Mean total response speed (R) as a function of median chronological age (A) for the two sexes. Each point is based on the data for 20 subjects averaged over the entire practice period. (From Noble, Clyde E.; Baker, Blaine L.; and Jones, Thomas A. Age and Sex Parameters in Psychomotor Learning, *Percept. Mot. Skills,* 19:935–945, 1964.)

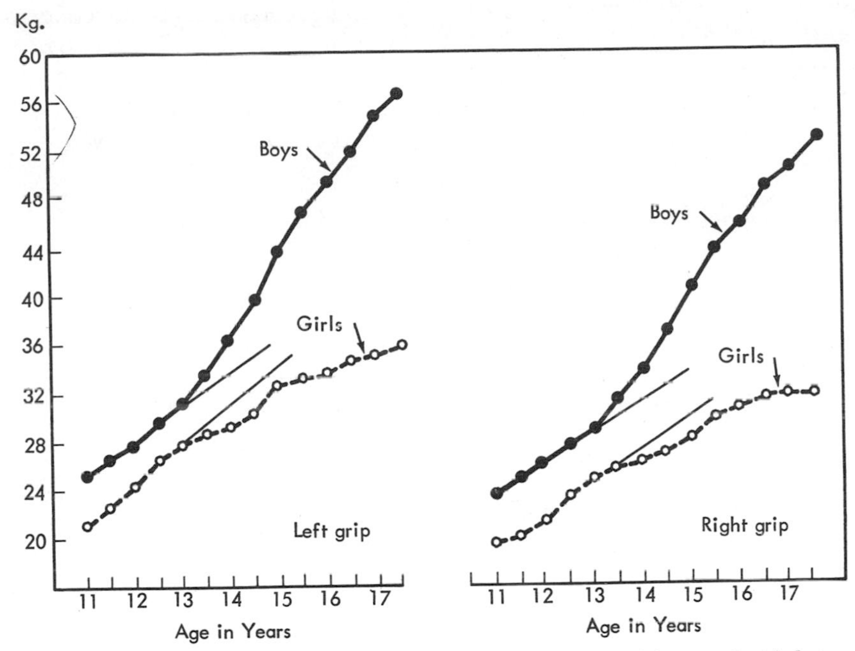

Figure 5–5. Comparison of right and left hand grip strength of boys and girls between the ages of eleven through seventeen. (From Jones, H. E. Motor Performance and Growth, *Univ. Calif. Publ. Child Develpm.*, 1949.)

reach, and distance throw are illustrated in Figure 5–6. The performance curves are similar for each activity. Other activities provide dissimilar curves, as can be observed in Figure 5–7. Girls were consistently better on an aiming task, which required motor coordination. Although the boys continuously improve on the other tasks, the girls worsen in performance in the baseball throw and balance skill, but do better each year on the basketball rapid pass.

In summary, generally it may be stated that boys typically increase in performance until the late teens, whereas girls decline in performance in the early teens. There are exceptions, of course. The relative performances of boys and girls at comparative ages may be attributed to many factors. One of the more prominent variables is the influence of social approval, which, of course, is culturally determined. For many years, while boys have been encouraged to develop their athletic prowess girls have been told to act feminine, to avoid most sports and vigorous activities. With a lack of incentive, performance levels naturally decline.

More factual evidence offered by Hirata (1966) indicates the relationship of achievements in various athletic endeavors with sex and age. Using the 1964 Olympic champion athletes as subjects, he found the mean age of the male champions to be twenty-six years, whereas the female champions were twenty-three years in age on the average. Most of the male champions were in the twenty to thirty age group whereas the majority of female champions were located in the seventeen to twenty-five age bracket. Hirata concludes that the male's motor and physical development is completed later than the female's and is maintained for a longer duration of time. However, other factors as well, perhaps social and psychological in nature, may account for some of the difference in peak-performance years between the sexes.

*Table 5–1. Performance Scores for Boys and Girls from Five to Seventeen Years of Age.**

Age	Run Yards per sec.	Standing Broad Jump (inches)	Jump and Reach (inches)	Brace (score)	Distance Throw (feet)
			BOYS		
5	3.8	33.7	2.5		23.6
6	4.2	37.4	4.0	5.5	32.8
7	4.6	41.6	6.1	7.5	42.3
8	5.1	46.7	8.3	9.0	57.4
9		50.4	8.5	10.0	66.6
10	5.9	54.7	11.0	11.0	83.0
11	6.1	61.0	11.5	11.1	95.0
12	6.3	64.9	12.2	12.7	104.0
13	6.5	69.3	12.5	13.1	114.0
14	6.7	73.2	13.3	14.5	123.0
15	6.8	79.5	14.8	15.2	135.0
16	7.1	88.0	16.3	16.2	144.0
17	7.2	88.4	16.9	(15.9)	153.0
			GIRLS		
5	3.6	31.6	2.2		14.5
6	4.1	36.2	3.5	5.5	17.8
7	4.4	40.0	5.7	7.5	25.4
8	4.6	45.9	7.7	9.0	30.0
9		51.3	8.7	10.0	38.7
10	5.8		10.5	10.5	47.0
11	6.0	52.0	11.0	11.1	54.0
12	6.1		11.2	11.8	61.0
13	6.3	62.1	11.0	11.8	70.0
14	6.2	62.7	11.8	11.9	74.5
15	6.1	63.2	12.2	11.5	75.7
16	6.0	63.0	12.0	11.8	74.0
17	5.9				

* From Espenschade, Anna. Motor Development, in Johnson, Warren R. (ed.), *Science and Medicine and Sports*, New York: Harper & Brothers, 1960.

From a physiological point of view, various differences between sexes usually favor the male in athletic performance, but not to the extent once supposed. With social encouragement, girls and women are displaying remarkable skills in a wide range of activities. Jokl (1964b) has accumulated much data from the 1952 Olympics, and he has found that some women's records in track and field and swimming at these Olympic Games were better than men's records in the early 1900's. He also concludes that "... the time-honored statement that women are invariably the weaker sex no longer holds true as an unqualified assertion." Constant hard drilling and training result in outstanding athletic performance, regardless of sex.

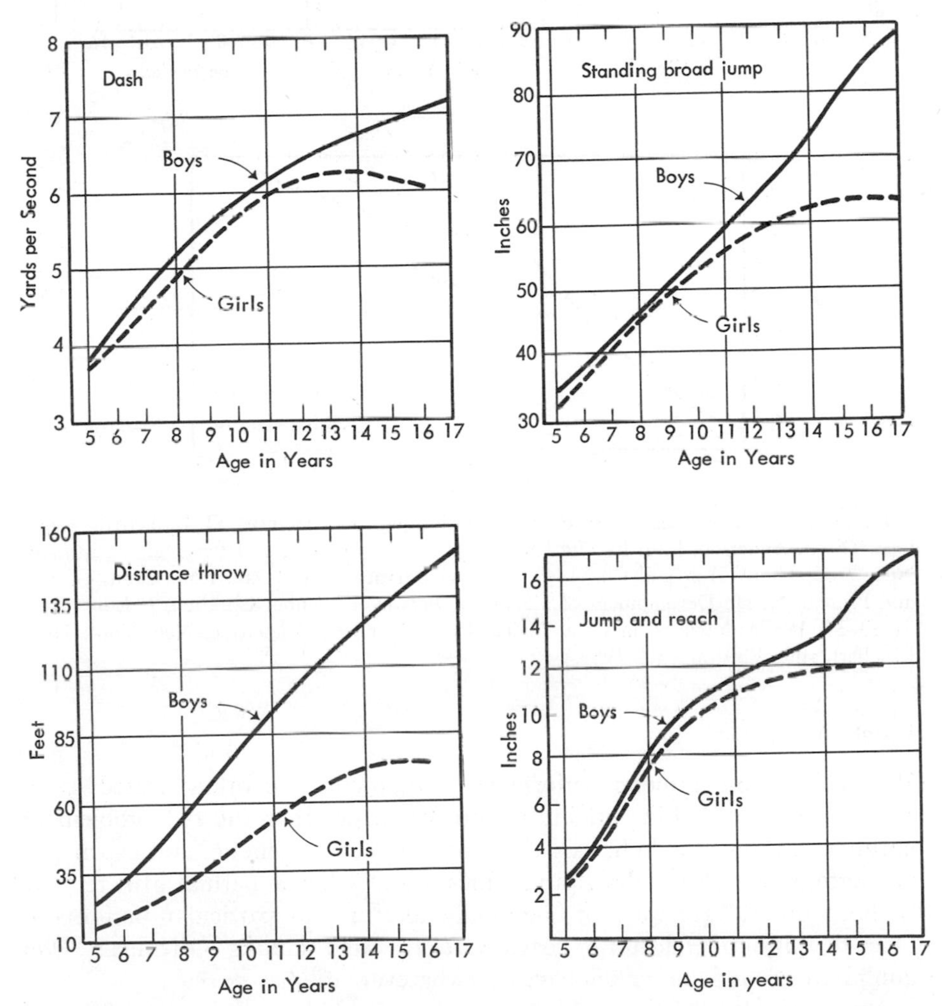

Figure 5–6. Age and sex differences in performing some motor skills. (From Espenschade, Anna. Motor Development, in Johnson, Warren R. (ed.), *Science and Medicine of Exercise and Sports,* New York: Harper & Brothers, 1960.)

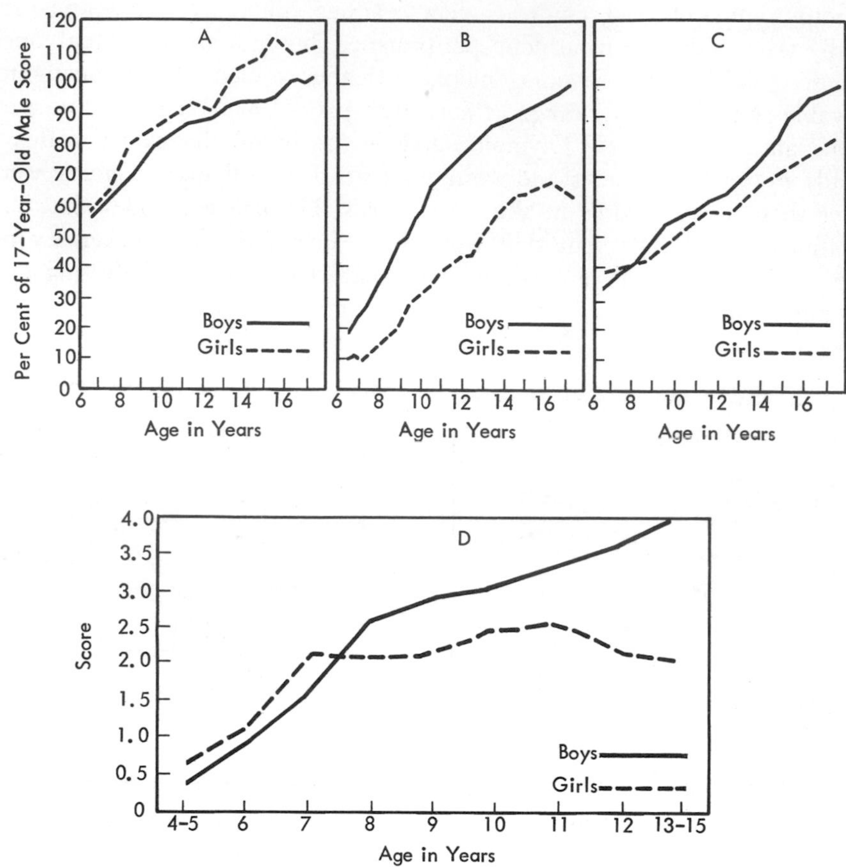

Figure 5–7. **A** Aiming Test; **B** Baseball Throw for Distance; **C** Basketball Rapid Pass. (From Anderson, John E. *The Psychology of Development and Personal Adjustment*, New York: Henry Holt and Co., 1949); and **D** Balance Test. (Data from Cron, G. W., and Pronko, N. H., Development of a Sense of Balance in School Children, *J. Educ. Res.*, 51:33–37, 1957; illustrated in Cole, Luella. *Psychology of Adolescence*, New York: Holt, Rinehart, and Winston, Inc., 1965.)

Innate Ability

When discussing athletic performance, arguments are often heated as to whether the outstanding athlete is born or made. It is the old problem of nature versus nurture. What are the relative effects of genetics and experience on performance? Such descriptive phrases as, "what a natural athlete," or, "a born hitter," are ways of commonly referring to particular performers. Does the physical educator or coach waste his time training individuals "who don't have it" and "never will have it" (whatever "it" may be)?

An examination of the problem should probably begin with the effects of heredity and environmental circumstances on intelligence, for it is the development of the cognitive processes that has been the primary concern of educators and psychologists during this century. The results of their research pave the way for understanding motor-skill accomplishment. No informed person would state that what we are is caused by purely genetic factors or solely environmental experiences, but rather that the end product is formulated by the interaction of both. The problem is in determining the relative contributions each makes to one's level of attainment in a particular endeavor.

Various methods have been employed in investigations concerned with the relative effects of heredity and environment on the organism. Families may be observed in order to find the characteristics that are prevalent among members, and correlations are computed so as to determine the degree of relationship among members on a specific variable.

Twins have been the subject of much research. If the twins are identical and raised in the same home, then behavior differences between them would probably be due to genetics. Twins who are reared apart also offer data valuable for gaining insight into the problem. Finally, a comparison of monozygotic twins (MZ) with dizygotic twins (DZ) permits further analysis of the relative effects of heredity and environment. Monozygotic twins are identical twins, coming from a single zygote and provided with identical hereditary endowments. Dizygotic twins are fraternal twins, coming from two separate zygotes and who may or may not be alike. When the genetic constitutions (genotypes) of the subjects are controlled and are more similar, deductions on environmental effects are more easily formulated. The particular characteristic of interest to the investigator and the level to which the observable attribute is affected by the genes is referred to as a *phenotype*.

It is no easy matter to control the many influencing variables adequately in order to estimate environmental versus hereditary effects accurately. Therefore, results of studies must be accepted with reservation. Such findings are more suggestive than conclusive, although certain general assumptions may now be made because of accumulating evidence.

Intelligence and Heredity. With intelligence as well as with any other factor, environmental variables operate within the limits offered by heredity. How influential is heredity in determining intelligence? Evidently, substantially. For example, Newman, Freeman, and Holzinger (1937) in their classic twin study found the IQ's of identical twins raised apart to correlate .76, whereas an r of .63 was yielded in comparing fraternal twins raised together. These authors rightly concluded that heredity was very important to the intellectual process. Environmental circumstances to a much lesser degree also affect intelligence, for it was noted that the IQ of one identical twin could be predicted from the IQ score of the other, the accuracy of which was dependent on their upbringing. When the IQ correlation of twins raised in the same house was squared for common variance, a predictability per cent of 80 was obtained. It was 60 per cent for identical twins raised apart. In other words, the twins living apart had a greater difference in IQ scores than those twins living together.

Burt (1958) also studied identical twins reared together and those separated early in life. He summarized his findings by indicating the relatively little effect environment had on intellectual growth, the figure approximating 12 per cent. Other investigators have found similar results, some as low as less than 10 per cent of the IQ variance being accounted for by the environmental component and up to 96 per cent of the variance contributed by the genetic background.

Although environmental factors have little effect on intellectual growth they have a great influence on achievement. Extremes in environmental surroundings will have a dramatic effect on IQ scores and academic achievement in general. It should go without saying that enriched environments will promote achievement but impoverished conditions will result in progressively poorer returns. The implication here is that although genetic factors limit potential, there is quite a distance between the operational level of an individual and his theoretical limits. Much can be done through environmental manipulations to raise the intellectual achievement of an average or below average youngster.

Athletic Accomplishments and Heredity. Just as differences in intellectual performance may be caused by hereditary and environmental factors, these same factors operate for potential success in motor skill performance. The extent of influence is not easy to ascertain, for most of the research has been completed on mental growth and is still inconclusive. However, it may be readily apparent that it does not necessarily follow that the same amount of practice on similar skills will benefit all individuals equally. Some people will perform more effectively after a few trials, some will show skill following many practice sessions, whereas others may never reach the level of performance which might be termed as skilled. Obviously dissimilar capacities for performing various tasks will be due to hereditary factors and/or previous experiences.

It is shown in Chapter 3 that there exists some relationship between the body build of the outstanding athlete and his chosen sport. To the extent that heredity might contribute to success in particular activities via physical characteristics, studies have found correlations approximating .50 between family physical qualities, such as height and weight (McClearn, 1964). Genetics will usually determine body types, and it is often witnessed that identical twins have similar body constitutions. Anatomically speaking, body structures may be greatly influenced by nonhereditary variables, such as health, nutrition, and exercise. A good example of an environmental factor exerting influence over genetic tendencies is the fact that first generation Japanese immigrants exceed their former countrymen in height by two inches. Nutrition and diet evidently had much to do with this situation.

As to actual research on the born-versus-made athlete, one of the leading contributors to knowledge in this area is Gedda (1961), who investigated the families of outstanding athletes as well as made comparisons of the sports practiced by twins. In this study, Gedda received data on genotype twins and twins with dissimilar genotypes. Among his many observations he noted a difference between type of twin and sports participation and success. Little dissimilarity in sports participation and practice could be found between genotype twins. It was equivalent to a 6 per cent difference in the case of identical genotype twins but was 85 per cent in the case of twins with different genotypes. Evidently, twins with contrary genotypes (fraternal twins) had individual interests and differed widely in general sports practice.

Gedda believes his data indicate that there is a great similarity between identical genotypes and the sports in which they participate successfully; hence the relationship of heredity factors to activity interest and certain characteristics to athletic success. He hypothesizes that sports aptitude is attributed to an exogenous factor or environmental conditions, including training, experiences, socioeconomic level, and an endogenous factor or inherited phenotype, which refers to the transmitted characteristics necessary for skill attainment in a specific sport.

In another investigation, Gedda (1964) and his co-workers surveyed the athletes who participated in the 1960 Olympic Games in Rome. After accumulating data on each athlete's family, the writers formulated two indices: an Index of Isosportivation (number of the athlete's family members participating in the same sport as he); and an Index of Allosportivation (number of family members practicing some other sport). Interpretation of the information allowed the following conclusions: (1) the athlete and his family practice similar activities and (2) specific physical and psychological qualities of the Olympians may be attributed to heredity. Family and environmental influences are not sufficient, for specific psychological and physical characteristics are needed for success in a particular sport. These occur repeatedly in the same family and are therefore attributed to heredity.

It appears therefore that motor capacity is determined by heredity. However, although achievement in intellectual pursuits and athletic endeavors will ultimately be determined by genetics, environmental experiences will do much to influence the level of achievement. Even the most favorably endowed individual, unless his energies are guided in a constructive manner and his abilities developed through instruction and practice, will not be an outstanding performer. Certain people are born with particular general talents or abilities, and these permit them to excel more easily in a given area. Yet, if all success were based on hereditary components, what would be the purpose in developing a psychology of learning, of developing learning techniques and theories? Why attempt to modify behavior? Obviously, much can be done with any individual if he is taught effectively, and his life's experiences will either facilitate or hinder his development and acquisition of motor skills.

Personality

Analysis of Personality. Everyday experiences and meetings with new individuals confirm our concept of individual difference in personality. Even as people display dissimilar physical, intellectual, and emotional characteristics their respective personalities are what sets them apart from others. A reference to one's personality usually indicates his identity, his uniqueness among many people.

Personality has been defined in many ways and the approach to the study of its development also varies. One of the more widely accepted definitions has been offered by Allport (1937) who suggests that personality is the "dynamic organization within the individual of those psycho-physical systems that determine his unique adjustment to his environment." When the researcher studies personality, he actually is studying behavior. Personality develops as a result of a person's adjustment to many situations, and his personality is reflected by his tendency to react in a certain way in a given situation.

Personality, intelligence, and motor capacity are all troubled by the same problem: the relative influence of heredity and environmental experiences. As is the case with motor and intellectual variables, it would appear that personality is a product of both environmental and genetic factors. It is the result of inheritance, habits, intelligence, emotions, drives, and experiences—all blending together to promote a characteristic way of behaving. Innate qualities influence personality development, but environmental factors determine the sort of influence.

Does a person exhibit a particular personality because of heredity? Because of maturity and matural growth processes? Learning? To a certain extent, personality characteristics appear to be congenital. This is evident, for behavior differences in babies are noted almost immediately after birth, too soon for experience to be the reason. Also, personality traits at an early age generally characterize a person later in life. Thompson (1962), a specialist in child psychology, writes that a child's personality structure is relatively consistent during the developmental period. With a certain degree of assurance one can predict later personality traits from those apparent at infancy.

Other psychologists insist that personality depends most on learning (Shaffer and Shoben, 1956). Since personality represents a characteristic way of behaving and much of behavior is learned, the hypothesis is reasonable. Learning principles operate in the development of a personality, for adjustment in life is learned. Personality, intellect, and motor capacity levels are difficult to ascertain because of a number of factors, which creates a problem in determining the relative contributions of genetics and environment to each. There are errors in measuring instruments and weaknesses. Changes take place because of the maturation-learning process, thus the problem in identifying true levels. Regardless of research technique and instrument problems, inheritance and environment are acknowledged influences on personality development.

Personality and Sports. Those familiar with and interested in motor–skill development feel that an individual's personality might very well determine his choice of activity as well as his accomplishments. In reference to activity selection, psychological needs are better met through certain sports than others for particular individuals. An aggressive person might choose a sport such as wrestling for his personal outlet. Someone else who enjoys a social environment provided by a sport might participate in team sports.

Athletes representing chosen sports have been found by some researchers to contrast in personality profile with so-called nonathletes. From sport to sport there is the suggestion that participants will vary in personality. Finally, even within a given sport, perhaps outstanding champion performers may be distinguished from average athletes in personality profile. The drive to excel, to be best, often distinguishes the champion from the almost champion.

Another consideration in this area of personality and sports is the possible changes which occur within a person as a result of his experience in sport participation. Although an individual's personality is formed early in childhood, it can be and is modified by later experiences in life. To display desirable personality and character traits is admirable and therefore encouraged by the parent, teacher, and most peer groups. Of the possible methods of molding a more socially-accepted personality, participation in organized physical activity has been acknowledged by many psychologists, sociologists, educators, and physical educators as one of the better means of transmitting this development. Then again, there are those who feel that this activity, especially in the more organized form of competitive athletics, would possibly have undesirable social and emotional effects on the participant.

A problem arises as to whether people choose to participate in activities because of what they are or change because of what they participate in. Perhaps both factors operate in a typical situation. Longitudinal studies in this area are lacking whereas cross-sectional studies having to do with the effect of programs of physical education and athletics on personal and social adjustment and emotional behavior of the participants are plentiful. Studies may also be found on the relationships between athletic ability, physical development, and personality traits.

An entire chapter in this book, Chapter 9, is devoted to the relationship of socio-psychological factors and physical activity. Therefore, suffice it to say here that personality, although difficult to measure accurately, is affected and modified by experiences in life, with sports participation included in those experiences. The influence of personality on athletic achievement, choice of activity for participation in leisure, and changes which occur because of this participation has not been well-researched. Heretofore, much of our knowledge has been based on subjective evaluations and empirical evidence. Nevertheless, latest evidence, more scientifically validated is presented and discussed in Chapter 9. It will be observed that this previously neglected area of study shows much promise for future research.

Summary

A study of growth and development includes inspection of the interactional effects of inheritance, maturation, and experience on the organism's motor development at different stages in life. It has been theoretically advanced and supported by a limited amount of human research that a critical-learning period exists for the learning of any type of behavior. These optimal stages for learning indicate the most effective and influential times in which to introduce new tasks. The critical period represents that time when the maximum sensory, motor, motivational, and psychological capacities are present for a given sort of learning.

During infancy and early childhood, a strong relationship between the physical, neurological, and intellectual processes has been demonstrated. Abilities are more general at this point in life, but become more specific with time. There is a similar development of motor patterns and intellectual skill, and it appears that achievement in basic motor movements will contribute to intellectual achievement. Complex skills and diverse sports are mastered with increasing age, especially during the first two decades of life. However, there is great difficulty in ascertaining the optimal age for athletic performance, for through ability and intensive training man can demonstrate superior skills at earlier and later ages than ever before. The optimal age for skilled performance in a given activity is affected also by the nature of the activity itself.

Sex differences in motor performance become more apparent with increasing age. Boys typically accelerate in motor performance during the teen years while girls level off and even demonstrate decline in performance. Physiological differences do not explain this phenomenon sufficiently, for additional considerations much be given to social and motivational factors.

Individuals are born with certain qualities and characteristics that provide them with higher potentials for motor achievement than others. However, since environmental experiences will actually determine the level of attainment, it must be concluded that motor skill is dependent on the interaction of both genetics and environment. Personality is developed and modified throughout life according to, and as a result of, the adjustments one makes to the situations he faces. Participation and success in sports would apparently be related to personality factors.

References

Allport, G. W. *Personality: A Psychological Interpretation*, New York: Henry Holt and Co., 1937.

Bachman, John C. Influence of Age and Sex on the Amount and Rate of Learning Two Motor Tasks, *Res. Quart.*, 37:176–186, 1966.

Bachman, John C. Motor Learning and Performance as Related to Age and Sex in Two Measures of Balance Coordination, *Res. Quart.*, 32:123–137, 1961.

BAYLEY, NANCY. *The Development of Motor Abilities During the First Three Years, Monographs for the Society for Research in Child Development,* Washington, D.C., 1935.

BEACH, FRANK A., and JAYNES, JULIAN. Effects of Early Experiences Upon the Behavior of Animals, *Psychol. Bull.,* 51:239–263, 1954.

BIRREN, JAMES E. *The Psychology of Aging,* Englewood Cliffs, N.J.: Prentice-Hall, Inc., 1964.

BRACE, D. K. *Measuring Motor Ability: A Scale of Motor Ability Tests,* New York: A. S. Barnes, 1930.

BROWN, ROBERTA W. The Relation Between Age (Chronological and Mental) and the Rate of Piano Learning, *J. Appl. Psychol.,* 20:511–516, 1936.

BRUNER, JEROME S. *The Process of Education,* Cambridge, Mass.: Harvard University Press, 1963.

BURT, CYRIL. The Inheritance of Mental Ability, *Amer. Psychol.,* 13:1–15, 1958.

CAPOBIANCO, R. J. Ocular-Manual Laterality and Reading Achievement in Children with Special Learning Disabilities, *American Educational Research Journal,* 4:133–138, 1967.

COWAN, EDWINA A., and PRATT, BERTHA M. The Hurdle Jump as a Developmental and Diagnostic Test of Motor Coordination for Children from Three to Twelve Years of Age, *Child Develpm.,* 5:107–121, 1934.

CRON, GERALD W., and PRONKO, N. H. Development of the Sense of Balance in School Children, *J. Educ. Res.,* 51:33–37,1957.

CUNNINGHAM, B. V. An Experiment in Measuring Gross Motor Development of Infants and Young Children, *J. Educ. Psychol.,* 18:458–464, 1927.

DELACATO, CARL H. *Neurological Organization and Reading,* Springfield, Illinois: Charles C. Thomas, Publisher, 1966.

DEMBER, WILLIAM N. *The Psychology of Perception,* New York: Henry Holt and Co., 1960.

ESPENSCHADE, ANNA. Motor Development, in JOHNSON, WARREN B. (ed.), *Science and Medicine of Exercise and Sports,* New York: Harper & Brothers, 1960.

FOWLER, W. Cognitive Learning in Infancy and Early Childhood, *Psychol. Bull.,* 59:116–152, 1962.

GEDDA, LUIGI. Sports and Genetics, A Study on Twins (351 pairs), in *Health and Fitness in the Modern World,* Chicago: The Athletic Institute, 1961.

GEDDA, LUIGI; MILANI-COMPARETTI, M.; and BRENCI, G. A Preliminary Report on Research Made During the Games of the XVIIth Olympiad, Rome, 1960, in JOKL, E., and SIMON, E. (eds.), *International Research in Sport and Physical Education,* Springfield, Illinois: Charles C. Thomas, Publisher, 1964.

GOODENOUGH, FLORENCE L. The Development of the Reactive Process from Early Childhood to Maturity, *J. Exp. Psychol.,* 25:431–450, 1935.

HENRY, FRANKLIN M., and NELSON, GAYLORD A. Age Differences and Inter-Relationships Between Skill and Learning in Gross Motor Performance of Ten and Fifteen-Year-Old Boys, *Res. Quart.,* 27:162–175, 1956.

HICKS, J. A. The Acquisition of Motor Skill in Young Children, *Child Develpm.,* 1:292–297, 1930.

HILGARD, JOSEPHINE R. The Effect of Early and Delayed Practice on Memory and Motor Performances Studied by the Method of Co-Twin Control, *Gen. Psychol. Monogr.*, 14, No. 6, 1933.

HIRATA, KIN-ITSU. Physique and Age of Tokyo Olympic Champions, *J. Sports Medicine and Physical Fitness*, 6:207–222, 1966.

HODGKINS, JEAN. Influence of Age on the Speed of Reaction and Movement in Females, *J. Gerontology*, 17:385–389, 1962.

HUMPHRIES, MICHAEL, and SHEPHARD, ALFRED H. Age and Training in the Development of a Perceptual-Motor Skill, *Percept. Mot. Skills*, 9:3–11, 1959.

ISMAIL, A. H., and GRUBER, A. H. The Predictive Power of Coordination and Balance Items in Estimating Intellectual Achievements, paper read at sixty-ninth annual meeting of the National Coll. Phys. Educ. Assoc. for Men, Philadelphia, Pa., 1965.

JENKINS, LULU M. A Comparative Study of Motor Achievements of Children of Five, Six, and Seven Years of Age, *Teach. Coll. Contr. Educ.*, Columbia University, No. 414, 1930.

JOHNSON, WARREN R. Critical Periods, Body Image and Movement Competency in Childhood, *Symposium on Integrated Development*, Purdue University, 1964.

JOKL, ERNST. *Medical Sociology and Cultural Anthropology of Sport and Physical Education*, Springfield, Illinois: Charles C. Thomas, Publisher, 1964a.

JOKL, ERNST; KARVONEN, M.; KIHLBERG, J.; KOEKELA, A.; and NORO, L. Olympic Survey (Helsinki 1952), in JOKL, ERNST, and SIMON, E. (eds.), *International Research in Sport and Physical Education*, Springfield, Illinois: Charles C. Thomas, Publisher, 1964b.

KEPHART, NEWELL C. Speech presented at Amer. Assoc. for Health, P. E., and Rec., Annual Convention in Chicago, Illinois, 1966.

KING, JOHN A. Parameters Relevant to Determining the Effect of Early Experience Upon the Adult Behavior of Animals, *Psychol. Bull.*, 55:46–58, 1958.

KLAUSMEIER, HERBERT J.; BEEMAN, ALAN; and LEHMANN, IRVIN J. Comparison of Organismic Age and Regression Equations in Predicting Achievements in Elementary School, *J. Educ. Psychol.*, 49:182–186, 1958a.

KLAUSMEIER, HERBERT J. Physical, Behavioral, and Other Characteristics of High- and Lower-Achieving Children in Favored Environments, *J. Educ. Res.*, 51:573–582, 1958b.

KLAUSMEIER, HERBERT J.; BEEMAN, ALAN; and LEHMANN, IRWIN J. Relationships Among Physical, Mental, and Achievement Measures in Children of Low, Average, and High Intelligence, *Amer. J. Mental Deficiency*, 63:647–656, 1958c.

KLAUSMEIER, HERBERT J., and CHECK, JOHN. Relationships Among Physical, Mental, Achievement, and Personality Measures in Children of Low, Average, and High Intelligence at 113 Months of Age, *Amer. J. Mental Deficiency*, 63:1059–1068, 1959.

LATCHAW, MARJORIE. Measuring Selected Motor Skills in Fourth, Fifth, and Sixth Grades, *Res. Quart.*, 25:439–449, 1954.

LORENZ, K. Z. The Companion in the Bird's World. *Auk*, 54:245–273, 1937.

McCLEARN, GERALD E. Genetics and Behavior Development, in HOFFMAN, MARTIN L., and HOFFMAN, LOIS, W. (eds.). *Review of Child Development Research*, New York: Russell Sage Foundation, 1964.

McGraw, Myrtle B. *Growth: A Study of Johnny and Jimmy,* New York: D. Appleton-Century Co., 1935.

McGraw, Myrtle B. Later Development of Children Specially Trained During Infancy: Johnny and Jimmy at School Age, *Child Develpm.,* 10:1–19, 1939.

Miller, James L. Effect of Instruction on Development of Throwing for Accuracy of First Grade Children, *Res. Quart.* 28:132–138, 1957.

Newman, H. F.; Freeman, F. N.; and Holzinger, K. J. *Twins: A Study of Heredity and Environment,* Chicago: University of Chicago Press, 1937.

Noble, Clyde E.; Baker, Blaine L.; and Jones, Thomas A. Age and Sex Parameters in Psychomotor Learning, *Percept. Mot. Skills.* 19:935–945, 1964.

Olson, Willard C. *Child Development,* Boston: D. C. Heath, and Co., 1959.

Radler, D. H., and Kephart, Newell C. *Success Through Play,* New York: Harper & Brothers, 1960.

Ravizza, R. J., and Herschberger, A. C. The Effect of Prolonged Motor Restriction Upon Later Behavior of the Rat, *The Psychol. Record,* 16:73–80, 1966.

Scott, J. P. Critical Periods in Behavioral Development, *Science,* 138:949–958, 1962.

Seils, LeRoy. The Relationship Between Measures of Physical Growth and Gross Motor Performance of Primary-Grade School Children, *Res. Quart.,* 21:244–260, 1951.

Shaffer, Lawrence F., and Shoben, Edward J. *The Psychology of Adjustment,* Boston: The Houghton Mifflin Company, 1956.

Sluckin, W., and Salzen, E. A. Imprinting and Perceptual Learning, *Quart. J. Exp. Psychol.,* 18:65–77, 1961.

Talland, George A. The Effect of Age on Speed of Simple Manual Skills, *J. Gen. Psychol.,* 100:67–76, 1962.

Thompson, George G. *Child Psychology,* Boston: Houghton Mifflin Company, 1962.

Tyler, Fred T. Concepts of Organismic Growth: A Critique, *J. Educ. Psychol.,* 44:321–342, 1953.

Wild, Monica. The Behavior Pattern of Throwing and Some Observations Concerning Its Course of Development in Children, *Res. Quart.,* 9:20–26, 1938.

Witte, Fae. Relation of Kinesthetic Perception to a Selected Motor Skill for Elementary Children, *Res. Quart.,* 33:476–484, 1962.

Annotated Student References

Motor Development

Bayley, Nancey, and Espenschade, Anna. Motor Development from Birth to Maturity, *Rev. Educ. Res.,* 11:562–591, 1941.

Summarizes the earlier research on motor development and children.

Birren, James E. *The Psychology of Aging,* Englewood Cliffs, N.J.: Prentice-Hall, Inc., 1964.

Provides a text on the psychology of adult life, specifically to apply the scientific method to the psychology of aging.

BRECKENRIDGE, MARIAN E., and VINCENT, E. LEE. *Child Development: Physical and Psychologic Growth Through Adolescence,* Philadelphia: W. B. Saunders Co., 1965.

Contains the latest evidence pertaining to child growth and development.

ESPENSCHADE, ANNA. Motor Development, in JOHNSON, WARREN R. (ed.), *Science and Medicine of Exercise and Sports,* New York: Harper & Brothers, 1960.

A summary of the research in motor development from infancy through adolescence by one of the outstanding contributors of knowledge to the area.

GEDDA, LUIGI. Sports and Genetics. A Study on Twins (351 pairs), in *Health and Fitness in the Modern World,* Chicago: The Athletic Institute, 1961.

A study on the effects of heredity on athletic success.

HOFFMAN, MARTIN L., and HOFFMAN, LOIS W., (eds.). *Review of Child Development Research,* New York: Russell Sage Foundation, 1964.

Reviews selective studies in child development research for the purpose of drawing conclusions for practice and furthering research.

McGRAW, MYRTLE B. *Growth: A Study of Johnny and Jimmy,* New York: D. Appleton-Century Co., 1935.

A classical study on the effects of early motor training.

MUSSEN, PAUL H.; CONGER, JOHN J.; and KAGAN, JEROME K. *Child Development and Personality,* New York: Harper & Row, Publishers, 1963.

The interrelatedness of the various growth variables are shown as they coincide with the chronological age.

RADLER, D. H., and KEPHART, NEWELL C. *Success Through Play,* New York: Harper & Brothers, 1960.

Logical theoretical deductions of the relationship between motor and intellectual factors in young children.

RAGSDALE, CLARENCE E. How Children Learn the Motor Types of Activities, in NELSON, HENRY B. (ed.), *Learning and Instruction,* Forty-ninth Yearbook, Part I, Nat. Soc. Study of Educ., Chicago: University of Chicago Press, 1950.

Generalized overview on the learning process as related to motor-skill learning in children.

TYLER, FRED T. Issues Related to Readiness to Learn, in HILGARD, ERNEST R. (ed.), *Theories of Learning and Instruction,* Sixty-Third Yearbook, Nat. Soc. Study of Educ., Chicago: University of Chicago Press, 1964.

This article discusses learning readiness—the when to teach—as it is affected by various factors.

6

Methods of Practice

Individuals possess unique qualities and specific characteristics because of inheritance, enabling some people to have greater potential than others for success with a given motor skill. However, actual skill attainment does not depend only on genetic factors. Environmental experiences qualitatively and quantitatively will promote learning and ultimately determine performance levels.

Recognition of individual differences requires allowance for the fact that all people will not benefit in the same way from the same practice techniques and methods of instruction. This does not mean, though, that we proceed in a haphazard way in attempting to attain skill. Research has cleared the way for a better understanding of the learning process, with the result that certain generalized learning principles may be applied to practice. These principles indicate the most effective and efficient means of attaining skill for the majority of people.

This chapter is concerned with the possible ways of manipulating environmental and practice conditions in order to obtain favorable performance in motor skills. Consideration is given to the nature of practice itself, the importance of motivation, the administration of practice sessions, and ultimate retention of that which has been practiced. Psychological concepts are introduced and research findings applied to the learning of motor skills.

Practice

Effect on Learning. For the majority of motor skills and under certain conditions, learning progresses with an increased number of practice trials. It is foolish to expect skilled performance at the onset, although there is no doubt that some individuals learn faster and are endowed more favorably than others for the task at hand. However, practice, as a rule, is a necessary prerequisite for learning.

Unfortunately, there is more to learning than mere practice, for *practice alone does not make perfect.* Practice must be accompanied by such conditions as the performer being aware of his direction or goal, and his results, and, in general, by motivation or the desire to improve. Repetition of an act may result in no performance increments and even in an inferior performance. The first situation (no increments) can occur if the conditions mentioned earlier in this paragraph are not present. The latter (inferior performance) will be manifested under these conditions or when the participant practices incorrectly and with erroneous goals. Thus, we can only assume the positive effect of practice on learning and performance when other desirable factors are operating in conjunction with practice, factors which are often taken for granted. (It might also be mentioned here that some learning theorists believe learning to take place in one trial and that further trials only enhance performance. However, this is a theoretical argument and does not concern us in this chapter.)

It is important to remember that drill may perpetuate error as well as eliminate error and improve skill. The advantage of practice lies in the attempts made to recognize and improve the human and environmental conditions surrounding the practice.

Attention. Practice is more meaningful and productive when the learner is attentive to particular cues. The learner, especially one who is a novice, typically experiences difficulty in isolating the most important elements in a given situation and concentrating on them. With practice and learning the individual becomes more selective in attending to stimuli—he even becomes conscious of less of them. The performer's attention is affected by the state of his organism as well as his knowledge of what to concentrate on. Improvement in motor performance during practice, then, is dependent on the attention the learner displays to the act in general and to certain cues in particular.

In psychological terms *attention refers to stimulus selection.* The following are some basic considerations of the selective process: (1) individuals differ as to what they will attend to when presented with identical situations; (2) stimulus selection will depend on the environment; and (3) stimulus selection will reflect the nature and state of the human organism. The problem of attention is not a simple one, for it encompasses many aspects of the learning situation. Its relevance to learning and consideration in practice is warranted.

Intent and Purpose. Practice is beneficial when it is purposeful. If the learner has the intention of improving and of attaining a goal, more than likely performance increments will be observed on succeeding trials. Thus, both the instructor and student are obligated: the instructor to set the goals and provide motivation, the student to follow the lead. Of course, if the task to be learned is meaningful to the student, there is less of a problem in creating interest to promote learning.

Merely going routinely through an act is a pure waste of time. It is not untypical for students in physical education classes to demonstrate the same low levels of skill at the termination of a unit as at the beginning. Although many reasons may be cited for this unfortunate circumstance, certainly one is a lack of purpose and direction. Many physical limitations can be overcome if the individual desires to improve in performance through practice. The reasons for wanting to develop a motor skill are varied ranging from pure enjoyment in skilled performance to building an ego, or for attention or for some material reward. Some reasons are better than others (who is to decide?) but the fact remains that any purpose is better than none at all, and performance will be contingent on intent to better oneself.

Amount of Practice. Of natural concern is the question of how much practice is necessary for a skill to be really learned. Where is that point of diminishing returns, that point when further practice will be wasted? Much depends on the criterion for skill attainment. Is the foul shot in basketball learned when the student can score one throw, five out of five, ten in a row, or twenty consecutive shots?

In psychological literature the criterion of success is usually one perfect trial or match. A trial may consist of learning ten nonsense syllables, tracing a maze, and the like. Any practice after the one-trial achievement, then, would be additional, and is termed *overlearning*. Researchers have investigated the effects of practice over and beyond the point when criterion learning has occurred and have invariably come to the same conclusion: overlearning results in better retention of the material learned than regular learning.

It is no secret that motor skills, e.g., bicycle riding, ball throwing, and typing are retained for a much longer period of time than many of the so-called intellectual or verbal skills. When one is asked to recall from childhood the skills involved in bicycling or to remember the lines of a poem, he typically demonstrates much greater performance with the motor skill. One school of thought advanced to explain this situation is that usually motor skills are overpracticed. How much time is spent playing baseball and learning the swing as contrasted with learning prose material? For the average youngster the answer is obvious.

However, overlearning is beneficial to a point, after which there are diminishing returns. In laboratory studies, 50 per cent overlearning is advantageous, but practice beyond this does not afford a proportional gain for the extended effort. Although 100 per cent overlearning results in a better performance yield than 50 per cent overlearning, the gains are not very worthwhile in terms of economy of the practice time.

Overlearning is associated with drill. The student as well as the teacher might very well ask how much drill is necessary in learning motor skills. The lack of research on motor skills, especially practical ones, necessitates a cautious application of the overlearning principle. Perhaps too much drill occurs in typical physical education situations: not only may this drill reach the point of diminishing returns, but it even may be detrimental because it (1) takes time away from learning other matter; (2) is boring to the learner; and (3) actually does not serve in improving skill retention significantly.

Enough practice to establish learning permanence is required for future success. But perhaps, instead of the number of repetitious trials providing greater motor-skill retention, the answer lies in the nature of the interpolated activity. From the time a skill is learned until it is to be demonstrated again, a few years later perhaps, a minimum number of competing responses has occurred. Most motor skills are somewhat unique. Not too many other learned skills will interfere with the originally learned skill. Therefore, it may be reasoned that motor skills can be retained with less practice, proportionally, than is associated with verbal learning.

The reply, therefore, to the question of how much practice is necessary is a difficult answer that can be made only after deciding on one of two possibilities. What is the object of the practice: immediate success or later retention? For many skills, reasonable achievement comes after not too many practice sessions. If the goal is immediate successful performance and there is no concern for the future, then the time spent on learning can be more limited. Contrarily, if later performance is an important consideration, then evidently more practice, hence more overlearning, will be beneficial in determining the length of time the tasks are to be retained as well as the amount of skill that will be displayed at that time of recall.

For the serious-minded athlete no amount of practice is enough for him. Is it any wonder that even after many years of no practice have elapsed, former college athletes can still demonstrate a reasonably high degree of proficiency in their areas of specialty? Of course, the average individual does not desire and perhaps lacks the ability to attain such a high level of skill. Although his time and energy involvement will be considerably less than the varsity athlete, it should be remembered that more practice will increase the potentiality for later-in-life leisure time skills to be available for use. Little early practice, which might result in immediate success, will certainly not produce beneficial long-range effects.

Early Achievement in Practice. Owing to the specific nature of individuals and their previous experiences, performers will vary in their rate of skill acquisition. With any given task, some people appear to be faster learners than others. The value of practice, especially over an extended length of time, is obviously more beneficial to those learners who demonstrate initial difficulty with the problem at hand. The necessity of practice of long enough duration has been established from research findings pointing to the fact that one cannot usually predict ultimate achievement from initial progress. Researchers such as Welch (1963) and Trussell (1965) have demonstrated that sufficient data, collected over approximately one-half the intended duration of the practice days, are needed to reflect final levels of attainment adequately.

However, there are evidently at least some tasks in which later proficiency is directly related to early proficiency. The data from Adam's study, acquired from performance on a discrimination reaction time test, nicely illustrate this point (see Figure 6–1). Ten groups of subjects were stratified into deciles on the basis of their first trial scores. They were given 160 trials, and although some individuals shifted status with practice, the groups maintained their relative positions throughout the experiment. The reader can observe the unique asymptote for each group, and it does not appear as if the groups would converge toward a common level. All groups showed improvement with practice, and as might be expected, more improvement was noted with the low ability subjects than the high ability subjects.

There is good reason to believe, though, that the relationship between initial and final status is quite low on more complex tasks, such as those taught by physical educators. Variations in the performance levels between learners throughout practice may be because of the relative ease of gaining insight into the problem; the transferability of related learned skills to the task at hand, which might be of special advantage in the early stages of practice; and various psychological, physiological, intellectual, and emotional adjust-

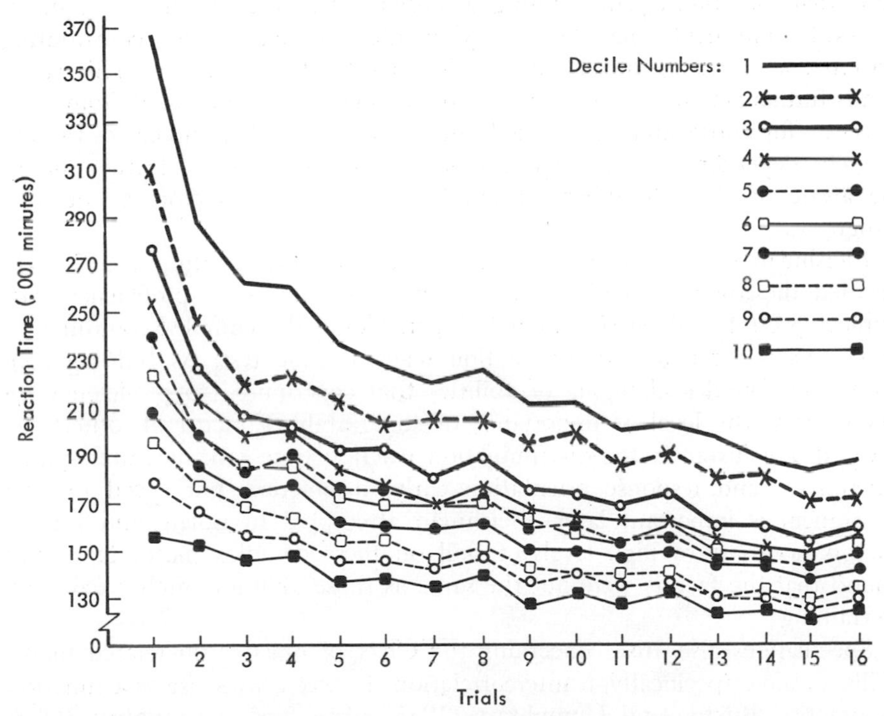

Figure 6–1. Mean performance curves for ten ability groups. (From Adams, J. A. The Relationship Between Certain Measures of Ability and the Acquisition of a Psychomotor Criterion Response, *J. Gen. Psychol.*, 56:121–134, 1957.)

ments that have to be made. Whatever the cause, initial individual differences will exist as will later differences, but apparently they are not related in gross motor skill learning. Hence, practice will benefit individuals in dissimilar ways and they will show varying rates of progress.

Changes During Practice. Observable changes in performance occur with practice. As learning increases, subjective evaluation or objective measurements will attest to this progress. Another aspect of change possibly associated with practice is that of different abilities being more important in the various phases of learning a skill.

The results of an investigation by Fleishman and Hempel (1954) would tend to support the idea of a change in factor pattern with practice. The Complex Coordination Test appeared to be more complex (in terms of the number of significantly important factors) in the initial phase of practice and less complex with the continuation of practice. Through the factor-analysis method, higher loadings on more factors were obtained at the beginning of practice. There were seven significant factors in the initial stages of practice but only three in the final stages. Beside this discovery, different abilities were found to be important during the various stages of practice.

To quote Fleishman and Hempel (on their results): "It is quite conceivable that the abilities contributing to individual differences in earlier stages of skill attainment...may be somewhat different than those contributing variance at more advanced and terminal levels of proficiency." This study lends further support for diffidence in predicting final achievement from early success, for those abilities needed for success are called upon in varying degrees, depending on the stage in practice. Also, teacher and learner should be aware of the desirability of emphasizing different factors as practice progresses.

Fleishman offered further evidence in another investigation (1957). He studied the abilities involved in early and late stages of proficiency. His subjects were tested on six motor tasks, including the complex coordination test, pursuit rotor, and discrimination reaction time test. As training continued he found a changing of abilities that contributed to proficiency on these tasks: the level of importance of some abilities increased, others decreased. For instance, the discrimination reaction time task measures spatial orientation and response orientation early in practice, but speed of arm movement is important later. Fleishman attempted to isolate and predict factors necessary to high levels of skill on these complex motor tasks and found that the factors were not the same as those abilities emphasized early in training.

Speculations also arise concerning the effect of practice on related motor skills, or more specifically, if intercorrelations between tasks rise as a function of practice. Buxton and Humphreys (1935) researched the problem. Their subjects were pretested, practiced, and post tested on four motor skills involving arm speed. The tasks included the Koerth Pursuit Rotor; the Brown

Spool Packer Test (speed in packing spools in a tray); and two tapping tests for speed, telegraph key tapping and alternating tapping of two brass plates with a stylus. At the beginning of practice, intercorrelations ranged from .08 to .40 and averaged .25. After practice, the correlations were surprisingly lower, ranging from −.02 to .39, with an average of .16.

Along with evidence presented in Chapter 4, this study lends further support for the specificity nature of skills and denies a general skill factor. If there were such a general factor as neuromuscular arm speed, the above reported investigation would have found high correlations between the tasks, if not at the beginning of practice, certainly at its termination. Evidently, even after practice a general factor cannot be used to determine success in a number of motor speed skills.

Owens (1942), corroborated these findings. The Minnesota Mechanical Ability Test consisting of seven tests of motor skills was administered eight times to two groups of junior high school boys. It was found that trait differences remained the same or increased with practice. The author concluded that it would be more favorable to have the individual specialize early in life in his greatest aptitude than learn general skills. The experiment also indicates the apparent genetic determination and uniqueness of motor skills.

Measuring Practice Effects. In order to determine the effects of practice, to see whether learning has taken place, the data obtained in a given situation must be analyzed. A brief glance at the research literature concerned with learning provides the reader with numerous methods of measuring the effects of practice and of designing studies. Some of these experimental designs have been employed more than others, but each has its own unique advantage in advancing information about the learning process.

First of all, practice sessions (length and frequency) and trials vary from study to study as does the nature of the material or skill to be learned. Many times these practice sessions, trials, and materials are arbitrarily selected by the investigator. Any variations of any one of the preceding variables between experiments may result in dissimilar findings.

Secondly, there are various methods of analyzing changes within practice. Measurement of these changes usually associated with differences between initial and terminal performances indicate the degree of learning that has occurred. McCraw (1951, 1955) has compared many of the possible ways of measuring and scoring tests of motor learning. In each of his two studies, McCraw obtained data from subjects performing two novel motor skills. Learning that has occurred because of practice may be measured by considering such factors as initial status versus final score, difference between first and last scores, and percentage of improvement. Also, there is the problem of ascertaining the number of trials that should represent the first score as well as the final score. How many trials are necessary for warm up and task familiarity are open to question, but most authorities agree that at least a few should be provided before an actual initial score is recorded.

In attempting to reconcile these problems, McCraw (1955) formulated eight methods, based on those found in other experiments, to score the practice effects on learning two tasks. Some of these procedures were

1. *Total Learning Score Method.* Consisted of cumulatively adding all the trial scores during practice.
2. *Difference in Raw Score Method No. I.* Required finding the difference between the final and initial trials.
3. *Three Per Cent Gain of Possible Gain Method.* Represented by the formula:

$$\frac{(\text{Sum of last "N" trials}) \text{ minus } (\text{Sum of first "N" trials})}{(\text{Highest possible score of "N" trials}) \text{ minus } (\text{Sum of first "N" trials})}$$

4. *Two Per Cent Gain of Initial Score Method.* Depicted by this formula:

$$\frac{(\text{Sum of last "N" trials}) \text{ minus } (\text{Sum of first "N" trials})}{(\text{Sum of first "N" trials})}$$

McCraw reported considerable variability in the scores as yielded by the diverse means of measuring improvement. As to a comparison of methods, he states that "...the most acceptable appear to be those that relate gain to possible gain...while the least desirable are those that interpret gain in relation to the initial score." The Total Learning Method and the Three Per Cent Gain of Possible Gain Method were the most valid measures in comparing individuals with dissimilar initial scores. The author generally found little relationship between the various scoring methods, i.e., each yielded different results.

Thus, it can be seen that varying the means of improvement measurement results in dissimilar outcomes and interpretations of the data. The nature of each study must be scrutinized before the procedure of data analysis is selected, although some methods are apparently more acceptable than others. One of the difficulties in determining laws of learning pertaining to any factor is the variation in design from investigation to investigation, including the selected method of data analysis.

Motivation

In any situation, at any time, and with any individual, performance is likely to fluctuate. Even outstanding athletes who have attained a high proficiency in certain skills do not perform consistently at a particular skill level. Variability in response can be caused by external factors. For the basketball player, the basketball, the court, the basket, the gymnasium, the spectators, all of which may vary from location to location, are sources of potential alternations in performance to which adjustments must be made.

Apart from environmental sources, internal variables such as physiological and psychological drives and needs contribute to levels of performance. The urge to push toward a specific goal has been termed *motivation.* Actually, motivation is a concept invented to describe the psychological state of the organism as it is affected by various influences. It is caused by specific motives (particular needs or drives), and attainment of the goal removes a particular need. A person is motivated when he desires some goal, a goal that will meet his needs or satisfy his interests.

Many psychologists believe that all behavior is motivated (by something), although it is extremely difficult to isolate specific motivational variables. Much research has been initiated having to do with motivation, although for many years animals have been the primary subject of the investigations. Currently, strong disagreement exists among theorists as to the nature and scope of motivation, and in general, the area may be considered fertile for extensive experimentation. The basic conflict is between the clinical psychologist's subjective evaluation and the experimental psychologist's restricted and contrived means of measuring motivation. Recent years have brought forth a more thorough examination of the motivational process as it pertains to the learning of motor skills.

Terminology and concepts related to motivation are often confusing because of the interpretations and interests of the particular investigator. It will not be the purpose of this book to present an extended treatment of such a complex field of study as motivation, but rather to interpret the basic research so as to satisfy the practical interests of the reader. Before delving into this research, further discussion is offered to clarify some basic terms.

Motivation in a practical sense encompasses wants, desires, wishes, and acts (Atkinson, 1964). *Motives,* specific causes of a motivational state, activate, direct, or select behavior. Motives are used to explain variable performances, for past behavior is not always indicative of present behavior. A change in performance may be caused by the presence or lack of one or more motives. Motivation and *incentive* are terms often used interchangeably, and, in fact, they have much in common. McGeoch (1961) describes the basic similiarities and distinguishes between the two concepts. An incentive is an object or condition that satisfies a motive and removes it, but, according to McGeoch, a person can be motivated without an incentive. Also, incentives may be present but appeal to no particular motive.

Motivation has been acknowledged to be of utmost importance during practice. In fact, McGeoch states that "...motivation is a necessary condition for the learning process (and) many motives are, themselves, the product of learning." Controversy has been raised over whether motivation affects learning or performance. Most psychologists agree that rewards in the form of praise, grades, candy, and the like operate on performance rather than learning. Unmotivated people do not perform the desired responses; therefore, they do not learn. The following formula represents the role of motivation.

Performance	=	Learning	+	Motivation
(behavior in a situation)		(past experience)		(reward, deprivation)

It should be pointed out that this scheme represents the thinking of most S-R theorists who are experimental psychologists. Other psychologists, for instance, Allport (1943), are interested in the individual and his unique personality and find fault with experimental psychologists who would emphasize enviornmental manipulations to the neglect of individual considerations. It appears evident that a satisfactory explanation of motivation must resolve the interaction of the basic process (environmental influences on behavior) and individual personalities.

Measuring Motivation. Many techniques have been employed to measure the effect of various motives. McClelland (1958) has done exceptional work in discussing these devices as well as general research problems related to the measurement of motivation. The different methods of measuring the presence or absence of a motive should reflect changes in motive strength in some way. Experimental research studies typically have investigated motivation in the following ways:

1. Providing special instructions or commentary.
2. Depriving the subjects (usually animals) of food or water.
3. Applying a strong persistent stimulus, such as an electric shock.
4. Varying the motivation by presenting objects of different magnitudes and attractiveness (rewards).
5. Measuring muscle-tension levels.

Further comment will be offered on motivation and muscle tension, as this technique is relatively new and a currently popular means for motivation assessment. Tension levels can be measured electromyographically and may be used to discover how well one performs on tasks relative to the amount of effort he exerts. Performance efficiency is equal to performance quality over tension level (Eason, 1963).

Eason noted in his investigation that coordination and skill on a tracking task increased daily without an increase in effort. Tension levels remained constant day to day as skill increased. Eason suggests that muscular tension levels may be used to solve a number of problems. The effects of practice (if any) after correction for motivation can be determined, and the plateau in learning can be analyzed to see if it is the result of a lack of skill change or a decrease in motivation.

McClelland (1958) warns that the measure of a motive should be represented by variations in only the motive of interest. The problem of isolating a specific motive in a situation in order to determine its effect on behavior is indeed perplexing and difficult. In addition, the effect of a particular motive, when determined, should be consistent when the same conditions are present. In other words, reliability is necessary before confidence can be given to the suggested effect of a given motive.

In measuring human motivation, three general methods have been employed. Firstly, self-ratings or reports have been provided by the subjects regarding their feelings toward or feelings following a particular event. Secondly, an outside observer may rate the subject's state of motivation, such as in a clinical assessment. Finally, motivation may be determined from a person's behavior in an experimental motivationally-induced situation. The ineffectiveness of these methods can be assessed from McClelland's general findings—that these three methods yield uncorrelated results.

One of the few relatively new attempts at measuring motivation in motor-skill performance was made by Eysenck (1963). Using the pursuit rotor, he demonstrated how S-R learning theory can explain and predict motivational effects. He suggested the consideration of reminiscence, an extended period of no practice between the end of practice and its resumption. Reminiscence scores (the difference between end of practice scores and resumption scores) measure drive. Eysenck was able to determine the effect of high-versus-low drive on the learning and performing of the motor skill, among other findings.

However there are standard laboratory methods used as motivational techniques for many years. Surwillo (1958) lists nine of them and suggests a tenth. They are

1. *Intrinsic interest.* The task is so interesting and challenging that S, the subject, on his own volition, applies himself to it.
2. *Social incentive.* Social incentives, in their simplest form, are E's (experimenter) requests of S, "Do well.", "Try hard.", "Try harder."
3. *Reporting scores and encouraging improvement.* E reports S's score at the end of each trial, indicates improvements or decrements, and and at times offers verbal encouragement. Cues pertaining to performance may also be given during a trial (e.g., a light may be flashed or an auditory signal given whenever S is off target, as in a tracking task). This motivational technique has been referred to in recent literature as *directive feedback.*
4. *Monetary incentive.* E offers S a sum of money for participating in the experiment.
5. *Importance.* S is told that the scores he achieves are important and may be used in the determination of norms.
6. *Social-competitive incentive.* The task may be arranged that S's engage in competition with each other or with some norm or previously-recorded high score. In some studies, the false-norm technique is used.
7. *Reward incentive.* Bonuses are given for improved performance.
8. *Threats of punishment.* Some form of electric shock is widely used.

To add to realism, electrodes may be attached and a mild shock administered with the threat that a stronger shock will be given if S does not meet some criterion.

9. *Administration of punishment.* Usually an electric shock is administered at the end of a trial for failure to reach a particular criterion.
10. *Heat-pain stimulation.* This is to be used in a lengthy experiment, where attention levels have a tendency to fall.

The Nature of the Task. Motivational effects depend not only on environmental manipulations and the individual's personality, but on the nature of the task itself. If motivational level can be held constant, it is observed that the relative simplicity or complexity of the skill to be learned will determine the ease with which it is learned. For instance, it is generally assumed that high or low motivation has the same effect on simple acts or skills.

However, the level of motivation will affect the performance of a complex skill. Evidence indicates that more difficult tasks require lower motivation, for high motivation has been found to impede skill acquisition in these tasks. Highest performance is attained by subjects with intermediate motivation (drive) and as tasks increase in complexity, subjects with less drive do better. The *Yerkes-Dodson Law* describes this phenomenon: there is an optimal level of motivation for the level of task difficulty. Although somewhat exaggerated, Figure 6–2 illustrates some possible effects of varying degrees of motivation.

In the study by Eysenck (1963) reported previously, no difference was

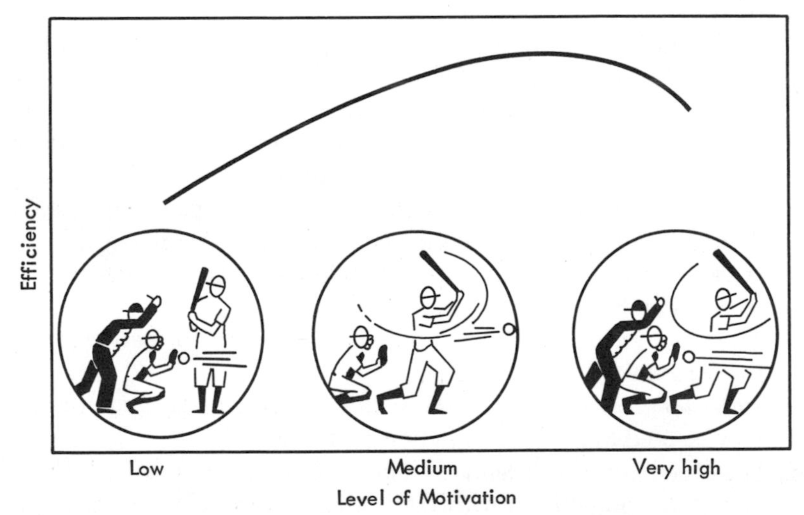

Figure 6–2. A schematic representation of the relationship between level of motivation and efficiency of behavior. At low and high levels of motivation the result is the same, a strike-out, but the behavior of the batter is quite different. (From Wickens, Delos D., and Meyer, Donald R. *Psychology,* New York: Holt, Rinehart, and Winston, Inc., 1961.)

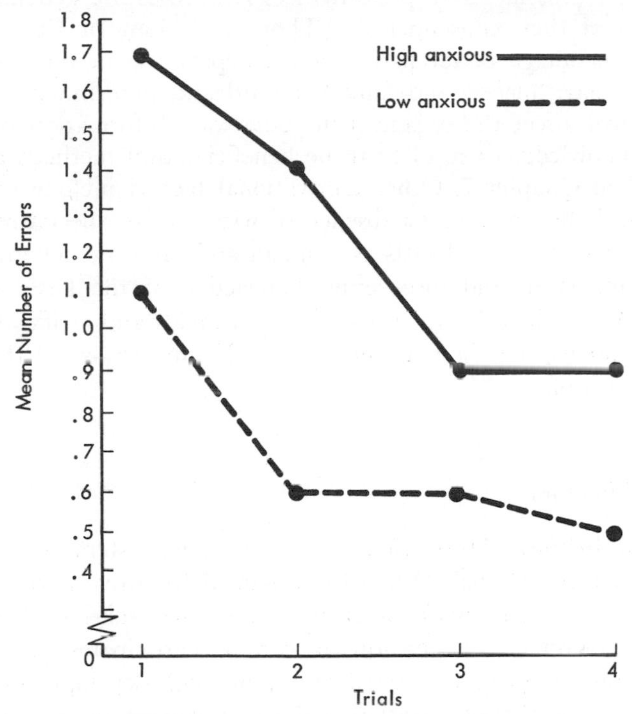

Figure 6–3. Error curves for anxious and non-anxious subjects. (From Palermo, David S.; Castaneda, Alfred; and McCandless, Boyd R. The Relationship of Anxiety in Children to Performance in a Complex Learning Task, *Child Develpm.*, 27:333–337, 1956.)

found between high and low drive groups on their initial performance on the pursuit rotor. However, a reminiscence test indicated a significant gain for the high drive group but not for the low drive group.

Hull's theory, extended by Spence, describes the relation of the task to the performer in the following way. If the correct response is dominant over incorrect responses (typical in a simple task), increased motivation or anxiety should facilitate performance. In a complex learning situation there are usually a number of competing incorrect responses that are more dominant than the sole correct response. Performance is predicted as poorer in this case in highly motivated subjects. Figure 6–3 illustrates the data obtained in an investigation concerned with testing the theory. The subjects were children who were placed in extreme groups as a result of their scores on the Taylor scale of manifest anxiety, which is a measure of motivation. Their task was to learn a light-button motor task that requires trial and error learning in attempting to find the correct button that turns off each light. As can be viewed in Figure 6–3, the nonanxious subjects were superior to the anxious subjects, thus substantiating evidence accumulated on adult subjects and further supporting Hull's theory.

Many environmental factors can be varied in order to promote optimal motivation and thus facilitate performance. Responses are generally learned as a function of their consequences (Thorndike's Law of Effect). Hence, rewards will encourage better performance, depending on the amount, frequency, and delay. Success and failure, reward and punishment, praise and criticism all will affect the organism in some way. Information provided in the form of knowledge of results can be beneficial, and methods and effects are discussed in Chapter 7. Other motivational factors include competition and rivalry and the presence or absence of witnesses or spectators.

The work of such psychologists as Tolman and Hull are acknowledged in promoting interest in and discovering knowledge of the basic needs and drives of animals. There is much research on animals and artificial means of motivating humans, but these are not reviewed here because of their lack of practical application.

Motivational Factors

Extrinsic and Intrinsic Motivation. Motivation may stem from two basic sources: internal or external. When the origin of the drive is from within a person, that is to say, he does something for its own sake, he is said to be *intrinsically motivated.* He performs a skill or participates in a sport for personal reasons, namely joy, satisfaction, or skill development. Intrinsic motivation implies self-actualization and ego involvement. An *extrinsically motivated* person persists at an activity for the material gain he can receive from it. He studies hard in a class not so much in order to acquire knowledge, but rather to attain a high grade. He may participate in a sport for the possible recognition and glory instead of for comradeship, inner satisfaction, and achievement. Extrinsic motivation is need-deficiency motivation.

From an educational and ideal point of view, intrinsic motivation is more desirable than extrinsic motivation. Unfortunately, because of cultural practices, we are frequently rewarded materially from childhood throughout life for demonstrating correct responses and acceptable behavior. We expect and become conditioned to rewards. Inner drive, though, is usually a more sustained and effective form of motivation. It should be acknowledged that in many situations both extrinsic and intrinsic factors operate, but with varying degrees of impact. If motivation from within is the primary source of the athlete's endeavors, he will be more likely to continue participating after the days of fanfare, hero worship, and excitement are over. Friedlander's (1966) study only partly supports the strength of intrinsic motivation. He used three measures of motivation and attempted to discover their relationship to two criteria of the job performance of white and blue collar workers. High performers reflected intrinsic motivation as most important to them, recognition second, and social environment as last in importance. Low performers were rated highest on social environment importance. However, within the blue collar group, there were no significant motivation-performance relationships.

External rewards may assume various objects and conditions. The effectiveness of these rewards, as Rotter (1966) points out, may very well be determined if they are perceived as being of external control, occurring by chance rather than one's own action; or of internal control, contingent on one's own behavior. Individuals differ in their attitude toward a situation depending on its control by external or internal factors and develop expenctancies accordingly. When individuals perceive a situation involves luck or fate, they have less expectancy for a reward. Performance is likely to deteriorate under this condition.

Most investigations have not been concerned with the subject's interpretation of a specific reward, but instead with the general effect of the reward on performance. Considering the possible variety of methods in motivating a person and the range of gross motor skills, it certainly is surprising to see the limited amount of work in this area. Here are some of the motivational techniques investigated: threats; praise; punishment; immediate knowledge of results; varying amounts of reward; prompting; introduction of bells, buzzers, sounds, and music during performance; cooperative ventures; and competition.

Ulrich and Burke (1957) found that by merely introducing a buzzer or bell at certain intervals of performance a greater work output was elicited from the subjects. Nine men and nine women were tested on the bicycle ergometer, and both sexes reacted similarly to the stimuli. The results of this study and others, especially those concerned with the military tasks of tracking and pursuit in which boredom from task monotony sets in, indicate the importance of novel stimuli interspersed during practice. If a motor skill is repeatedly performed, motivation, which might normally lessen, will probably increase with the introduction of various stimuli throughout a practice session.

Strong (1963) investigated the effect of six motivation conditions on 434 sixth grade boys and girls performing the American Association of Health, Physical Education, and Recreation Physical Fitness Test (a battery of seven tests). The motivating conditions were competition with a partner; competition with oneself; group versus group competition; competition against records; level of aspiration; and competition with a peer of unequal ability. Results indicated the level of aspiration and team competition to be the most effective motivators.

Sometimes experimenters do not find that various motivational factors influence performance. This may be because of the fact that the subjects are already operating at a high-level of drive on the task, therefore additional inducements will be ineffective. Perhaps this is why Ryan (1961) reported no difference in grip strength between four groups operating under four different motivational conditions. The subjects were threatened with shock, provided with a knowledge of their results, given constant exhortation, or asked to do as well as possible. Nelson (1962, 1963) found that music varying in rhythm, sound, and tempo did not affect an all-out ride on the bicycle ergometer.

Noble (1955) analyzed the effect of special verbal inducements on a co-ordination task which was fairly well learned by the subjects. Thirty-two one-minute trials were administered to the subjects, and additional motivation was provided at trials eight, sixteen, and twenty-four to three groups picked at random. The treatments were found to be ineffective as to improving performance. Noble did speculate that the subjects were probably operating at a high degree of motivation and the verbal motive-incentive instructions might be irrelevant to the situation.

Employment of verbal instructions or inducements is one of the most widely used motivational techniques. Research evidence does indicate this method helps in the learning of written materials and there is some evidence to support the idea that it is also beneficial to motor performance. Fleishman (1958) provides interesting data on the relation between ability levels and motivation. Four-hundred subjects were trained on the Complex Coordination Test, on which a subject must make appropriate stick and rudder control adjustments in response to successively presented patterns of visual signals.

All of Fleishman's subjects were given five one-minute trials and then divided into two groups, one of which received continual verbal encouragement during certain rest periods between the remaining fifteen trials. In analyzing the data, high and low ability groups, based on scores made on the initial trials, were determined and compared under motivating and non-motivating conditions. It was found that each group improved at about the same rate and in the same fashion. However, in the high ability subjects, there was a significant difference in favor of the motivated group over the unmotivated group. The performance curves are presented in Figure 6–4.

There is probably much speculation as to the effect of the crowd and band on athletic performance. Although audience impact on performance is treated in Chapter 7, an early study is inserted here to indicate band influence on performance. Ayres (1911) noted a real influence on the physical effort of cyclists when a band played compared to when it was silent. Environmental factors usually do not affect the performance of skills too much that are well learned. There is a general stability in performance unchanged despite different situations. However, personal observation and empirical evidence would point to the fact that it is possible for performance levels of the skilled to rise or fall when certain factors are present.

It is more likely, though, that during the acquisition-of-skill stage the effect of varying motivational conditions will be more noticeable. Before routines become well established and responses somewhat conditioned, environmental variations act as temporary depressants or facilitators to performance.

Varying the amount of reward appears to produce a change of performance in favor of the reward with the greatest magnitude. Studies on verbal materials have repeatedly demonstrated this occurrence. The same results appear in

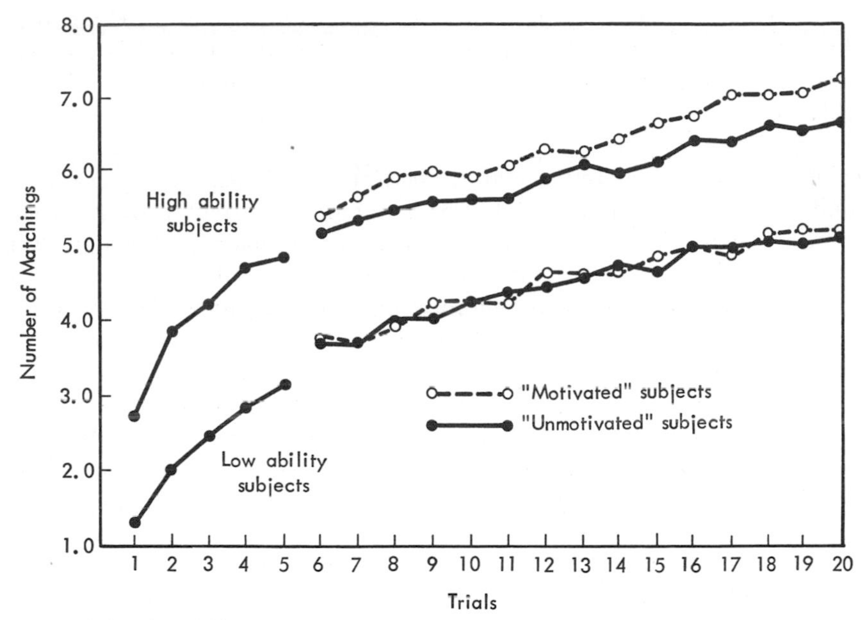

Figure 6–4. Acquisition curves for subjects of different ability and motivation levels. (From Fleishman, Edwin A. A Relationship Between Incentive Motivation and Ability Level in Psychomotor Performance, *J. Exp. Psychol.*, 56:78–81, 1958.)

measuring short-term retention, for Weiner and Walker (1966) found that a greater strength of motivation during learning led to less forgetting. Four different incentives were used: one-cent reward, five-cent reward, shock for no recall, and withheld motivation. This investigation concerned the selecting of consonants for various colored slides, but it is inviting to speculate on the effect of similar incentives on motor performance. Assuming little or no inner drive of the learner, the instructor would have to turn to the most extreme motivating conditions in order to hasten skill acquisition. Once again, it is necessary to realize that individuals are not all motivated in the same manner by a particular form of motivation. Some respond better when they are yelled at and incited; others need inspiration as provided through different approaches. A grade, a position in the class or on the team, punishment, a note to the parents—these and many other techniques are specifically appropriate for a certain kind of person. Most ideal would be an at depth analysis of the performer's personality and nature, so that the most appropriate motivational method, if needed, could be applied without subjecting an entire group to the same condition.

Coaches are often guilty of approaching all their boys in the same way. One type of coach continually yells at his players to "fire them up." Unfortunately, some individuals will respond in a negative way when they are constantly under dramatic vocal fire. On the other hand, a mild mannered coach who offers only praise when deserved and sympathy where warranted may be guilty of neglecting those athletes who need to be inspired vigorously. Anyone interested in motor learning must be aware of the desirability of instilling an inner drive in the performer, understanding his personality, and applying the appropriate motivational technique at the right time.

Reinforcement. The term *reinforcement* refers to the occurrence of any event that increases the probability or maintains the strength of a particular act or behavior. For all intents and purposes, a reinforcer is a form of reward, and perhaps *reward* is a more general term than reinforcement. However, reinforcement has attained specific meanings with regard to the classical and instrumental learning experiments designed by psychologists. In unique animal experiments, men like Pavlov and Skinner have demonstrated the effect of a reinforcer on conditioning an act or directing behavior.

With reference to motor-skill learning, any statement that could be said about reward holds true for reinforcement. If the student is learning a motor skill, the encouragement, praise, grade, or money awarded to him after he performs correctly serves as a reinforcer. These rewards reinforce the act; they tell the individual that he is doing what is desired and that possibly further good performances will be rewarded in the same way. It has been found that more immediate reinforcement is more effective than any delay in reinforcement. Association of a correct response with a given stimulus becomes strengthened with immediate reinforcement, for during any delay other activity occurs and the individual is apt to confuse which response he is being rewarded for.

Another aspect of reinforcement to consider is its ideal frequency. Although continual reinforcement is effective, it appears that random reinforcement is better. In other words, there is improved performance with uncertainty in a situation. Actually, typical situations do contain a large amount of uncertainty in reward. The baseball batter does not get a hit every time at bat, but certainly one hit in three attempts (unpredictable in occurrence) is sufficient to act as a reinforcer. He never knows when or what kind of hit he will make, but by achieving an adequate number of them, he is continually motivated whenever he goes to bat.

Success and Failure. In any given endeavor, the outcome will be viewed as relative success or failure, depending on the criteria for success. It may be recalled from Chapter 4 that personal success or failure is dependent on the level of aspiration, which in turn serves as a motivational force. The traditional concept of encouraging successes and avoiding failures in order to elevate motivation and at the same time improve performance is perhaps too simply stated. Recent evidence has shown that the relative effects of success and failure on motivation are much more complex than once believed.

Atkinson (1957) offers research and theory to describe the probability of motivation increasing or decreasing as a result of experienced success or failure. For example, the expectant probability of success with a task of intermediate difficulty is .50. For a difficult task, one of say a .20 probability of success, motivation steadily increases with repeated success until the probability of success is .50. Motivation after that point *decreases* as the probability increases to certainty (1.00). The probability of success is so high that there is no interest or incentive. Atkinson concludes that one should always look for new and more challenging tasks.

Atkinson (1964) considers another aspect of the problem when he writes on the results of repeated failure in an easy task (p or expectant probability = .80). Motivation should *increase* with failure until the expectant probability has been lowered to .50, and after that, the motivation should weaken. The motivation should lessen with the first failure on a difficult task. Success with simpler tasks increases motivation on subsequent more difficult tasks; the level of aspiration rises with success.

The old assumption that success automatically increases motivation and failure automatically decreases it is not always true as has been shown theoretically. On the other hand, not all current research substantiates all of Atkinson's concepts on motivation (some of which are mentioned in Chapter 4). Nevertheless, there appears to be justification for a number of these concepts. The difficulty of the task as it appears to the performer and his initial success with its undertaking contribute to his motivational level. Another consideration for probabilities and motivation is the anxiety level of the individual. An anxious indiviual confonts a new challenge with a probability of success different from less anxious people. Fear of failure results in quickened loss of motivation.

Finally, the number of successful acts before failure occurs may affect performance in various ways. Bayton and Conley (1957) divided seventy-five college students into three groups and administered the Minnesota Rate of Manipulation Test to them. One group received five trials of success before experiencing failure; for the second group failure came after the tenth trial; and the third group experienced failure after the fifteenth trial. Results indicate that early failure has an inhibitory effect upon that experience. As success increases through time, subsequent failures increase motivation. After ten and fifteen successful trials, a shift to failure increased the level of performance, whereas this was not so after five trials. Evidently, an application of these results to the learning of any motor skills would call for the learners to experience as much success as possible in the early stages before failure.

Reward and Punishment, Praise and Criticism. Although there have been many methods developed to influence the motivational process, perhaps the most widely used in everyday situations fall into reward and punishment categories. Examples of rewarding good behavior and correct responses and punishing the undesired are familiar to everyone that there is no need to list them here. However, the relative effectiveness of each, as demonstrated by practical experience and research evidence, deserves examination.

Thorndike influenced ideas on punishment through a good part of this century. At first, on the basis of experiments with animals, he concluded that reward and punishment had equal effects on behavior. He later modified this position as evidence indicated reward to be a more stable and a stronger influence for desirable behavior than punishment. Skinner, working with rats, noted the more temporary and unpredictable effect of punishment. Punishment inhibits behavior, but wears off. Hence, it has a temporary effect unless it is administered continually.

At the present time, psychologists and educators agree that of the two, it is better to take a positive approach to the learning situation. Praise, since it is specific to the act and informative, tells the person when he does the correct thing. Punishment tells the person what not to do instead of what to do. After punishment, the desired response still has to be discovered. In our society, even the threat of the most dire consequences for antisocial behavior does not totally inhibit these acts. The implementation of threats, criticism, or pain, no matter how severe, does not always work. The effects of punishment are not consistent from individual to individual or situation to situation.

The ineffectiveness of punishment can be explained also by the usual delay between the time an act takes place and the administering of the punishment. Reward is almost always immediate; that is, the type obtained by the individual for himself. The youngster may take a cookie without permission from the jar—thus he is rewarded. When mother discovers what has happened, perhaps hours later, he is punished. The situation results in a conflict for the child. In a specific motor–learning situation, praise or criticism can occur immediately or else be delayed, with immediacy the more desirable.

Yelling and screaming at a child or striking him for performing a skill incorrectly may help in improving his skill level, but it also may cause confusion, anguish, and resistant behavior. On the other hand, positive reinforcement for ideal or near ideal performances by praise and encouragement will probably be more effective in attaining hoped–for goals. The work of Skinner has demonstrated the heights one can reach in controlling and hence predicting behavior through constant reinforcements.

A study by Hurlock (1925), although using addition problems as the task to be learned, serves to demonstrate the relative effects of various incentives. Children in four groups were tested under four different conditions: praise, reproof, no comment, and ignored (but heard praise and reproof given to others). The praised group did best, the reproved group was second best, the ignored group third, and the no-comment group finished last.

Knowledge of Results. An early experiment contributing to the concept that practice does not always make perfect was one in which the subjects had to draw a line of so many inches when blindfolded. Because they were never informed as to how they were doing, the subjects did not improve in their performances. Many studies since then, analyzing a wide range of methods and materials, have tended to demonstrate the importance of knowledge of results.

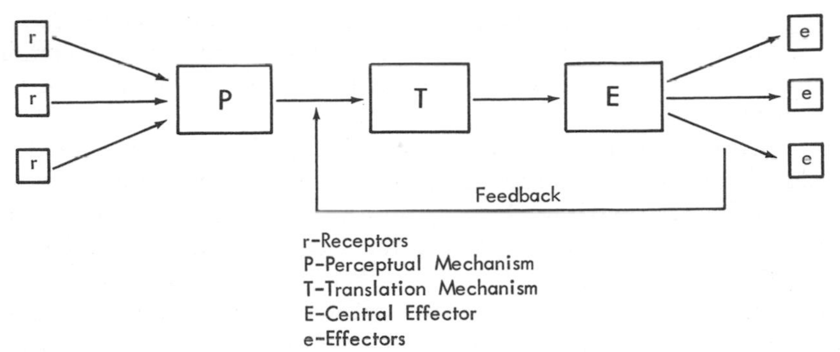

Figure 6–5. Feedback with relation to the other major mechanisms in the information-process concept.

Knowledge of results (KR) is a form of reinforcement, for the individual is informed as to the correctness or incorrectness of his responses. This information may come from an external source, e.g., the teacher, or from the person's own performance on a skill in which he knows right from wrong. Although *KR* is a term widely used in the literature, present-day terminology, engrossed in man-machine dynamics, has popularized another term, *feedback,* which basically refers to the same state of affairs as knowledge of results. Feedback can best be understood when viewed in relation to the three major mechanisms needed for information processing. *Information processing* is another recently popularized term describing human behavior.

As can be seen in Figure 6–5, the receptors stimulate the Perceptual Mechanism to perceive and identify the information (stimuli). Then the Translation Mechanism is activated to decide on a choice of action. The Central Effector coordinates and phases the action, innervating specific effectors. Feedback, in this case proprioceptive information, comes from the Central Effector and influences the future information which might have to be monitored by the perceptual-translator process. This descriptive mechanical operation system has proven to be an interesting method to evaluate motor-skill performance, especially as far as industrialists, engineers, and certain psychologists are concerned.

We typically receive feedback or KR when we perform most athletic skills. In performing a swimming stroke, if it does not feel right, we try to adapt and correct our movements. The quarterback who continually attempts to pass into a particular zone, only to find it well covered by defenders, adjusts his offense. The archer can see if he is missing the target and compensates accordingly in his next responses. From merely making a basket, serving in the proper court, or making a putt, we are informed if our response is correct.

There are other cases when it is necessary for an outsider to provide relevant information. Sometimes we are not aware of what we do wrong to cause an inappropriate response. A violation of a mechanical principle, bad form resulting in inefficient performance, or other errors can be relayed to the performer by an instructor. Knowledge of results are just as important to the individual whether provided by external sources or through one's own movement.

In practice or actual competition, knowledge of results serves a definite purpose. If the fencer is not rewarded by a point when he legally touches an opponent, he may make unnecessary adjustments. Enjoyment and learning are hampered. The same holds true for fouls not called in a basketball game. The foul call informs the player that the referee knows he violated a rule, and no call permits the player greater freedom and perhaps more violations of other rules. Without a knowledge of results, improvement cannot occur. Violations not called in practice severely limit the performance in a game, especially if the player is not aware he is committing illegal acts.

Research on the topic of knowledge of results is too vast to be presented here. Among the theoretical and minor issues raised are two questions: is the intertrial interval more important than the knowledge-of-results delay?; and, will a delay of KR have the same effect on all types of tasks? Generally speaking, as far as the motor skills typically taught by the physical educator are concerned, immediate KR is most beneficial. After having their blindfolded subjects draw a three-inch line, Greenspoon and Foreman (1956) found that an increase in the KR delay interval resulted in a decrease in the rate of learning. The KR delay periods were zero, ten, twenty, and thirty seconds. Tasks such as line drawing and tracing do not typify the gross motor skills encountered by physical educators, hence these results probably do not mean much in their area of teaching. In continuous, complex tasks, the activity itself (if results can be seen or movement is not restricted) plus the cues from the instructor enable the learner to hasten his skill attainment.

The terms *knowledge of results* and *reward* are not interchangable terms, even though there are many likenesses between them. Bilodeau and Bilodeau (1958), eminent researchers in the area of KR, state the effects of KR and reward as similar but not necessarily equivalent. Both are the terminal effect of the subject's responses. However, reward is usually associated with a dictonomy of responses, e.g., right or wrong; KR varies with the degree of response error. In motor skills, we typically learn to make graded responses by a graded error signal—knowledge of results is the index of how to modify responses.

In those activities where visual results constitute the major source of KR, performance is improved through being able to see how one has done. Motivation is increased. Pierson and Rasch (1964) tested their subjects for isometric strength twice a day, once with the dial in view and once when it was not. Higher scores were attained when the subjects were aware of their performance achievements.

Ammons (1956) has summarized the research on knowledge of results and states eleven empirical generalizations from the research.

1. The performer usually has hypotheses about what he is to do and how he is to do it, and these interact with knowledge of performance.
2. For all practical purposes, there is always some knowledge of his performance available to the human performer.
3. Knowledge of performance affects rate of learning and level reached by learning.
4. Knowledge of performance affects motivation.
5. The more specific the knowledge of performance the more rapid the improvement and the higher the level of performance.
6. The longer the delay in giving knowledge of performance, the less effect the given information has.
7. In the case of discontinuous tasks where knowledge of performance is given, small intervals between trials are generally better for learning than are longer ones.
8. When knowledge of performance is decreased, performance drops.
9. When knowledge of performance is decreased, performance drops more rapidly if trials are relatively massed.
10. When subjects are not being given supplementary knowledge of performance by the experimenter any longer, the ones who maintain their performance level probably have developed some substitute knowledge of performance.
11. When direct (supplementary) knowledge of performance is removed, systematic "undershooting" or "overshooting" may appear in performance.

Administration of Practice Sessions

Anyone interested in the most efficient means of skill learning must invariably consider the length of the practice sessions, their frequency in a given period of time, and the work-rest ratio within a practice period. The effective use of time, as defined by maximum productivity or skill development in minimum practice time, can be determined theoretically from the results of countless investigations found in psychological literature. From a practical point of view, though, there is the problem of generalizing in a particular task from data collected under a wide range of experimental materials and methods.

Of course, many factors other than time allotment and distribution are involved in the eventual acquisition of a skill. Some factors are obvious and observable, e.g., the relative complexity of the skill, the amount and quality of instruction offered, facilities and equipment, the motor abilities of the learner, his past experiences in relevant skills, and his maturity. Other factors are not so apparent and might include motivation and determination, emotional status, and mental and physical readiness. All these factors operating in various combinations in turn affect the outcome of the administration of practice sessions.

Many of these variables are difficult to isolate and control. One aspect of the learning situation that can be directed by the instructor is the amount and distribution of time to be designated for the acquisition of a skill or a group of skills. Any teacher or coach is interested not only in providing a period of long enough duration for skill attainment, but also in proportioning the time so that it might bring the most desired immediate and future results. Attempts to improve learning efficiency in any field of activity must consider the problem of optimal spacing of training sessions and the practice session itself.

Length and Spacing of Practice Sessions. What is the ideal length of practice periods and rest intervals? Although it would be satisfying to be able to provide the teacher and coach with a set answer, the problem is not so simple. Obviously, if the activity is a physically demanding one, attention to cues will diminish and learning in general will suffer as fatigue increases. In this case the length of the session should be relatively short if maximum learning potential is to be realized.

The skill level of the performer is another consideration. Beginners normally have shorter spans of attention than advanced performers and their motivation is extremely more variable. Hence, as a general rule, practice periods may be increased in length (to a point) as skill is attained. Children usually sustain interest in a specific activity for briefer time periods than adults, and instructional periods should be weighed accordingly. These are but two of the common-sense approaches toward practice scheduling.

In one of the more novel experiments on practice schedules, Knapp and Dixon (1950) had two groups of college students learn how to juggle. One group juggled three balls for five minutes each day while the other group practiced fifteen minutes every second day until the criterion of successful juggling was met: 100 consecutive catches. An analysis of the data indicated that the first group learned the task much faster, with one minute of practice in Group I equal to one minute and eighty seconds of practice in Group II. The investigators concluded from these results that learning a task such as juggling was enhanced by shorter practice and shorter rest periods.

In an early study, Lashley (1915) investigated the acquisition of skill in archery, using twenty-six subjects divided into five groups. Each group shot either five, twelve, twenty, forty, or sixty arrows every day until they all had made 360 attempts. During the first 180 attempts, little difference was found; but an analysis of the later attempts showed a greater proficiency for the groups who shot less each day and had their practice periods distributed over a longer period of time. For instance, the group which shot twelve arrows a day improved 47 per cent whereas the sixty-shot group showed an improvement of 29 per cent.

These and other studies support the belief in shorter practice and rest periods and, in general, practice extended over a longer duration of time. Murphy (1916) investigated optimal practice conditions for acquiring skill in javelin throwing. His groups practiced either five times a week, three times, or once a week until a total of thirty-four practice sessions were completed. On the basis of his findings, Murphy favored practicing the skill three times or once a week over five times a week. Young (1954) studied the learning of skill in archery and badminton. She found archery to be learned better when practiced four days a week, whereas badminton skill was acquired faster when the activity was practiced two days a week. Both groups, in learning these activities, received a total of twenty lessons.

From a practical standpoint, many educators wonder whether the semester or trimester college plan is best for the assimilation of knowledge. Similarly, physical educators are concerned with the relative effects of each plan on skill acquisition. Waglow (1966) observed the effects of a seventeen-week semester and a fourteen-week trimester on skill achievement in tennis, golf, and handball. Actually, 1,800 minutes of class time were devoted to each activity under the semester plan and 1,820 minutes were likewise appropriated under the trimester plan. Even so, Waglow found a significant difference in favor of the semester plan for tennis and golf, but not for handball.

It would generally appear, then, that gross motor skills can be learned more efficiently with shorter but more numerous sessions spaced over a longer time period. Although the writer has made a deliberate attempt to review studies concerned only with the learning of athletic skills here, many other studies can be found employing such tasks to be learned as prose, nonsense syllables, inverted alphabet writing, digits, mazes, concepts, symbols, aerial gunnery, typing, piano playing, and pursuit rotors. Summarizing all this research, it is apparent that the optimal rest period necessary for the acquisition of verbal, written, or motor skills varies with the material used. Of twenty-four studies reviewed under the topic of optimal rest intervals between practice periods, thirteen showed superior performance with a greater distribution of practice, eight studies indicated a preference for a rest interval somewhere in the middle of those used, and three investigations did not find any difference in performance with the various intervals employed.

However, these results are somewhat misleading, as what may have been a minimum rest between trials for one study may have been the maximum rest interval used in another study. It is difficult to reach a conclusion, except perhaps that somewhere between too little rest and too much layoff is the desired condition for practice. Also, gross motor skills can be learned with more of a rest interval between practices than can other types of learning material, e.g., nonsense syllables and pursuit rotors.

In motor learning as in weight training there seems to be a point of diminishing returns. Present evidence does not support the contention that five days a week of weight lifting is more effective in increasing strength than three days a week of lifting. Similarly, Massey (1959) found very little difference in the manner in which three groups performed on a stabilimeter (hand–tracing) task as a result of their prescribed practices. One group practiced three days a week for five weeks, a second group practiced five days a week for five weeks, and a third group had only nine days of practice. On this particular task, nine days of practice were sufficient for skill acquisition, which means that actually sixteen of the twenty-five practice days that the second group had seemingly were wasted.

The work of Harmon and Oxendine (1961) is in apparent agreement with these findings. Three groups of junior high school boys learned a mirror tracing task, with all the subjects practicing two days per week for five weeks. The groups differed in the number of practice trials that were allowed each testing day. Although a greater number of practice trials resulted in better performance at first, the groups improved at the same rate throughout the remainder of the experiment.

Oftentimes thought is given to manipulating the practice schedule. Oxendine's (1965) groups of subjects learned a mirror-tracing task based on the following practice schedules: increased succeeding practice periods, decreased succeeding practice periods, and constant units of practice. The three groups completed the same amount of practice time. The constant-unit practice group did best on the task and the decreasing-practice group was found to do the poorest.

There are many ways in which practice and rest schedules can be altered. Most of the studies discussed here and even research not mentioned in this section have been interested primarily in immediate performance rather than in ultimate retention of that which has been learned. The next section, which deals with massed and distributed practice, also will include a number of investigations primarily concerned with the immediate effects of the varied practice schedules. The reader should wait until he examines the material on retention later in this chapter before he forms any conclusions on the relative effectiveness of various training procedures.

Massed Versus Distributed Practice. The distribution of time allotted for the learning of a specific skill has posed a serious problem to physical educators and coaches, especially since there are usually many skills to be learned in a limited period of time. Ultimately, the instructor may utilize one of the following methods of practice.

On the one hand, he could have his students consistently and continuously practice the skill to be learned without any intermittent pauses. This method is termed *massed practice.*

On the other hand, the students might learn the skill in shorter but more frequent practice sessions. These practice periods would be divided by rest intervals or intervals of alternate skill learning, a condition known as *distributed practice.* Is the continuous practice period more effective in skill acquisition and retention than one broken by spaced rest periods? Is it better to practice a task with very little interruption for rest or is rest beneficial to learning and performance? If pauses are desired, what are the optimal intervals between practice trials?

Attempts to improve learning efficiency in any field of activity must consider the problem of optimal spacing of training sessions. Some instructors are in favor of teaching a skill in one session and having the students practice this skill repetitiously in the one period. Other instructors believe in requiring the students to practice different skills for a short duration at each meeting. The actual length of time devoted to the learning of a skill under massed and distributed conditions might be the same. However, under massed conditions the practice of the skill occurs continuously in one session whereas the practice of this same skill under distributed conditions would be limited each session but practiced in a number of sessions.

The relative effectiveness of concentrating all practice or study into one sitting as compared with dividing it into smaller units sampled at varying intervals of time is an important problem in the study of the learning process. The problem exists throughout a wide range of activities from academic preparation to athletics. Numerous studies have been completed in psychology on the distribution of practice effects on learning, with the first demonstrated in 1885 by Ebbinghaus. Unfortunately, very little work may be found in the experimental literature relating to the effects of distribution of practice on the learning and retaining of gross motor skills, or more specifically, athletic skills. Nevertheless, leading physical educators are in general agreement in their opinion that short, frequent performances are more favorable and profitable to learning than long sessions crowded into a brief span of time.

Many studies dealing with massed and spaced practice have been undertaken. Two of them using a pursuit rotor apparatus, are reviewed here. In pursuit rotor learning, the subject attempts to hold a stylus on a target located on a phonograph-like platform that moves in an unpredictable manner and with controlled speeds. Ammons (1951) had two groups of ten subjects perform thirty-six practice trials on the pursuit rotor. The massed practice group was not allowed any rest between trials whereas the distributed practice group paused five minutes between trials. Distributed practice was favored under the various performance achievement criteria used by the experimenter.

Travis (1937), using the Koerth pursuit rotor, utilized the services of only four subjects who every other day alternated under massed and distributed practice conditions. He found distributed practice (two minutes of work and one minute of rest repeated six times) to result in a consistent rise in the learning curve. The massed practice (twelve continuous minutes of practice) resulted in a progressive decrease in efficiency.

Crawford and others (1947) studied the training missions of 221 students and found that ammunition distributed over many training missions resulted in a much greater percentage of target hits than if all the ammunition was fired in one session.

In an athletic situation, Griffith (1932) noticed similar results. He had one group of basketball players continuously shoot a basketball for an hour, whereas another group shot three minutes and relaxed two minutes for an hour. The next day the procedures were reversed. Both groups shot about an equal amount of time; but when shooting with frequent rest periods, the men averaged 15 per cent more baskets than when shooting steadily.

These are but a sample of the investigations in this area of learning. Figure 6–6 typifies the relationship of massed and distributed practice effects.

To summarize, a number of randomly selected investigations reviewed by the author will now be presented. Eighteen studies demonstrated superior performance with distributed practice, five fared better under massed practice, and six studies resulted in no appreciable differences attributable to the effects of the practice conditions. Three studies favored early massing and later distributing, one showed no difference early in practice as a result of practice conditions but demonstrated better later performance under distributed practice, whereas a fifth investigation favored early distribution of practice.

In spite of the general findings indicating the preferability of some form of distributed practice over massed practice, leading physical educators have

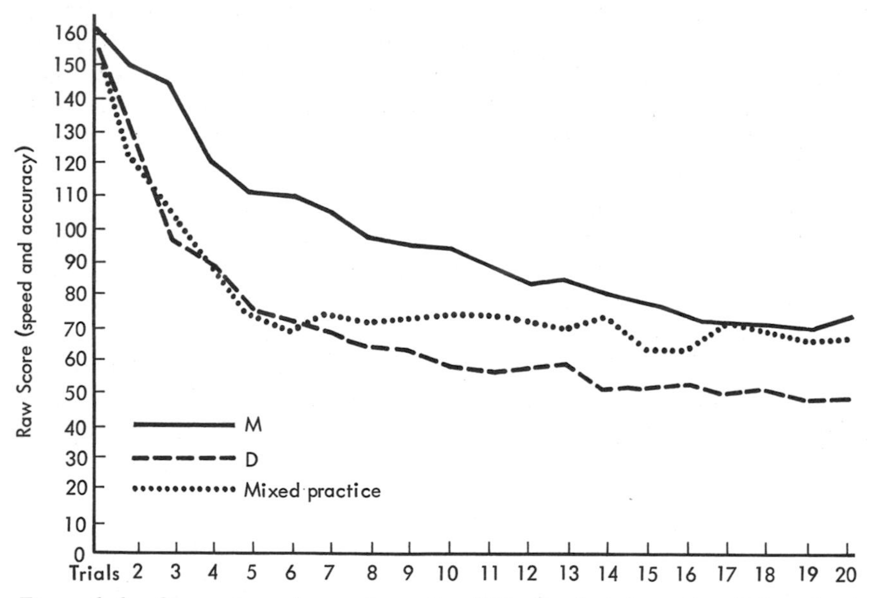

Figure 6–6. Comparison of massed practice (M), distributed practice (D), and mixed practice on a stabilimeter task. The massed-practice group had 20 consecutive trials, the distributed practice group was allowed a 1-minute rest period between trials, and the mixed practice group had 5 trials of distributed practice and the remaining fifteen of massed practice. Notice how the mixed-practice learning curve assumes the characteristics of each practice method at the different points of the experiment. The distributed practice method is clearly more effective throughout the practice trials. (From Lorge, I. Influence of Regularly Interpolated Time Intervals upon Subsequent Learning, *Teach. Coll. Contr. Educ.*, No. 438, 1930.)

had reservations in advocating this procedure. After summarizing much of the pertinent research, Mohr (1960) concluded:

> Although the sum of the physical education findings agree with those in psychology, the evidence is far too scanty to uphold the assumption that distributed practice will result in more effective learning than massed practice.

Rarick (1960) also warns:

> Psychologists have studied extensively the effect of duration and distribution of practice sessions upon verbal and fine motor learning, but the applicability of these generalizations to the learning of gross motor skills needs further study.

There is a distinct hazard in applying inferences from one experimental area to another one, even if apparently related. However, there is little reason to doubt the superiority of a distributed form of practice over massed practice for *immediate skill acquisition and retention.* As is shown in the next few pages, *skill retention* is not favored so clearly under one practice condition. After a rest interval, tests of retention usually indicate a lessened dissimilarity in performance between groups trained under massed and spaced practice conditions. In other words, it would appear that varied practice conditions, because of the temporary aspect of their influence, affect performance more than they do learning. If distributed practice primarily affected learning, the wide differences at the end of practice in favor of distributed practice would remain the same on later recall tests.

Retention and Forgetting

Motor skills are often learned with the intention of successfully performing them at a later date. Although immediate performance is also a consideration, written or skill tests and athletic contests are examples of occasions when later recall of that which has been learned is demanded. Retention may be dependent on a number of factors, namely the nature of the task, its meaningfulness to the learner, the time lapse between the original learning and recall, and the conditions under which the task was learned. Let us examine such factors as well as prominent theories describing this aspect of the learning process.

Retention and forgetting are terms used to describe the same process. Whereas *retention* refers to that which is remembered and can be determined by measuring the difference between the amount originally learned and the amount forgotten, the amount *forgotten* is equal to the amount learned minus the amount retained.

Normally we might expect to find a decrease in retention with the passage of time in which there is no practice, but research results indicate that this is not always the case. A number of studies have demonstrated that the retention curve does not always drop rapidly following the post-rest learning period but instead continues to rise. This improvement instead of a decrement in the recall of a task after a period of rest has been termed *reminiscence*. It appears that certain practice conditions may be more advantageous for reminiscence than others.

Methodology of Retention Experiments. Three measures have generally been used in investigations concerned with retention. These include recognition, relearning, and recall. *Recognition* is the method so often used in written testing, an example of which is the multiple-choice test. A *recall* score is informative in that it indicates how much or how well something is remembered.

A *relearning* score is determined in the following way. The number of trials the subject needs to relearn a task, for example, twelve, is subtracted from the number of trials it originally took him to learn it to a particular criterion, say, fifteen. The figure obtained, three, is placed over the original learning trials, fifteen, and this results in a *savings score*. In this case, the savings score, otherwise known as the *retention score*, is 20 per cent. Conversely, the forgotten score would be 80 per cent. In terms of their retention effectiveness, recognition is best whereas recall results in the poorest performances.

When testing for retention, two methods have been employed. Older studies used repeated tests on the same subjects in order to measure retention at various intervals after the completion of practice. This procedure has been rightfully attacked, for each test influences the next test and becomes but another form of practice. This flaw in experimentation undermines the effectiveness or desirability of such a method. A designation of the subjects into subgroups after the practice periods are over to be tested at different times for retention adds precision to the experiment. This desired method requires the investigator to have an ample number of subjects at the beginning of his study.

Retention as a Function of Practice Methods. Most investigators concerned with varying the practice-rest ratios have been interested primarily in the immediate acquisition of the tasks whereas few have extended their investigations to observe retention effects of the practice conditions. Typical results are those reported in the following experiments.

Reynolds and Bilodeau (1952), using apparatuses involved in the rudder-control test, a complex coordination test, and a rotary–pursuit test, had groups practice under massed and distributed conditions. The subjects were given retention tests ten minutes, fifteen minutes, and ten weeks after the termination of practice. The effects of distributing practice were notably more advantageous throughout the experiment and on the first two retention tests, but both groups demonstrated similarity in performance on the retention test given ten weeks later. Using the SAM Complex Coordinator, Lewis and Lowe (1956) had one group of subjects practice steadily for twenty minutes in each of fifteen sessions. The distributed practice group was allowed thirty-second rests after every trial. Although distributed practice resulted in immediate superior performance, a four-month-later retention test suggested that the conditions of practice seemed to have no differential effects on retention.

Massey (1959), in a study already reported, had her subjects learn a tracking task under different practice conditions. No superiority of any one of the patterns investigated was noticed on a retention test given one week after the conclusion of practice. Cook and Hilgard (1949) practiced groups of subjects on a pursuit rotor for three days with decreasing and increasing rests between trials. After long periods of rest, performances tended to be alike, regardless of the arrangement of the prior practice.

Singer (1965) investigated the retention of a novel skill practiced under massed and distributed practice conditions. Figure 6–7 illustrates the results. During the actual practice, the effectiveness of a lengthy rest between sessions is evident as are the inhibiting effects of continuous practice. However, retention tests, administered one day, one week, and one month after the conclusion of practice indicated different trends. No significant differences between the groups were noted on the first two retention tests, but a signifi-

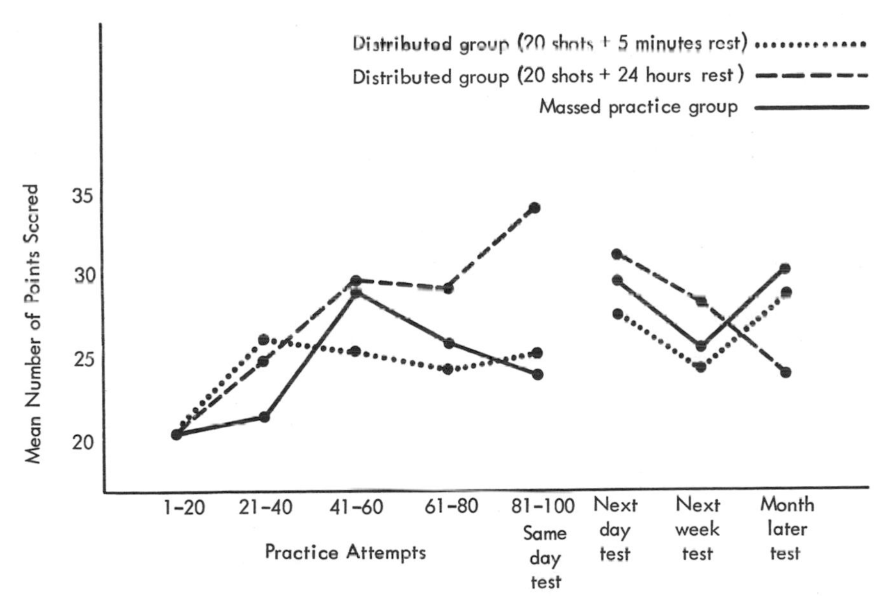

Figure 6–7. Massed and distributed practice effects on the acquisition and retention of a novel basketball skill as measured by the mean number of points scored. (From Singer, R. N. Massed and Distributed Practice Effects on the Acquisition and Retention of a Novel Basketball Skill, *Res. Quart.*, 36:68–77, 1965.)

cant difference was obtained in favor of the originally massed practice group over the most widely distributed practice group.

It might be added that this final result is unusual and hard to explain. More in line with the research evidence are the findings from another experiment, depicted in Figure 6–8. Although initial differences are small, there evidently is a critical point where massed practice inhibits and worsens performance whereas distributed practice appears to be continually beneficial. A test one week after the termination of practice, indicated little difference between the groups.

A survey of research investigating retention effects after a period of at least twenty-four hours from the final moment of practice indicates little difference between groups as a result of their practice methods. However, more research findings favor the retention effects of distributed practice over the effects of massed practice.

Reminiscence. Reminiscence is the opposite of forgetting, for it is the phenomenon in which performance increases after a rest interval and is therefore attributable to rest. It is also believed to occur only when the task has been partially learned. Reminiscence was not isolated as separate from the distribution effects of practice until the work of Ballard (1913). He read passages from "The Ancient Mariner" for fifteen minutes to elementary school children and then required them to write all that could be remem-

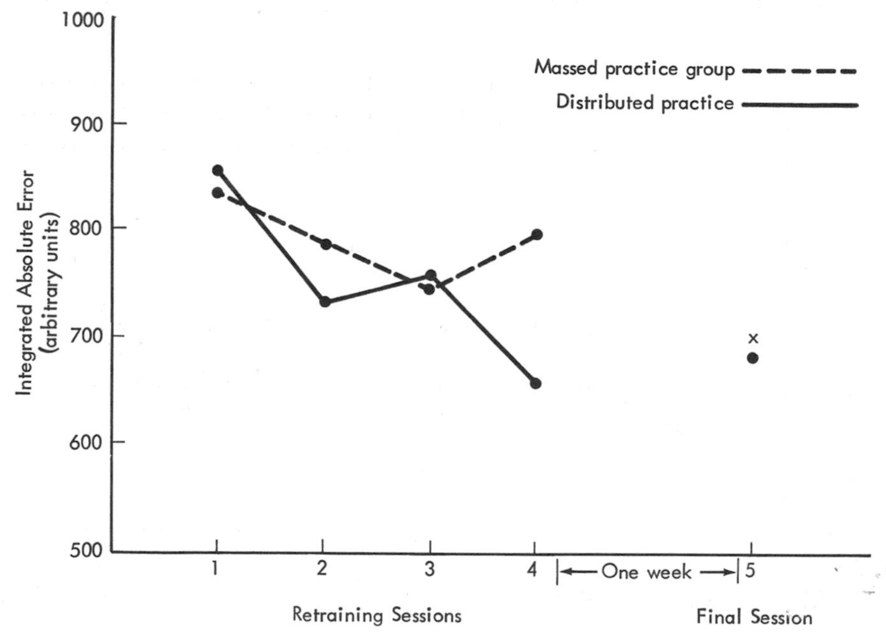

Figure 6–8. Effect of different retraining programs during retraining and after a further 1-week rest. The subjects were tested on a tracking task. (From Fleishman, E. A. and Parker, James F., Jr. Factors in the Retention and Relearning of Perceptual-Motor Skill, *J. Exp. Psychol.*, 64:215–226, 1962.)

bered. The students were then divided into smaller groups and were tested from one to seven days later. The reminiscence peak was found to be greatest after a two-day delay, as the students remembered more at that point than immediately after the reading.

Since the publication of this study, researchers have manipulated numerous variables in order to determine the effects on reminiscence. According to Buxton (1943), reminiscence may be dependent upon a number of factors, such as the type of learning technique employed, type of subject matter, degree of mastery before rest, type of practice (degree of distribution), and the length of the rest interval. Although reminiscence in motor-learning studies has not received a great deal of attention, a few representative ones are reported briefly here.

Fox and Young (1962) instructed two groups of students for six weeks and nine weeks in badminton skills. They were tested after six weeks and twelve weeks of no practice on a wall–volley test and short serve test. No reminiscence was noticed on the short service test. The group instructed for nine weeks did significantly better after six weeks than the group given six weeks of instruction, but there was no difference between the groups after twelve weeks. The former group regressed while the latter group improved and displayed the effects of reminiscence. Evidently, the additional three weeks of instruction did not contribute to long-term retention.

Purdy and Lockhart (1962) tested subjects one year after they had learned five novel skills, e.g., ball toss and foot volley. These investigators discovered that 89 per cent of the subjects displayed reminiscence in one or more of the skills, an incidence of reminiscence much higher than found in other studies. It is difficult to generalize how long after the termination of practice performance increases, and if indeed it will increase. The method most used in measuring reminiscence is a comparison of skill demonstrated after a specified interval of time with the amount displayed at the end of formal practice. Thus far, it appears that studies yield inconsistent results as to the optimal rest period following practice for reminiscence.

Consider, for example, further confusing findings in this area. Fox and Lamb (1962) studied the effects of reminiscence following the learning of softball skills. No reminiscence effects appeared after a five-week period of no practice, but improvement in skill was noticeable after a seventeen-week layoff. It appears that studies investigating an optimal period for the demonstration of reminiscence effects have shown these periods to vary with the learned tasks, from a few minutes with nonsense syllables to a few months or more with athletic skills.

Research also indicates that the method of distributing practice might reflect greater or lesser degrees of reminiscence. It seems that relative massing of practice trials will afford the greatest amount of reminiscence which in turn will result in a similar performance or in a performance slightly below that of a distributed practice group. A possible explanation is that at the immediate conclusion of practice the distributed practice usually yields a superior performance but after a rest period the distributed group performs less effectively, the massed group better, and therefore ultimately both are approximately equal. Theoretical explanations of reminiscence, especially in conjunction with massed and distributed practice, are presented later in this chapter.

Retention as a Function of Material Learned. As a general rule, it may be stated that gross motor skills are retained for many years at a higher skill level than any other learning materials, such as fine motor skills and prose. We may have last performed on a bicycle when twelve years of age, but even after an eight-year layoff, cycling ability would be extremely high. Compare this situation with a passage memorized from a poem or from history, also learned years ago and not practiced for a long period of time. Would you expect to recall the passage with the same degree of accuracy and proficiency as you demonstrated on the bicycle? Of course not.

The long-term retention permanence of motor skills was demonstrated in a series of experiments undertaken by Swift at the beginning of the twentieth century. Swift (1906), using himself as the subject, learned to type over a fifty-day period. Two years elapsed before he touched a typewriter again, and it took him only eleven days to reach the same proficiency he had attained after fifty days. Swift (1905) had two subjects practice keeping two balls going with one hand, one ball being caught and thrown while the other was in the air. After rest periods of over 600 days, retention tests indicated that the subjects in all but two instances performed better than they had at the close of regular practice. Employing the same skill (ball juggling), Swift (1910) practiced for forty-two days and then waited six years before attempting the skill again. It took him only eleven days to relearn the act and demonstrate a performance equivalent to that at the end of the original practice.

An important consideration as to what is retained is the meaningfulness to the learner of that which is learned. Nonsense syllables are forgotten very quickly (compare the learning curves in Figure 6–9). Some prose is retained longer than other prose, depending on its meaningfulness, not only logically but also in importance to the person. Motor skills, especially to children, are held high in personal worth and efforts to achieve are intensive and extensive. There is a relative permanence to the meaningful material which we learn.

Although motor skills are generally retained better than other types of learned material, the more abstract they are the more the retention curve resembles that of verbal or written matter. For instance, Adams and Dijkstra (1966) had their subjects learn a motor task that required mastering the positioning of sliding elements on a bar. Retention was tested in intervals ranging from five to 120 seconds. The results fundamentally agreed with the findings of verbal research on short-term memory: that rapid forgetting occurs with the passage of time but the performance becomes more stable with reinforcement.

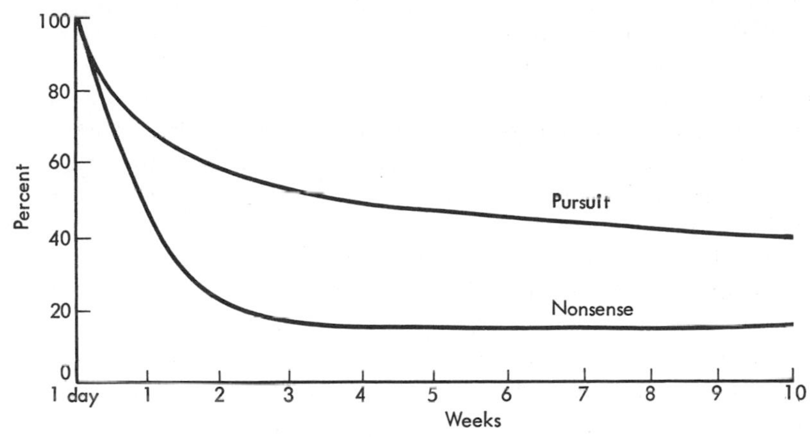

Figure 6–9. Retention comparison of verbal material (nonsense syllables) and a motor skill (pursuit rotor). (From Leavitt, Harold J., and Schlosberg, H. The Retention of Verbal and of Motor Skills, *J. Exp. Psychol.*, 34:404–417, 1944.)

Ryan (1962) tested eighty men after three, five, seven, and twenty-one days had lapsed from practice on stabilometer and pursuit rotor skills. Little or no loss in performance was found on the retention days tested, and the pursuit rotor skill was retained better than that of the stabilometer. Ryan was interested in extending the retention periods to determine the lasting effects of a once-learned motor skill. In a second study (1965) Ryan gave eleven initial learning trials on the stabilometer to his subjects, who were divided later into three groups to be tested three months, six months, and one year after the termination of practice. There was no significant difference on the first retention trial for all three groups; all showed a loss in proficiency. A longer nonpractice period resulted in more trials needed to regain the earlier proficiency.

Once again, unusual motor tasks will not be retained as well as the familiar ones, for example, sports skills. Everyday experience and empirical evidence support the notion of the long-lasting effects of once-learned athletic skills. Explanations for this phenomenon may lie in one or all of the following suggestions. It may be due to the relative importance motor-skill achievement has to the individual. Perhaps it occurs because of the total body effort intellectually and physically needed to perform an athletic skill successfully. Athletic skill retention can also be explained by simply examining the number of hours devoted to its learning as compared to the time spent in learning a literary passage. Whereas a child may allocate a few hours for memorizing a poem, he plays softball incessantly. Is it any wonder, then, that the greater number of stimulus-response occurrences in the athletic situation results in superior retention?

Amount of Practice and Overlearning Effects on Retention. How much should a task be practiced for it to be learned sufficiently? The rub in this question is the word *sufficiently*. Perhaps the question should be restated to read: How much practice is necessary for the greatest amount of retention (assuming this is what is desired)?

All things being equal, the amount of initial practice is directly related to the amount retained, as retention has been demonstrated to be higher when the task is well learned. Partially-learned material is forgotten faster than mastered material. Of course, it would be extremely difficult to know when the skill is learned well enough and the individual has had enough practice. But, as Fleishman and Parker (1962) have demonstrated, the most important factor in retention is the initial level of proficiency. These investigators practiced their subjects on a highly complex tracking task over a six-week period. Other interesting results of the study were (1) the amount of verbal guidance during practice had no effect on retention; (2) massed and distributed practice effects did not differ on a retention test given one week after practice; and (3) retention on this motor task was quite high, even after a rest period of twenty-four months.

Retention will be even more enhanced if the skill is overlearned. *Overlearning*, as defined earlier, refers to practice provided on a task after it has been learned according to some criterion. The criterion in many psychological studies dealing with the learning of written material is one perfect recitation. If precise experimental control is wanted, the number of trials it takes the subject to achieve the criterion measure is recorded. The researcher can then arbitrarily provide the subject with more practice trials on the task, and by dividing this figure by the original number of practices, the percentage of overlearning is derived. Invariably, studies concerned with overlearning find that greater practice beyond the learning criterion results in better retention performances.

There is some practical concern as to who are the best retainers, fast or slow learners. If a person acquires skill quickly, will he also retain it at a high level of proficiency? Early studies showed that fast learners were better retainers than slow learners. However, a weakness in testing procedure was that both types of learners had the same number of learning trials. The fast learners retained more because they learned more initially. Later studies have demonstrated that if all the subjects have to reach an initial learning criterion regardless of the number of practice trials, the slow learner will score higher on retention tests. This could be explained by the overlearning effect.

Proactive and Retroactive Inhibition. The things we typically learn are not isolated, but rather fall into sequential patterns of various learning materials. Because of this fact, the learning and retention of a particular response might very well be affected by what is learned, especially of a related nature, before and after training on this response. Going a step further and translating this to psychological terms, if a specific response is desired for a given stimulus ($S_1 - R_1$) and a second response is learned for this same stimulus

($S_1 - R_2$) either before or after $S_1 - R_1$ occurs, interference in retention of $S_1 - R_1$ will be observable.

Psychologists have designated terms for these two situations. *Proactive inhibition* refers to the negative effect one learned task has on the retention of a newer task. *Retroactive inhibition* describes the condition when a recently learned task impairs the retention performance of an older learned task. Generally, experimental designs to measure proaction or retroaction are as follows:

Proaction

Groups	Prior Learning	Desired Learning	Recall
Experimental	Task B	Task A	Task A
Control	None	Task A	Task A*

Retroaction

Groups	Original Learning	Interpolated Learning	Recall
Experimental	Task A	Task B	Task A*
Control	Task A	Rest	Task A

* Although Task A recall is desired, Task A and Task B responses will conflict.

Proactive inhibition has been investigated considerably less than retroactive inhibition and, at one time, was thought to be less of an influence on retention than retroactive inhibition. However, what is true of one condition is usually true of the other. It does not matter whether related tasks are learned before or after the desired learning task; inhibition of varying degrees will occur on retention tests. With retroaction, the desired response has been weakened by the second learned response; but in proaction, it is the competing response that has been weakened by the learning of the desired response.

Forgetting is thought to occur because of a competition of responses, and certainly this is the case in proaction and retroaction. We live in a verbal world and learn many, many words in a lifetime. Retroaction and proaction are constantly building up, causing relatively much and rapid forgetting. Motor skills are not forgotten quickly, mainly because there are not that many to learn, many are unique, and they are practiced at great length. In learning to ride a bicycle, one has to adjust to such factors as balance and gravity. Bicycle riding will not be unlearned for there are no competing responses to this situation. It should be remembered, though, that negative transfer can occur in motor-skill learning, and any time S_1 is presented after R_1 and R_2 have become associated with it, there is the danger of conflict.

Theories of Retention and Forgetting. It is usually felt that forgetting is a decline in performance caused by the passage of time. However, experimental evidence points to the fact that ultimate retention will be more dependent on the intervening events rather than merely on time per se. Greater activity brings about the development of competing response tendencies, thus resulting in a higher degree of forgetting.

Experimentally, this idea is verified by holding the time period constant between the last original learning trial and the recall test but varying the amount of intervening activity. If time alone is responsible for forgetting, the recall scores should be the same, regardless of time spent in activity. But this is not the case. If four groups had learned certain material and were tested after twenty-four hours on a retention test, with Group A allowed only two hours of activity during this rest period, Group B four hours of activity, Group C twelve hours, and Group D actively responding for the entire twenty-four hour period, performance on the recall test could be predicted. Whereas the least active group during the retention period would do best on the recall test the most active group would perform worst of all.

One can gather from this discussion that we should be able to retain more after sleep than following waking activities. Whether something, once learned, is ever truly forgotten is open to question. Freud's work as well as that of others interested in psychoanalysis indicates that not only are early life experience and behavior important in determining later life behavior, but also that many childhood experiences can be recalled under emotional recall situations. Things learned can be retained better under more favorable learning situations and more efficient learning techniques. Currently major advances are being made in the memorization of written and verbal material through coding techniques. However, the process of forgetting is still not well understood, from both psychological and physiological viewpoints.

How can we explain what is retained and the strength of this later performance? Theorists representing different schools of thought approach the matter in various ways. Walker (1958) believes that high arousal during the associative process (practice) results in greater permanent memory. Koffka (1935), a leader in Gestalt psychology, states that a greater organization of the stimulus trace results in less probability of its weakening over time. Broadbent (1958) writes that perceptual filters operate during attempted retention, and recall will occur if the correct channel is monitored and monitored at the right time. These general statements should suffice at least to familiarize the reader with some possible directions they may take in describing retention.

Interesting theories have been advanced to explain performance during and after massed and distributed practice. McGeoch (1961) has reviewed numerous theories and categorizes them as follows: work theories, perseveration theories, and differential forgetting theories.

Differential forgetting theories, according to McGeoch, generally handle massed and distributed practice effects by stating that during practice a subject learns incorrect and conflicting responses as well as correct ones. Because the conflicting associations are probably less well learned than the appropriate responses, the conflicting ones will dissipate with rest at a faster rate than during practice. Therefore, according to the theory, learning will take place faster during distributed practice because the incorrect responses will have had an opportunity to drop out more quickly than under massed practice conditions. However, there are theoretical limitations as to the desirable length of the rest interval.

Reminiscence would be explained in a similar manner: rest intervals provide an opportunity for the dropping out or forgetting of wrong associations that are less strongly favored than the right ones and hence are forgotten more rapidly. Under this theory, massed practice would probably be expected to yield a greater reminiscence effect than distributed practice.

Perseveration theories tend to hold that some activity persists in the individual after the termination of practice, therefore resulting in the learned response becoming more strongly fixated than it was previously. Muller and Pilzecker formulated the classical perseveration theory, and Hovland (1938) explains it as follows: "The neural processes perseverate for a considerable time following learning. Distributed practices permits the setting-in process to proceed with minimal interference," whereas massed practice would not allow enough time to permit this activity to occur.

Work theories generally state that the act of repeating a response tends to build up either a loss of interest, boredom, physical fatigue, or mental fatigue. The interfering processes presumably disappear with rest and the more permanent learned responses would supposedly remain.

Hull's (1943) theory, based on a theoretical construct called *reactive inhibition,* is most representative of the work theories and probably has encouraged more investigations in the area of massed versus distributed practice than any other theory. Hull postulates that two inhibitory processes occur when responses are made, reactive inhibition (I_R) and conditioned inhibition (S^IR). I_R is temporary by nature and dissipates with time whereas S^IR is relatively permanent. With increased practice the temporary work decrement increases and explains the poorer performance of subjects learning under massed practice conditions. By the same token, distributed practice permits I_R effects to disappear more easily; hence, the superior performance of distributed-practice subjects. Also, reminiscence is described as occurring when the I_R effects have been rendered ineffective as a result of rest from repeating the desired responses.

However, Hull's work theory holds that over a long time interval reactive potential diminishes. Supposedly, reactive inhibition disappears after ten to twenty minutes of rest, resulting in increased performance at that time. Some writers are of the opinion that perhaps I_R lasts for a day or even a week. Even if it lasted for a month, there is no logical explanation as to why the disappearance of I_R should result in an eventual superior performance for massed-practice subjects than for distributed-practice subjects. Considering that all subjects had experienced the same number of practice trials, the associated strength for the habit should at best be equal under massed and distributed conditions.

Some investigators have applied Hull's basic concepts to motor-skill learning, more specifically, rotary-pursuit learning. Kimble (1949) calls his theory a "Two-Factor Theory of Inhibition." Proponents of this theory state that in many studies, especially those employing motor tasks, rest periods are too short to allow for the dissipation of the majority of the reactive inhibition. Figure 6–10 illustrates how pursuit-rotor performance would fit into this theory.

When a subject learns under relatively massed practice, an inhibition develops that hinders performance rather than learning. Therefore, performance would be weaker under massed conditions rather than under distributed

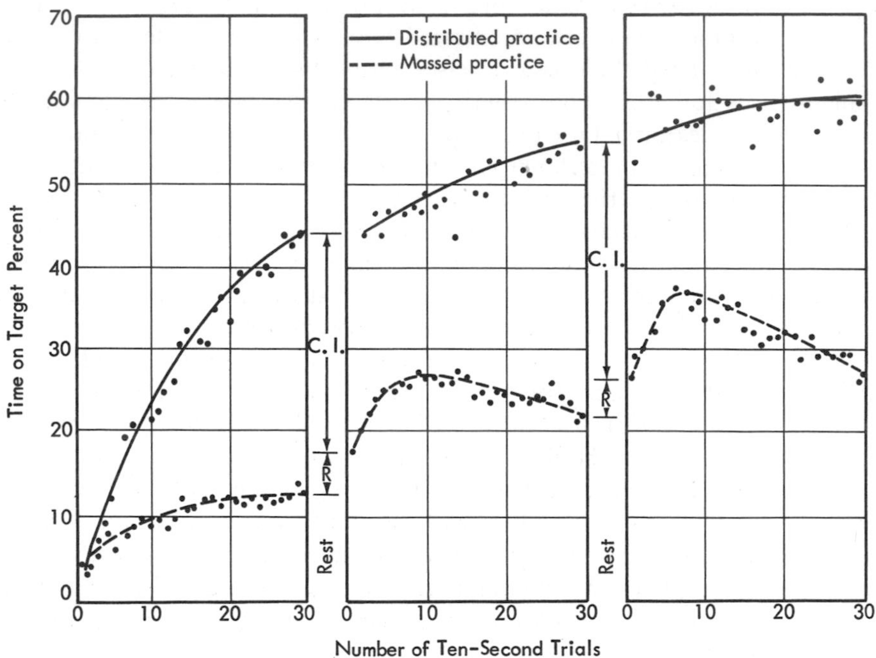

Figure 6–10. Motor performance as it represents learning and retention during and after massed and distributed practice conditions and according to Hullian Theory. Pursuit-rotor performance varies markedly with the spacing of the trial, or practice, periods. Each dot represents the average time-on-target during a 10-second period. The upper curve shows the performance of subjects who were allowed a 30-second rest pause between each 10-second trial. The lower curve shows the performance of subjects denied such a rest. Both groups were given two 10-minute rest periods. The improvement in performance shown by the massed-practice group immediately following the 10-minute break is called reminiscence (R), which is believed to be a measure of reactive inhibition accumulated during massed practice. The major depressant on scores of the massed-practice group, however, is conditioned inhibition (C.I.). (From Eysenck, H. J. The Measurement of Motivation, *Scientific American*, 208:130–140, 1963.)

practice since the inhibition dissipates rapidly with rest. Precisely what the optimal rest period is for superior performance has been disputed as a result of the findings of various studies. Gagné and Fleishman (1959) believed that the inhibition affects performance rather than what is learned. They wrote concerning motor skills:

> If one concentrates the learning of a motor skill . . . we have no reason to believe that this is a particularly inefficient learning procedure, although its effects on immediate performance may be detrimental.

Evidently, the amount of effort exerted by the subject in learning will have its effects on performance (Ellis, 1953). More effortful behavior perhaps results in the greater amount of I_R present and therefore a greater need to cease activity. Effortfulness would depend on the physical energy required for the learning of the task and the length of time without rest while practicing.

The fact that greater overall bodily effort is required for the mastery of athletic skills as contrasted to learning nonsense syllables or rotary-pursuit tasks may be one of the reasons why reminiscence has been demonstrated after twelve or more weeks of no practice of athletic skills. Massed practice would theoretically be less effective with the learning of gross motor skills than other learning materials because of the effort involved. On the same explanatory grounds, reminiscence should then be greater after practicing these gross motor skills.

Hovland and Kurtz (1951) feel that verbal learning can be explained in terms of associative interferences; on the other hand, in motor-learning work decrement factors (motivation, boredom, and physical fatigue) have to be stressed with the possible supplementation of the reactive inhibition concept.

Evidently, the theoretical approach to explain aspects of the learning process is limited to the nature of the task and a host of other variables. Learning theorists have great difficulty in attempting to formulate theories to be used as the general operational framework to govern all learning materials and situations. This problem becomes more obvious in Chapter 8 in which learning theories are presented and discussed.

Summary

Since practice does not always make perfect, it is obvious that certain conditions would be more favorable to the learning of a task if they are applied in the training period. The learner should be attentive to the necessary cues; the practice must be purposeful with the learner attempting to attain a goal; and he must practice increasingly to strengthen learning bonds. Individuals vary in their abilities to learn different tasks as well as in speed of skill acquisition. Ample practice must be provided for the slow learner if he is to have the opportunity of demonstrating success.

Motivational factors and techniques have been the subject of intensive investigation, but thus far the results have not been extremely rewarding. However, the values of extrinsic and intrinsic motivation cannot be denied. The effects of success and failure on future performance depend on such factors as task difficulty or perceived task difficulty, previous number of successes and failures on the task, and the emotional characteristics of the individual. Reward and punishment are not equally effective motivational measures. Encouragingly, there is much evidence favoring reward or praise rather than punishment or criticism as the ideal motivational technique.

Practice sessions can be administered in varying lengths with varying interpolated rest periods. Within each practice session, a skill may be practiced continually or with designated rest periods or alternate skill learning between trials. It appears that gross motor skills can be learned more efficiently with shorter but more numerously spaced sessions over a longer time period. Of the many studies found in experimental literature, the vast majority have demonstrated the immediate superiority of distributed practice over massed practice using a wide range of learning materials and methods. As to the optimal rest interval between trials, wide variations are found depending on the task employed. It would probably be safe to assume that rest periods should be neither too brief nor too extensive, and that some learning materials are learned more effectively than others over relatively greater rest intervals.

Although little difference may be found in the eventual retention of a learned skill that has been practiced under continuous practice and spaced practice, there is a slight inclination to favor distributed practice for retention success. Reminiscence has been obtained in many studies investigating for the occurrence of this phenomenon. It is not limited to a specific task or under a special learning condition, although it appears that massed practice tends to lead to greater reminiscence effects.

Gross motor skills are usually retained for a greater period of time than written or verbal material. These skills, or any material that is overlearned, will result in greater retention performances. It remains for investigators to study further such variables as those discussed in this chapter, variables associated with practice, and their effects on the learning and retention of physical education skills. Methods for facilitating skill acquisition and retention should be the primary concern of those in the motor learning area.

References

Adams, Jack A., and Dijkstra, Sanne. Short-Term Memory for Motor Responses, *J. Exp. Psychol.*, 71:314–318, 1966.

Allport, G. W. The Ego in Contemporary Psychology, *Psychol. Rev.*, 50:451–478, 1943.

AMMONS, ROBERT B. Effect of Distribution of Practice on Rotary Pursuit "Hits," *J. Exp. Psychol.*, 41:17–22, 1951.

AMMONS, ROBERT B. Effects of Knowledge of Performance: A Survey and Tentative Theoretical Formulation, *J. Gen. Psychol.*, 54:279–299, 1956.

ATKINSON, JOHN W. *An Introduction to Motivation*, Princeton, N.J.: D. Van Nostrand Co., Inc., 1964.

ATKINSON, JOHN W. Motivational Determinants of Risk-Taking Behavior, *Psychol. Rev.*, 64:359–372, 1957.

AYRES, L. P. The Influence of Music on Speed in the Six Day Bicycle Race, *Amer. Phys. Educ. Rev.*, 16:321–346, 1911.

BALLARD, PHILIP B. Obliviscence and Reminiscence, *Brit. J. Psychol. Monogr. Suppl.*, No. 2, 1913.

BAYTON, JAMES A., and CONLEY, HAROLD W. Duration of Success Background and the Effect of Failure upon Performance, *J. Gen. Psychol.*, 56:179–185, 1957.

BILODEAU, EDWARD A., and BILODEAU, INA McD. Variable Frequency of Knowledge of Results and the Learning of a Single Skill, *J. Exp. Psychol.*, 55:379–383, 1958.

BROADBENT, D. E. *Perception and Communication*, London: Pergamon Press, 1958.

BUXTON, CLAUDE E. The Status of Research in Reminiscence, *Psychol. Bull.*, 40:313–340, 1943.

BUXTON, CLAUDE E., and HUMPHREYS, L. G. The Effect of Practice upon Intercorrelations of Motor Skills, *Science*, 81:441–442, 1935.

COOK, BARBARA S., and HILGARD, ERNEST R. Distributed Practice in Motor Learning: Progressively Increasing and Decreasing Rests, *J. Exp. Psychol.*, 39:169–172, 1949.

CRAWFORD, MEREDITH P., et al. Psychological Research on Operational Training in the Continental Air Forces, *Army Air Forces Aviation Psychol. Program Research Reports*, No. 16, 1947.

EASON, ROBERT G. Relation Between Effort, Tension Level, Skill, and Performance Efficiency in a Perceptual-Motor Task, *Percept. Mot. Skills*, 16:297–317, 1963.

ELLIS, DOUGLAS S. Inhibition Theory and the Effort Variables, *Psychol. Rev.*, 60:383–392, 1953.

EYSENCK, H. J. The Measurment of Motivation, *Scientific American*, 208:130–140, 1963.

FLEISHMAN, EDWIN A. A Comparative Study of Aptitude Patterns in Unskilled and Skilled Psychomotor Performers, *J. Appl. Psychol.*, 41:263–272, 1957.

FLEISHMAN, EDWIN A. A Relationship Between Incentive Motivation and Ability Level in Psychomotor Performance, *J. Exp. Psychol.*, 56:78–81, 1958.

FLEISHMAN, EDWIN A., and HEMPEL, WALTER E., JR. Changes in Factor Structure of a Complex Psychomotor Test as a Function of Practice, *Psychometrika*, 19:239–252, 1954.

FLEISHMAN, EDWIN A., and PARKER, JAMES F. Factors in the Retention and Relearning of Perceptual-Motor Skill, *J. Exp. Psychol.*, 64:215–226, 1962.

FOX, MARGARET C., and LAMB, ETHEL. Improvement During a Non-practice Period in a Selected Physical Education Activity, *Res. Quart.*, 33:381–385, 1962.

FOX, MARGARET C., and YOUNG, VERA P. Effect of Reminiscence on Learning Selected Badminton Skills, *Res. Quart.*, 73:386–394, 1962.

FRIEDLANDER, FRANK. Motivations to Work and Organizational Performance, *J. Appl. Psychol.*, 50:143–152, 1966.

GAGNÉ, ROBERT M., and FLEISHMAN, EDWIN A. *Psychology of Human Performance*, New York: Henry Holt and Co., 1959.

GREENSPOON, JOEL, and FOREMAN, SALLY. Effect of Delay of Knowledge of Results on Learning a Motor Task, *J. Exp. Psychol.*, 51:226–283, 1956.

GRIFFITH, COLEMAN R. *Psychology of Coaching*, New York: Scribners, 1932.

HARMON, JOHN M., and OXENDINE, JOSEPH B. Effect of Different Lengths of Practice Periods on the Learning of a Motor Skill, *Res. Quart.*, 32:34–41, 1961.

HOVLAND, CARL I. Experimental Studies in Rote-Learning Theory. III. Distribution of Practice with Varying Speeds of Syllable Presentation, *J. Exp. Psychol.*, 23:172–190, 1938.

HOVLAND, CARL I., and KURTZ, KENNETH H. Experimental Studies in Rote-Learning Theory. IX. Influence of Work-Decrement Factors on Verbal Learning, *J. Exp. Psychol.*, 42:265–272, 1951.

HULL, CLARK L. *Principles of Behavior*, New York: D. Appleton Century Co., 1943.

HURLOCK, E. B. An Evaluation of Certain Incentives on School Work, *J. Educ. Psychol.*, 16:145–159, 1925.

KIMBLE, GREGORY A. An Experimental Test of a Two-Factor Theory of Inhibition, *J. Exp. Psychol.*, 39:15–23, 1949.

KNAPP, CLYDE G., and DIXON, W. ROBERT. Learning to Juggle: I. A Study to Determine the Effect of Two Different Distributions of Practice on Learning Efficiency, *Res. Quart.*, 21:331–336, 1950.

KOFFKA, K. *Principles of Gestalt Psychology*, New York: Harcourt and Brace, 1935.

LASHLEY, K. S. The Acquisition of Skill in Archery, *Papers from the Department of Marine Biology of the Carnegie Institute of Washington*, 7:105–128, 1915.

LEWIS, DON, and LOWE, WILLIAM F. Retention of Skill on the SAM Complex Coordinator, *Proceedings of the Iowa Academy of Science*, 63:591–599, 1956.

MCCLELLAND, DAVID C. Methods of Measuring Human Motivation, in ATKINSON, JOHN W. (ed.), *Motives in Fantasy, Action, and Society*, Princeton, N.J.: D. Van Nostrand Co., Inc., 1958.

MCCRAW, L. W. Comparative Analysis of Methods of Scoring Tests of Motor Learning, *Res. Quart.*, 26:440–453, 1955.

MCCRAW, L. W. A Comparison of Methods of Measuring Improvement, *Res. Quart.*, 22:191–200, 1951.

MCGEOCH, JOHN A. *The Psychology of Human Learning*, New York: David McKay Co., Inc., 1961.

MASSEY, DOROTHY. The Significance of Interpolated Time Intervals on Motor Learning, *Res. Quart.*, 30:189–201, 1959.

MOHR, DOROTHY R. The Contribution of Physical Activity to Skill Learning, *Res. Quart.*, 31:321–351, Part II, 1960.

MURPHY, HERBERT H. Distribution of Practice Periods in Learning, *J. Educ. Psychol.*, 7:150–162, 1916.

NELSON, DALE O., and FINCH, LEWIS W. Effect of Audio-Analgesia on Gross Motor Performance Involving Acute Fatigue, *Res. Quart.*, 33:588–592, 1962.

Nelson, Dale O. Effects of Selected Rhythms and Sound Intensity on Human Performance as Measured by the Bicycle Ergometer, *Res. Quart.*, 3[illegible]-488, 1963.

Noble, Clyde E. An Attempt to Manipulate Incentive-Motivation in a Continuous Tracking Task, *Percept. Mot. Skills,* 5:65–69, 1955.

Owens, W. A., Jr. A Note on the Effects of Practice Upon Trait Differences in Motor Skills, *J. Educ. Psychol.*, 33:144–147, 1942.

Oxendine, Joseph B. Effect of Progressively Changing Practice Schedules on the Learning of a Motor Skill, *Res. Quart.*, 36:307–315, 1965.

Pierson, William R., and Rasch, Philip J. Effect of Knowledge of Results on Isometric Strength Scores, *Res. Quart.*, 35:313–315, 1964.

Purdy, Bonnie J., and Lockhart, Aileene. Retention and Relearning of Gross Motor Skills After Long Periods of No Practice, *Res. Quart.*, 33:265–272, 1962.

Rarick, Lawrence G. Physical Education, in Harris, Chester W. (ed.), *Encyclopedia of Educational Research,* New York: The Macmillan Co., 1960.

Reynolds, Bradley, and Bilodeau, Ina McD. Acquisition and Retention of 3 Psychomotor Tests as a Function of Distribution of Practice During Acquisition, *J. Exp. Psychol.*, 44:19–26, 1952.

Rotter, Julian G. Generalized Expectancies for Internal Versus External Control of Reinforcement, *Psychol. Monogr.*, 80: No. 1, 1966.

Ryan, E. Dean. Effect of Differential Motive-Incentive Conditions on Physical Performance, *Res. Quart.*, 32:83–87, 1961.

Ryan, E. Dean. Retention of Stabilometer and Pursuit Rotor Skills, *Res. Quart.*, 33:593–598, 1962.

Ryan, E. Dean. Retention of Stabilometer Performance over Extended Periods of Time, *Res. Quart.*, 36:46–51, 1965.

Singer, Robert N. Massed and Distributed Practice Effects on the Acquisition and Retention of a Novel Basketball Skill, *Res. Quart.*, 36:68–77, 1965.

Strong, Clinton H. Motivation Related to Performance of Physical Fitness Tests, *Res. Quart.*, 34:497–507, 1963.

Surwillo, Walter W. A New Method of Motivating Human Behavior in Laboratory Investigations, *Amer. J. Psychol.*, 71:432–436, 1958.

Swift, Edgar J. Memory of a Complex Skillful Act, *Amer. J. Psychol.*, 16:131–133, 1905.

Swift, Edgar J. Memory of Skillful Movements, *Psychol. Bull.*, 3:185–187, 1906.

Swift, Edgar J. Relearning a Skillful Act: An Experimental Study in Neuro-Muscular Memory, *Psychol. Bull.*, 7:17–19, 1910.

Travis, Roland C. Practice and Rest Periods in Motor Learning, *J. Psychol.*, 3:183–189, 1937.

Trussell, Ella. Prediction of Success in a Motor Skill on the Basis of Early Learning Achievement, *Res. Quart.*, 39:342–347, 1965.

Ulrich, Celeste, and Burke, Roger K. Effect of Motivational Stress Upon Physical Performance, *Res. Quart.*, 28:403–412, 1957.

Waglow, I. F. Effect of School Term Length on Skill Achievement in Tennis, Golf, and Handball, *Res. Quart.*, 37:157–159, 1966.

Walker, E. L. Action Decrement and Its Relation to Learning, *Psychol. Rev.*, 65:129–142, 1958.

WEINER, BERNARD, and WALKER, EDWARD L. Motivational Factors in Short-term Retention, *J. Exp. Psychol.*, 71:190–193, 1966.

WELCH, MARYA. Prediction of Motor Skill Attainment from Early Learning, *Percept. Mot. Skills*, 17:263–266, 1963.

YOUNG, OLIVE G. Rate of Learning in Relation to Spacing of Practice Periods in Archery and Badminton, *Res. Quart.*, 25:213–243, 1954.

Annotated Student References

PRACTICE EFFECTS ON LEARNING

MCGEOCH, JOHN A. *The Psychology of Human Learning*, New York: David McKay Co., Inc., 1961.

Extensive treatment of factors affecting learning, with exhaustive review of experimental literature.

MOTIVATION

ATKINSON, JOHN W. *An Introduction to Motivation*, Princeton, N.J.: D. Van Nostrand Co., Inc., 1964.

Identifies and clarifies basic concepts of motivation, especially designed for the beginning student interested in human motivation analysis.

ATKINSON, JOHN W. (ed). *Motives in Fantasy, Action, and Society*, Princeton, N.J.: D. Van Nostrand Co., Inc., 1958.

Presents representative studies of the different methods of measuring motivation.

BINDRA, DALBIR. *Motivation: A Systematic Reinterpretation*, New York: The Ronald Press Co., 1959.

Contains meaningful aspects of the study of motivational phenomena and describes a new approach to the problem of motivation.

EYSENCK, H. J. The Measurement of Motivation, *Scientific American*, 208:130–140, 1963.

Provides a new method of measuring motivation, with a discussion on how the results fit into basic S-R theory.

MURRAY, EDWARD J. *Motivation and Emotion*, Englewood Cliffs, N.J.: Prentice-Hall, Inc., 1964.

Introductory book on the emotional aspects of motivation handled from both psychological and physiological viewpoints.

ADMINISTRATION OF PRACTICE SESSION

KNAPP, CLYDE G., and DIXON, W. ROBERT. Learning to Juggle: I. A Study to Determine the Effect of Two Different Distributions of Practice on Learning Efficiency, *Res. Quart.*, 21:331–336, 1950.

A truly novel study indicating the effectiveness of short practice and short rest periods.

MOHR, DOROTHY R. The Contributions of Physical Activity to Skill Learning, *Res. Quart.*, 31:321–351, Part II, 1960.

Reviews literature pertaining to different aspects of practice and performance.

OXENDINE, JOSEPH B. Effect of Progressively Changing Practice Schedules on the Learning of a Motor Skill, *Res. Quart.*, 36:307–315, 1965.

An investigation of the effects of various practice schedules on learning a mirror-tracing task.

RETENTION

FLEISHMAN, EDWIN A., and PARKER, JAMES F. Factors in the Retention and Relearning of Perceptual-Motor Skill, *J. Exp. Psychol.*, 64:215–226, 1962.

An interesting study examining the effects of a number of variables on retention.

GAGNÉ, ROBERT M., and FLEISHMAN, EDWIN A. *Psychology and Human Performance*, New York: Henry Holt and Co., 1959.

Contains a basic discussion on retention and is a good general book for those interested in human performance.

NAYLOR, JAMES C., and BRIGGS, GEORGE E. Long-Term Retention of Learned Skills: A Review of the Literature, *ASD Technical Report 61–390*, U.S. Air Force, Dayton, Ohio, 1961.

A report summarizing the research related to techniques of sustaining and promoting retention.

PURDY, BONNIE J., and LOCKHART, AILEENE. Retention and Relearning of Gross Motor Skills After Long Periods of No Practice, *Res. Quart.*, 33:265–272, 1962.

The long-term retention of motor skills is demonstrated in this study.

7
Teaching Methodology

Regardless of his area of interest, each teacher searches for methods of improving his teaching effectiveness. An understanding of learners and their individual characteristics, the knowing of oneself, including teaching strengths and weaknesses, and an awareness of varied teaching techniques will all contribute to the elusive objective: a more effective teacher. This chapter is concerned with the last area, methods of teaching.

There is no one way to teach. Some teaching methods are better than others, and a method's effectiveness may very well depend on the teacher and the task as well as the learner. To limit and direct all teachers to one procedure would be erroneous; certainly we do not attempt to require every baseball batter to stand and swing in exactly the same way! General principles should not be violated, but there is leeway for individual variation and initiative. A comparison of teaching techniques indicates that certain ones are more beneficial than others to the average learner. Because of the complexity of the problem and the many operating and interacting variables, however, it should be apparent why conclusive evidence in favor of certain approaches is somewhat lacking.

Methods of Instruction

In any given lesson or unit, the instructor is apt to face a series of challenges. Instructional techniques applicable to certain situations vary, and he should settle on those that are most appropriate and effective. Often these decisions are based on his own educational background, for there is much truth in the statement that we teach as we have been taught. The physical educator may select from a number of general teaching methodologies and many more instructional techniques, some of more proven merit than others.

All teachers must make certain judgments before class begins. These judgments involve various dimensions of the class situation, and, in a sense, reflect an individual's teaching style. Mosston (1966) categorizes preclass decisions in the following order:

1. Selection and apportionment of subject matter, e.g., time allotted for practice.
2. Quantity of an activity, e.g., consideration for individual differences.
3. Quality of performance, e.g., measurement standards.
4. Teacher involvement, e.g., to what extent and how.
5. Student involvement, e.g., to what extent and how.

Although Mosston is concerned with these variables primarily as they relate to teaching styles, the purpose of this chapter is to examine research having a bearing on preclass decisions. In what manner should new material be presented to students? How should the student be guided during the practice of skills? How does a class, or social situation, assist or hamper individual progress? These questions are a few that, hopefully, are answered in this section.

Whole, Part, and Whole-Part Learning. Most skills can be taught in their entirety or broken down into parts. For example, the side stroke in swimming contains a coordinated leg pattern, a breathing phase, and a relaxation stage. All these aspects of the stroke may be learned separately before the completed stroke is attempted, or the stroke may be practiced in its totality at the initial stages of learning.

The basketball lay-up is an example of another skill that can be learned by the whole method or in parts (the approach and dribble, aim, the release, and the follow through). Many times it is not so easy to distinguish whole from part learning. *Whole* could refer to the sport itself, a skill in that sport, or even a part of that skill. In the latter case, when the arm stroke in the side stroke is taught so that each arm is practiced independently, that is an example of part learning. But if the arms are practiced as they coordinate with each other, it could be argued that whole learning is now exemplified. It could also be argued that this is still part learning since the complete side stroke is not being practiced. Therefore, it is possible to confuse the terms and what they label; and one should view these terms as relative to each other and to the material learned. Broadly speaking, the problem concerns separate practice on each of several components compared to practice on the whole task.

Some researchers have attempted to combine the features of both whole and part methods, creating whole-part and progressive-part methods. Whereas the part method implies equal practice or equal time devoted to the units, the whole-part method, as described by Brown (1928) in her study, refers to sequential practice on all the parts with additional repetitions on weak units.

The latter procedure allows the student to move from unit to unit only after he has mastered each one. The whole-part method, according to some researchers, also may describe the situation wherein the learner views the desired end product and then practices each part until the skill is finalized. The progressive-part, repetitive-part, or continuous-part procedure requires the individual to practice preceding learned units with each newly-introduced unit. In other words, the subject practices one subtask, then the second subtask with the first, the third with the first two, until all subtasks are learned and performed together. For example, Barton's (1921) subjects learned a maze that was divided into quarters. After the first quarter of the maze, the subjects practiced on one half of the maze, then three quarters, and finally the entire maze under the continuous-part method.

As to the preferability of one method over the others, the teacher must first analyze the complexity of the learned skill. Consider, for example, the following three investigations. Barton (1921) found that, in learning a maze, the part method was best (57 per cent less errors than the whole method), the continuous-part method was second in effectiveness (47 per cent less errors than the whole method), and, of course, the whole method yielded the poorest performance.

Brown tested her pianists under three conditions. The whole method constituted a score played from beginning to end without corrections; the part method referred to the score divided and practiced in equal units; and the whole-part method indicated the units were practiced from beginning to end but repeated where errors occurred. She found the whole method to be most efficient and the part method to be the least beneficial.

In the third study, Cross (1937) instructed ninth grade boys in three different ways in order to determine the most effective manner of teaching basketball. Play was the whole method; the whole-part method included a breakdown of fundamental skills; and a minor game method, which included lead-up games to build up fundamentals, was his third instructional procedure. Cross concluded that the simpler skills were taught best by the whole method, the most complex by the whole-part method, and those skills of intermediate difficulty were best enhanced by the minor-game method.

Psychologists would generally agree with the findings of Cross. If a skill is relatively simple, the advisable procedure is to employ the whole method. More complex skills require some sort of breakdown, for, as Barton indicated, the whole in his study was too large and overwhelmed the learners. Although Briggs and Brogden (1954) found a superiority of whole over part practice on a complex coordination test, an analysis of their data suggests that the "...superiority of whole practice may disappear at high levels of task complexity." It is believed that if the learner knows his goal, is aware of how the final act should be executed, he will gain quicker insight into the problem. The parts will be more meaningful and will be more easily coordinated into the desired ultimate skill.

In recent years, researchers such as Naylor and Briggs (1963) have distinguished two aspects of the task that might be considered before designating the learning to proceed under part or whole conditions. Task complexity refers to the demands made on a person's memory and is a function of information processing. Task organization indicates the nature of the interrelationships of several task dimensions or components. A task has a low organization when there are only a few independent components comprising the task. The studies of these and other researchers suggest that part practice is more favorable for tasks of high complexity and low organization. When the organization is high, i.e., there is an increase of the component interaction, the whole method is preferable.

This problem of whole versus part learning is more complex for motor skills than verbal materials. The fractionation of a task requires isolating components equal in difficulty and length, which is not easily done with typical motor skills. A survey of the research on physical education activities indicates little preference for one method over the other. One of the more recent studies, completed by Wickstrom (1958), compared learning of basic gymnastics and tumbling stunts by the whole method to the whole-direct repetitive method (similar to the progressive-part procedure, for the subjects practiced a part of a stunt and then moved on to the second part, combining both). He found little difference in the performances of the groups. In the teaching of sport skills, perhaps common sense might dictate which skills can be taught as wholes and which should be fractionated. Whole methods are to be advocated where possible if for no other reason than efficiency, for as Wickstrom and other investigators have observed, whole learning methods generally permit the student to reach a criterion in fewer trials than part methods.

Neimeyer's (1959) results further complicate the matter. His subjects were taught swimming, badminton, and volleyball under whole and part methods. The data indicate the favorability of the part method for teaching volleyball, the whole method for swimming, and either technique for the teaching of badminton. These results serve as a further reminder not to generalize from task to task in favor of one particular method. Rather, it is more important to analyze what is to be learned. Perhaps the concepts of task complexity and task organization should be applied to the numerous physical education motor activities for a more accurate indication of those skills that might be favored under whole or part learning conditions.

As a final thought, there is some opinion that more intelligent subjects are likelier to fare better under the whole method. At least one investigation would tend to support this hypothesis. McGuigan and MacCaslin (1955) collected data on rifle marksmanship for four days of firing at different yard markers. Groups were taught either under the whole method, which consisted of watching a demonstration and being instructed and practicing on all the subtasks together; or with the repetitive-part method, learning one subtask for firing, then the second at the same time with the first, and so on. Although the whole method yielded superior performance for all levels of intelligence in slowfire, a more challenging task, sustained fire, was learned more effectively under the whole method for only the subjects with above-average intelligence.

Active and Passive Learning. For many years, physical educators thought of their discipline as pertaining to education through physical means. One aspect of this education includes the learning of motor skills, and there certainly is enough evidence to justify the impression that this learning will occur in organized programs of physical education in which students actively participate. Active participation has traditional connotations, for we think of it as primarily emphasizing physical movement; and although no act is purely physical or solely cognitive, we will refer to such terms in their usual context for the sake of convenience. Just how much activity is necessary, or to put it another way, to what extent the active participation can be exchanged with other forms of involvement is not clearly understood.

Time spent in overt physical activity may be replaced with verbal instructions and directions, films, viewing another's performance, reading material, and mental imagery or practice. The effectiveness of these techniques alone and in conjunction with actual physical involvement are of great interest to educators who are concerned with the best combination teaching method.

Numerous experiments support the contention that learning motor skills occurs with active practice and specific instruction. Evidence on ideal ratios of physical practice to other means of learning is conspicuous by its absence. There are many people who feel the only way to learn a motor skill is through active physical participation. The results of studies on mental practice serve to question this belief; and certainly the value of lecture, films, reading material, and the like cannot be denied. How much time should be devoted to any of these techniques as a replacement for activity?

Empirical evidence suggests that beginners profit more from actual physical involvement in the activity. One investigation that provides contrary data is worth reporting here. Jones (1965) found that physical practice was not necessary for his subjects to learn a gymnastic skill, the hock-swing upstart. Mental practice was a sufficient condition for learning, and interestingly enough, undirected mental practice was found to be more effective than directed mental practice. Verbal and written instructions appear to be more beneficial and meaningful as an individual's skill level increases. This would be especially true with complex skills. Although there is no total substitution for participation, as the learner progresses he may obtain greater skill when the activity is supplemented with various teaching aids, such as detailed verbal and written directions.

Worthy of our attention is the current interest in mental practice, which is a form of passive learning in the sense that overt physical practice does not take place. In order not to offend those who would claim that the individual actively responds even during mental practice, it must be restated that this concept is indeed true. However, relatively speaking, the learner *appears* to be passive. *Mental* or *image practice* or *conceptualization* refers to task rehearsal in which there are no observable movements. Researchers have compared the effectiveness of learning tasks through actual physical practice with mental practice or a combination of physical-mental practice.

As far back as 1899, the question was raised as to whether gymnastic movements could be learned through mental practice even if they were not practiced physically. The relationship of skill learning and muscle activity to conceptualization has been demonstrated in various ways in a number of experiments since that time. One of the earlier studies was completed by Perry (1939) in which he administered five tasks to his subjects, tasks which ranged from simple motor tasks to those demanding ideational and symbolic activities. The tasks were a three-hole tapping test, a peg-board test, a card-sorting test, a symbolic digit-substitution test, and a mirror-tracing test. Perry compared the effects of actual to mental practice on the performance of each task.

Mental rehearsal was found to yield significantly better performances on four of the five tasks than no practice at all. Physical practice was superior to conceptualization on three tasks, however the mental practice group was favored on the peg board task. Other studies have, in general, obtained similar results. Typically, physical practice is better than mental practice which in turn is better than no practice at all. Clark's (1960) results are of interest since they were derived from practice on a physical education skill. His subjects learned the Pacific Coast one-hand foul shot under conditions of physical and mental practice and he found mental practice to be nearly as effective as physical practice.

Other researchers, although noticing the significant beneficial effects of mental rehearsal, have not obtained such effective results from this form of practice. More in line with the general research findings in this area is a study by Twining (1949) in which ring tossing was the skill to be learned. Three groups were involved, one that threw 210 rings on the first day and the twenty-second day; a second group that threw 210 rings on the first day and 70 rings each day from the second through the twenty-first day and 210 rings on the twenty second day; and a third group that threw 210 rings on the first day, mentally rehearsed the skill for fifteen minutes daily from the second through the twenty-first day and threw 210 rings on the twenty-second day. The subjects without practice showed no significant learning. The subjects receiving physical practice improved 137 per cent. The subjects who had mental practice improved 36 per cent. The improvement was statistically significant in both groups.

In investigations comparing a third group, one which is physically and mentally practiced, usual results indicate this method to be as effective as physical practice or slightly inferior to it. A combination of physical-mental practice is probably better than mental practice alone.

Present-day investigators have attempted to come to grips with the many variables that possibly might affect learning by mental practice. Some of these include the skill level of the learner on the skill to be learned, the novelty of the task, intelligence, kinesthetic sense, and ratios of physical to mental practice.

Start (1964) tested forty-four male college students on the single leg upstart on the Olympic High Bar with five minutes of mental practice on six successive days. Performance ratings, when compared to IQ scores, yielded a correlation of .08. Other studies also, reviewed in previous chapters, have demonstrated that intelligence has a low correlation with various estimates of physical performance.

Corbin's (1965) results suggest that mental practice is only effective with tasks previously experienced by the learners. Mental practice alone was found not to be effective in learning a juggling task novel to the subjects, but it was most beneficial when used in conjunction with physical practice. The data point to the fact that physical practice is the best method to develop motor skill.

Perhaps previous physical practice on the task at hand facilitates the ease with which conceptualization takes place. It is quite difficult to envision the intricacies of an act unless one has had actual experience performing it, a hint that mental practice has more value with the highly skilled individual. A number of studies indicate that the novice gains faster with physical practice than with mental practice alone.

Another consideration is the ability level of the individual in a given task; that is, the person must have the necessary skill to perform the actions if instructions of any kind are to be valuable. Organized actions must correspond to verbal concepts. Words and concepts are only valuable in the motor-learning situation to the extent that they can be translated into coordinated movements.

Aside from experimental data, empirical evidence indicates that almost all athletes subject themselves to some form of mental rehearsal before, during, and even after competition. They constantly review, analyze, and conceptualize their performances, although in a less structured manner than has been employed in formalized experimentation. Nevertheless, at least one high school tennis coach has turned to planned mental practice periods which precede and complement the actual play of the athletes. Following one of these conceptualizing sessions, a player was overheard to comment, "Hope I do in practice as well as I think!"

Mental rehearsal, under many but not all conditions, has been shown to be beneficial as a method of learning and improving motor performance. Exactly how this information may be applied practically to the learning situation faced by the physical educator has not been worked out as yet. It seems reasonable to expect, though, that in the future there will be a greater recognition of the cognitive processes in the learning of motor skills. The ratio of time allocated for mental and physical practice will be designated as will designs of mental practice provided for different skills to be taught in the physical education class.

Concentration on One Aspect of Skill Rather than on Another. Most activities require the learner to master different skills before proficiency is attained. For example, in sports where the activity is continuous and situations change unpredictably, it is not at all improbable that such factors as speed, accuracy, and timing will be of equal importance for success.

Many times the question is raised as to whether one should emphasize speed or accuracy in the early stages of learning. The tennis player might initially attempt to master accuracy in stroking by standing relatively still and concentrating on the stroke and the direction of the ball. On the other hand, he could practice under game-like conditions, striking the ball when constantly on the move, in and away from the net. The fencer might learn how to lunge by practicing slow, carefully calculated movements that emphasize form and accuracy. Or, he could practice making the swift and agile movements associated with actual competition.

When learning motor skills, accuracy has usually been emphasized first. However, there is evidence enough to justify that practice should resemble game situations, that a skill should be rehearsed as it would be performed in the contest. Many basketball players shoot well by themselves or even under lessened pressures of practice sessions. However, defensive hands in their faces, shooting on the move, game pressures, boisterous spectators, and other variables contribute to the downfall of these same players. Skill attainment implies the ability to adjust to changing conditions. Practice sessions that simulate contest situations will be more effective in preparing the performer for what to expect and what is desired of him in these contests.

Two interesting experiments serve the purpose of emphasizing the need for practice to resemble ultimate desired performance. In one study, reported in greater detail in Chapter 4, subjects had to lunge at a target (Solley, 1952). He found the group that emphasized speed in learning performed better when speed was the necessary factor for successful performance. Equal emphasis on speed and accuracy in practice yielded the most favorable results when both these factors were important to effective performance.

Fulton (1945) tested sixty college women on two tasks, tracing movements required on the Snoddy stabilimeter and a striking movement at a target. During training, one group of subjects was encouraged to speed, the other to attain accuracy. Early emphasis on speed for both tasks was more effective, as stronger transfer was noted of the speed-set than the accuracy-set. When an individual practices at a high speed and then attempts to attain accuracy along with the speed, he does not have to change the movement of the act. However, low speed practice transformed to the greater speed demanded in competition requires a new movement, a change in body control. No negative transfer effects on accuracy resulted from early speed emphasis in Fulton's investigation. In interpreting her data for athletic skill learning, Fulton concludes: "Therefore, movements such as tennis strokes, golf strokes, and hammer throws in which the accumulation of momentum is essential for effective performance would be particularly adversely affected by early emphasis on accuracy."

Sequential Order of Learning. In any sport, there are a series of skills that must be mastered before total satisfaction can be enjoyed when participating in that sport. Typically, more complex skills are taught after simpler ones have been experienced. As we shall see later, this practice is not always advisable or necessary. For now, though, let us be concerned with skills of approximately equal difficulty which comprise a particular sport.

Physical educators often touch the various skills of a sport at different class meetings. Traditionally they begin with one skill and usually progress according to a well- accepted, predesigned plan. Volleyball is an example of a sport composed of at least four distinct, unique skills: spiking, serving, digging, and setting. Volleyball instructors often teach the set first, the spike last, and serving and digging in interchangeable order. The concern here is for the acquisition of one part of a sport facilitating the learning of other phases, of placing the skills in such an order so as to best promote ultimate game performance.

If, in a series of things to be learned, some are more important than others, where should they be placed in the learning order? Psychologists have been able to control extraneous variables to a great extent by studying the learning of lists of nonsense syllables, prose, and poetry. The learning of sequential materials, a particular order of parts comprising a whole, has been termed *serial learning*. When nonsense syllables are presented at random arrangement and subjects are allowed to recall them in any order they desire, studies have usually found the words at the end of the list to be most frequently recalled (see, for example, Deese and Kaufman, 1957). However, when nonsense syllables are presented serially or organized material such as prose is learned, that which has been learned first is retained best, the last material is mastered second best, and the middle is last to be recalled.

Returning to the volleyball example, it seems only natural to ask if one skill is deemed most important and useful for satisfactory participation in a sport, will it be most effectively learned and retained if it is taught first, last, or in the middle of all the skills to be learned for that sport? Since the set is considered by many volleyball experts as the one skill most often used in a game, what should the position of this skill be in relation to others which will be taught?

Although the order in which skills are learned might affect later performance, it is surprising to discover how little research work has been done on this topic. In an attempt to gain some insight into the problem, Singer (1968) obtained data from college volleyball classes on the learning and retention effects of volleyball skills taught in an ordered sequence. Each of four classes learned four skills in a different order. Immediate and later retention tests indicated that the order in which the skills were learned had little bearing on test scores. Isolated significant differences demonstrated lack of noteworthy pattern in between and within group differences.

Although one might have speculated from other research and theory that those skills learned first and last would be best retained, Singer's study does not substantiate the premise. Possibly, because of the nature of gross motor-learning, one should not expect much difference in retention in a short period of time as a result of the sequence in which skills are taught.

That the learning of certain matter might promote the learning of other matter is a concept much relied on in educational thought and practice. A logical sequence of material presentation is the desired structure of the unit outline. There is still much debate as to what constitutes a "logical sequence," and an obvious consideration is the arrangement of tasks by their apparent difficulty. Transferring elements must be contemplated, and the topic of transfer is covered in detail later in the chapter.

Drill Versus the Problem–Solving Approach. Different educational teaching philosophies have been emphasized at various periods in this century. The revolt against the traditional method of learning (concerned with course content) inspired learning not by mere repetition but through questioning and probing. Deweyism brought about consideration for individual differences in interests, rates of learning, and, in general, a problem-solving approach to learning. Lately, many experts on educational curriculums have spoken out against so-called student-oriented courses in favor of teacher-oriented courses. The plea is for a return to traditional teaching methods, i.e., "the command performance." Whether material can be learned more effectively through drill and memorization or problem solving and probing is the current argument. Perhaps different material can be learned better under either condition.

What about a comparison of the application of these methodologies to motor-skill learning? Drill has always been the basic means of teaching motor skills, primarily because it does provide results and possibly because it does not require much creativeness and ingenuity on the part of the instructor. Arranging a situation which encourages the students to think, reason, and then act toward a goal is a methodology rarely practiced by physical educators and coaches; hence, its merits are difficult to ascertain. However, it should be of interest to speculate on the effectiveness of drill and problem solving with motor learners.

There has been considerable attention given lately to exploration skills, especially by women physical educators interested in educating elementary school children. Instead of perpetuating traditional teaching methods, these people have attempted to guide youngsters to a greater awareness of factors associated with any activity, namely time, force, and space. The approach is such as to initiate individual creativity in mastering basic movement skills, those which underlie simple and complex sport activities in varying degrees. This rationale appears to be justifiable and the approach is refreshing. How effective the immediate and long-term results are in comparison with those of traditional teaching methods is a question unanswerable at the present time.

As to the athletic skills of older children, the drill method has the advantage of facilitating the execution of an act until it is habit-like. This method is fine for the high jumper, broad jumper, and diver, to name a few, who basically demonstrate a skill under the same static environmental conditions with each performance. Comparing this situation to the one faced by the tennis player, basketball player, and soccer player, we can observe that in the former case the environment is relatively stable; fixed responses are not only allowable, they are encouraged.

In the latter circumstance, environmental conditions are dynamic. Unpredictable stimuli require the performer to have a flexible repertoire of responses. If the player (say, the basketball player) becomes routinized in his movements, an alert opponent will take advantage of him. The player who can drive to the right side and invariably stops short to take a jump shot is easier to defend against than the player who is a threat to move in any direction and who varies his shots. A team which is overcoached may reflect this practice in the following manner. The offensive pattern calls for the guard to dribble the ball toward the side-line and pass it to the forward and then cut through the middle on the opposite side. From there perhaps a few team patterns may be executed. A smart defensive team expects the guard's initial pass to the forward and intercepts one or two passes. The guard has been so trained to perform the same routine that he does not adjust properly and perhaps his and the team's play may disintegrate totally.

Players who have been exposed to diverse game circumstances, who are not overdrilled, will react more favorably to the unexpected. Drill has its function. It encourages a consistency in performance and a skillfully executed act. Obviously, certain skills must be developed before complex movement patterns may be elicited. But if coaches or physical educators merely *train* instead of *educate*, if they make robots of their pupils, they have done them a great disservice. Active youngsters must be able to reason quickly in challenging situations and have the abilities to express their thoughts. Therefore, both drill and problem-solving approaches serve in meeting teaching and student goals.

Even in sports that demand a skill to be performed in a relatively predictable environment, the problem-solving method might promote the learning of more complex skills. When the student is introspective and does not only repeat an act continually without understanding what he is really doing, he probably will gain quicker insight into other relevant skills. Perhaps overall swimming objectives are taught more effectively when the student, with teacher guidance and supervision, is encouraged to think of means of propulsion through the water on the side, back, and front, and then to react in a supervised trial-and-error method. The drilled individual learns the skill but maybe nothing more; the individual who has to reason and learn in a loosely structured situation may learn the skill as well as water principles, confidence, safety, and ways of transferring elements to other strokes and water conditions.

Traditional and innovated methods of teaching physical education skills are in existence throughout the world. Supporters of the teacher-completely-dominating drill approach, however, appear to be diminishing. Perhaps because the value of drills has been questioned, Wickstrom (1967) has seen fit to present a strong argument on behalf of the utilization of this teaching methodology. His emphasis is on skill development, however, and the importance of strengthening S-R bonds for the play that will follow later. Drills, like other teaching techniques, must be administered in an effective manner if their true value is to be realized. Wickstrom offers the following suggestions for successful results from the usage of drills:

1. Concentrate on drills until basically correct form starts to become automatic and thereby habitual. Drills need not be the only form of skill practice employed but they should be emphasized.
2. Encourage students to concentrate on the correct execution of the skill or skills used in the drills. Drills which are performed sloppily are useless and probably far more harmful than beneficial. If students do not improve in performance the situation must be analyzed to determine the cause.
3. Constantly make corrections during drills to keep attention on the proper techniques of performance. Early corrections of a general nature made with enthusiasm and to the entire group are stimulating and effective. Along with the corrections, general comments on the correct fundamentals are positive in nature and of particular value. The students should be kept aware of the purpose and objectives of the drill while they are doing it. It should be remembered that the drill is an opportunity to concentrate on certain aspects of correct performance and develop a consistency in the performance.
4. Make drills game-like as often as possible. Drills of this sort are more interesting and challenging because they are a movement in the direction of regular play.
5. Advance to the use of multiple-skill drills to emphasize the proper use of combined skills. The transition from drills to the game is easier if drills have been devised to reflect the choices and problems possible in the actual game.
6. Make extensive use of modified games to create the much desired competitive atmosphere. Most games can be modified to emphasize one or two skills and still offer controlled practice. The modified game is one of the easiest ways to maintain a high level of interest and still retain the essential spirit of the drill.
7. Keep drills moving at a brisk pace and involve as many participants as possible. This procedure will increase the amount of individual participation and practice. Since motor learning involves the factor of trial-and-error, the student needs many opportunities to participate, evaluate and change. One or two chances per individual in a drill would not have much impact on learning.

Other physical educators are looking beyond the teaching approach that treats all individuals alike and in which the teacher dominates the activity. A stimulating new book by Mosston (1966) offers modern ways of teaching physical education students. After discussing the weaknesses of the traditional teaching method, which he calls the "command style," he delves into more desirable techniques, culminating in the *guided discovery style,* of which the problem-solving approach is an extension.

The individualized learning process, according to Mosston, brings the learner to a high level of development in four dimensions: the physical, the social, the emotional, and the intellectual. The teacher induces discoveries to problems in all activities, the solutions of which are not predetermined. That is to say, there are a number of ways of approaching a situation, and each student may cope with the problem in his own individualized manner. After all, there are many means by which one can express himself whether they be oral or physical. Examine the following example found in Mosston's book of a problem to solve in movements on the parallel bars:

> The first area of problem design is the initial relationship between the body and the parallel bars. How do we get on? In relating the body to the given equipment (Level 1 in the structure of subject matter), one can observe that several possibilities exist in terms of *where* to mount the parallel bars. Thus, there is a need to develop problems, the solution of which will establish the possible relationships between the position of the body, the movement, and the position on the equipment.
>
> Mounts onto the parallel bars are possible at the following locations:
>
> 1. At the end of both bars, outside the bars.
> 2. At the end of both bars inside the bars.
> 3. In the middle of both bars, inside the bars.
> 4. At *any* point of both bars, inside the bars.
> 5. At the above proposals, entry can be performed above, below, and between the bars.
> 6. 1–4 can be done from under or over the bars.
> 7. Some of the above can be done using only *one* bar. Which ones?
> 8. Some of the above can be done alternating one and two bars. Which ones?
> 9. Are there other locations?
> 10. Are there other possible bar combinations (excluding for a moment various slope arrangements)?
>
> Let us examine some problems to solve in mounting *at the end of both bars (from the outside), facing the bars:*
>
> 1. Design two mounts from a standing position which will land you in support position.
> 2. Using each one of the solutions of the previous problems, *end* in three different support positions.
> 3. Design four different mounts from four starting positions *other than* standing, ending in each of the suggested supporting positions of 2.

4. Are there still other alternative starting positions from which you can execute four discovered mounts? How many? Are they all good? How do you determine that?
5. Using the new alternative starting positions, can you still find another mount to a support position?
6. Is it possible to end the previously discovered mounts in positions other than the front support position?
7. Can you end *any* of the previously discovered mounts with a turn? What kind of a turn?
8. Can you end any of the mounts on top of both bars?
9. Can you find three different end-mount positions on top of both bars?
10. On top of one bar?
11. Could you end the mount on no bars? Would this constitute a mount?

Although there are more steps on the parallel bars offered by Mosston, the quoted material should be adequate to reflect some possible procedures to follow in the problem-solving approach. The approach could be utilized with all sports, and Mosston does present some sports examples such as soccer, tumbling, and football. However, the approach need not be consistent from teacher to teacher, and there is plenty of room for individual creativity in the formulation of problems.

There is no firm evidence to support a stand for the drill or problem-solving approach to all types of motor-skill learning. One may assume the prerogative of conjecture, as the writer has just done, to determine the values of each method. From an educational point of view, a problem-solving approach certainly is consistent with the philosophy of our leading physical educators. From a skill-learning point of view, arguments can be justified for either method. Perhaps, to be considered at the onset, is the nature of the skill, its relation to other material to be taught, and the objectives of the teacher.

Whilden (1956), although not comparing the drill to the problem-solving approach, did investigate the effects of pupil-dominated and teacher-dominated groups. Two classes of junior high school girls learned beginning basketball skills. At the end of the unit, the teacher-dominated group (traditional instructional methods) was judged to display better basic skills, but the pupil-dominated group demonstrated a greater knowledge of the rules, a better attempt at improving the social status of near-isolated girls, and played together better as a team. Each learning method had unique value, and certainly an approach other than the conventional one apparently can fulfill particular objectives more nearly.

Programmed Learning. Our society is so besieged with technological advancement and innovations, it is not surprising that some enterprising educators rebel against the traditional classoom learning situation. Since man-made machines have substituted for human productivity and have been demonstrated to be more efficient in industry in certain cases, these educators suggest that machines can serve a similar purpose in education.

Actually, the concept of a teaching machine is by no means new. Pressey is credited for creation of a teaching machine in the twenties and Skinner for streamlining it in later years. Skinner applied his laboratory research on reinforcement in learning to the device's design and is acknowledged as the leader in convincing the public of the machine's value as well as influencing its widespread popularity. In its simplest form the machine is constructed for individual usage, with the content of a course or course area presented to the learner in simple to more difficult sequence form. The learner has to respond correctly to the questions and is informed by the machine as to the correctness of his answer. Proper responses permit him to advance through the material; complex and more difficult material is learned only after simpler material has been mastered.

Courses have to be programmed in a logical way. The material is presented in detail step by step, ensuring progressive knowledge acquisition. The Skinner method encourages only correct responses whereas the Crowder technique permits errors, operating under the philosophy that a learner may profit from his mistakes. For an interesting discussion on programming and teaching machines, the reader is encouraged to read Travers' book, *Essentials of Learning* (1964).

Schramm (1964) has listed the essential characteristics of programmed learning:

1. An ordered sequence of stimulus items.
2. A response by the learner to each of the stimuli.
3. Reinforcement of the response by immediate knowledge of results.
4. Progession in small steps.
5. Practice consisting of mostly correct responses and few errors.
6. Learning proceeding in successively closer approximations to the desired objectives.

Presently, there are many types of teaching machines and programmed texts on the market. Some are relatively inexpensive but others, such as computer-assisted machines, can be quite costly. Basically, though, all these machines are geared to operate under certain accepted learning principles. One of these is the imparting of immediate knowledge of results, of reinforcing correct responses. Reinforcement, especialy when directy following a response, is essential for learning. Obviously, a teacher faced with a number of pupils in his class cannot provide individual attention. Hence, another strong feature of the machine; it permits students to work at their own pace and within their own abilities. Whereas the teacher must gear his lesson to the average learning speed of the class, programmed individualized units meet specific needs and abilities. There are other merits to teaching machines, but they need not be analyzed here.

Of most concern with these machines or programmed texts is their effectiveness in educating students. Athough research is not yet ample enough nor experimental designs sufficiently sophisticated to warrant any conclusive statements, results are most promising. A number of investigations, if not finding programmed material to be better learned than material taught by traditional teaching methods, have noted greater efficiency in the form of time-saving benefits of the programmed method. As an an example, Rawls, Perry, and Timmons (1966) found psychology course material to be learned at a substantial time saving with a programmed group as compared to a lectured-to group. Although no significant difference was noted between the groups on a knowledge test administered at the end of the unit, a six-weeks later retention test favored the programmed group.

The advantages associated with these various devices have been derived when the material to be acquired was *not* in the motor-skill area. This is understandable, for motor skills have yet to be programmed. Programmed texts and teaching machines can be used, if desired, for the learning of information related to athletic skills. With regard to a particular sport, programs can be developed containing such matter as relevant physiological and mechanical principles, rules, strategy, and history. What about programming movement skills? Is it possible? Skinner (1961), although not addressing the problem directly, expressed a need for many types of teaching machines. He writes that rhythm is the temporal patterning of behavior, and effective behavior has to be properly timed. Rhythm, according to Skinner, can be taught through the program method.

Possibly the future will bring attempts at programmed instruction of motor patterns. These efforts would certainly coincide with those in industry and education. Although some people would replace teachers altogether with machines, most educators favoring programmed instruction view the teacher as playing an important role in individual guidance along with the programmed material. The teacher is not to be replaced, but rather freed to devote more of his time to individual instruction and assistance.

Teaching Cues and Aids

Not only does every teacher differ with respect to communication techniques and unit planning, but also in methods of implementing and enriching particular lessons. Although some teachers adhere to routinized teaching procedures, others look to supplemental materials and methods to fulfill certain objectives perhaps more effectively attained by these techniques. Traditional teaching units may be altered in many ways. Some of these approaches to motor learning are presented here, along with an evaluation of their worth as indicated by published research.

Verbal Instruction. It is most uncommon to discover an organized learning situation where verbal directions are not issued by the instructor before and during practice. These verbal cues help to direct the student, to make him more attentive to certain stimuli. The meaningfulness of verbal comments and written material can be evaluated partially by their explicitness and simplicity. Also, consideration must be given for the task to be learned as well as the skill level and unique personality of the learner.

Some individuals respond better to certain modes of instruction than others. Drawing from this premise, certain people will learn faster than others from verbal comments on their motor activity. At the present time beginners as a group seem to benefit less than advanced learners from extensively detailed verbal directions. Younger children have less patience than mature learners and need to be immersed in activity. With respect to the nature of the task, a more complex one would probably require greater explanation and more teacher direction.

Actually, as Miller (1953) points out, the things we usually learn are mediated by words. In the beginning stage of learning a task, the individual has to learn instructions to know how and what to perform. He must learn directions before he can obey. Not only are there words from external sources (instructors, teachers, and coaches) but words spoken to oneself during activity. This latter theoretical state has been termed *verbal mediation* and has also been referred to as conceptualization, ideation, or thought processing.

The ability, then, to succeed in motor performance may very well be related to a certain extent to being able to apply external and internal words to motor acts. Sometimes, however, the verbal mediation process may interfere with skilled performance. Consider, for example, the performer who thinks too much and gets confused, resulting in a delayed reaction to a given situation. This is especially detrimental in a game, where players have to respond immediately to unpredictable openings and occurrences.

The effectiveness of oral directions along with demonstrations has been reported by Goodenough and Brian (1929). These researchers trained three groups of young children to throw rings over a post. After fifty days and 1,000 trials, the group that received demonstrations and comments, and had to follow definite patterns of performance improved more in this skill than the other two groups. The second group had experienced brief demonstrations and some comments, while the third group had been given no instruction or comments.

Experimenters have researched some of the unique problems associated with verbal transfer to motor proficiency: What is the most effective point in motor skill practice for the introduction of cues? How much verbal training is necessary to transfer successfully to motor performance? What are the effects of verbal training on complex and simple motor tasks? As far as tracking skill is concerned, Trumbo, Ulrich, and Noble (1965) observed that written materials and verbal cues were important in early but not in later practice. These results do not necessarily imply the same outcome with practice on physical education skills. There is much empirical evidence that in those motor acts in which there is a progression of skills from simple to complex, and in game situations that are rarely stable, continuous verbal cues are of assistance in stimulus discrimination and serve as a motivating factor.

Figure 7–1 illustrates the effects of tuition and a lack of it on learning archery skills. One group received regular and systematic instruction; the other had none. An interesting sidelight in this study was that brighter students, as measured by a mental ability test, tended to profit more from the instruction than the duller students. If the task to be learned is relatively easy, written material and cues will help the individual in the beginning to proceed on the right track. With practice on this type of task, further assistance from an outsider is usually unnecessary.

Verbal training that precedes motor training must be of sufficient quantity and quality in order to transfer favorably to motor skill performance. This condition becomes evident in reviewing Baker and Wylie's (1950) experiment. Before practicing on a discrimination problem involving matching the correct switch to a light stimulus, their subjects received verbal training and memorized by the oral paired–associates method. The group which had eight verbal training trials did not show evidence of significant transfer to motor performance when time or the number of errors were used as measurements.

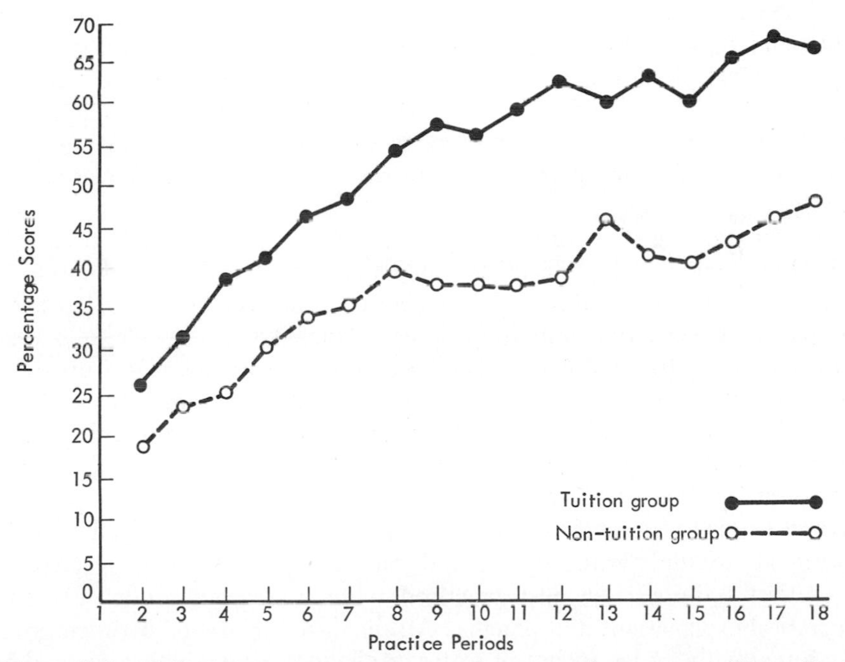

Figure 7–1. Daily average percentage scores for two archery groups. (From Davies, Dorothy R. The Effect of Tuition Upon the Process of Learning a Complex Skill, *J. Educ. Psychol.*, 36:352–365, 1945.)

However, the twenty-four verbal training trials brought about a significant transfer effect on both these measurements.

When verbal training is offered only at the beginning of a task, it is the simple task, not the complex one, that will be most positively affected. Battig (1956) found verbal pretraining to facilitate performance on simpler motor tasks but no benefit was shown from this pretraining on complex tasks. The subjects were tested on a finger-positioning apparatus.

It is doubtful whether verbal or written instructions can completely take the place of actual motor-skill practice, especially on skills containing a certain degree of challenge. Descriptions and ideas are one thing, experience another. The body must actively respond, and the kinesthetic receptors must be stimulated, if a high skill level is to be reached on complex motor tasks.

Mechanical Principles. From a theoretical point of view, it makes good sense to believe that if the individual understands what he is doing his performance should be facilitated. The ability to succeed in athletic skills is dependent many times on both intended and unintentional application of mechanical and kinesiological principles. Intentional usage of scientifically accepted movement patterns would seem to be a desirable objective. It is reasoned that the knowledge of mechanical principles will assist the learner in gaining quicker insight into and mastery of a given gross motor task.

Unfortunately, this "sound reasoning" of transfer has not been upheld consistently enough in experiments to gain acceptance. On the positive side, Mohr and Barrett (1962) found that the learning of mechanical principles beyond actual physical activity was an effective teaching technique. In their study an experimental group of women learned mechanical principles associated with swim strokes; the other group did not. After fourteen weeks, the experimental group improved more than the control in all strokes except the elementary back stroke.

In an interesting study of principle transference to an assembly task, Johnson (1963) compared performance of experimental and control groups of normal and retarded children. With eighteen subjects in each of the four groups, the two experimental groups were instructed in a principle to facilitate performance on the motor task. Both experimental groups were superior to both control groups when they were timed on their rate of assembling ten items. The unusual finding was that the performance of the retarded experimental group was significantly better than that of the intellectually normal control group. One of the earliest studies on the problem of principle transference to task was reported by Judd (1908). The task involved was dart tossing at an underwater target, and one group of subjects received no theoretical training, they just practiced while the other group was given theoretical explanations and practice. Although no difference between groups was found with twelve inches of water, a change to four inches favored the experimental group. These subjects evidently applied the theory in this transfer situation.

Some sample experiments obtaining contrary results follow. Colville (1957) attempted to determine the effect of knowledge of three mechanical principles on the learning of a number of motor skills. Two groups of college women were formed, one of which spent their time learning and practicing the skills, the other learned mechanical principles as well as having skill practice. The results indicated that (1) instruction in mechanical principles did not promote the initial learning of a motor skill any more than did an equal amount of time spent in skill practice; and (2) such knowledge did not facilitate subsequent learning as evidenced when similar or more complicated skills were learned, even though the same principles were applicable.

Sorenson (1966), an industrial researcher, was interested in the importance of a knowledge of mechanical principles for on-the-job success of mechanical repair men. He reports that "the better mechanics appeared to rely on mechanical intuition and experience rather than formally taught principles (e.g., physics, mechanics, electricity, etc.)....They seem to fit a picture of born mechanics rather than made mechanics."

Thus the question is raised once again of the importance of intellectual knowledge as contrasted to supposed "innate ability" on motor achievement. Perhaps the safest statement, in view of conflicting research results, is that some individuals will prosper more, some less, when time is devoted to learning mechanical principles, especially when this time is taken away from potential physical participation. On the more optimistic side is a study completed by Kittell (1957) investigating the effect of learning principles on learning other principles. His sixth grade subjects had to solve multiple-choice verbal problems. After analyzing his data, he states that "evidence... indicates that...underlying principles promote transfer and retention of learned principles and may provide the background enabling future discovery of new principles."

The context in which the principles are learned and insight into how they are to be applied in given situations are conditions to be considered if such knowledge is to be beneficial to motor performance. Unfortunately, educators sometimes orate too much and expect the learner to know many things which do not interest him. To conclude, perhaps the following words of Hilgard and Marquis (in Kimble, 1961) demonstrate practical insight into the problem:

> There is a limit to the learner's curiosity in understanding something. The understanding which the learner wishes in a problematic situation is knowledge of the essentials to economical goal-achievement, and nothing more can be counted on. The mistake is sometimes made in teaching students of assuming that they wish to understand what lies behind a process which for them is just a tool. They wish to know how to use the tool to reach immediate goals; the further curiosity is related to different goals, which may be goals for the teacher but not for them.

Visual Cues. It is interesting to analyze just how visual stimuli facilitate or hamper the learning process. With a newly-introduced skill, the learner typically attends to too many stimuli and he has to learn to be more selective, which will occur with experience and expert guidance. Too many visual stimuli can be distracting, and, in fact, perhaps none are necessary in the beginning stages of learning certain skills.

Let us examine the golf swing as an example. One of the greatest problems with the beginning golfer is to get him to concentrate on the swing and to feel the movement rather than worry about how far the ball has gone. A few instructors believe in blindfolding these beginners so that this kinesthetic sense may be developed further. Indeed, one study reported early in this century did show blindfolded golfers to demonstrate greater ultimate proficiency than golfers taught with full vision. Unfortunately, not enough carefully controlled investigations have been completed in this area to advocate one method over the other method. Other skills require the presence of a certain amount of visual cues. Gymnastics, diving, and trampolining stunts necessitate vision for equilibrium, balance, and safety. And, of course, for many activities vision provides a knowledge of results, e.g., basketball shooting, archery, tennis, and the like, enabling the individual to know when to compensate for inaccurate responses.

Visual guidance can be provided for the learner by allowing him to view expert performance. This is a procedure usually advocated and practiced by many physical educators. It allows the beginner to visualize what the desired act looks like and supplies him with the ideal goal for which to strive. Merely watching others perform a task while not expecting to have to do it results in more effective learning. Twitmeyer (1931) presents evidence on this point. His subjects viewed others undertaking a pencil-type maze task not knowing they would have to solve it. He concluded that visual guidance, even if of "undirected intention," was very effective for the early acquisition of skill.

Oftentimes certain visual cues are emphasized or artificial ones introduced in order to promote the learning of various skills. Examples of the artificial visual cues are found in (1) basketball, where spots or marks on the backboard provide specific points at which to aim for backboard shots; (2) archery, where sometimes the point-of-aim method is employed (a marker placed before the target is sighted upon); and (3) bowling, where the spot method of aiming is often used (a spot placed on the alley is aimed at instead of the pins).

Artificial visual cues are used either as an initial learning technique, to be disregarded later, or as a continual performance aid. Although research is scattered and inconclusive on the value of these techniques, it does appear as if many of them are of value in fulfilling certain objectives. Theoretically analyzing the problem, specific and precise visual cues are easier to attend to than general and vague ones. Furthermore, nearer cues should be easier to aim for than those more removed. However, not all learners will benefit equally from the identical cues in the same task.

Anderson (1942) studied the benefits of spot aiming in basketball with junior high school girls. After six weeks of practice, a significant difference in performance was found in favor of a group learning the backboard spot-aiming technique over a group not using the spots. Twenty-five per cent more improvement was noted for the spot group than the no-spot group.

On the matter of spot-versus-pin bowling, two investigations have yielded contrary results. Summers' (1957) subjects, college women, demonstrated the spot-aim method to be significantly more effective in bowling achievement than the pin-aim method. Of further interest is the observation that there was no difference in performance between the women who learned with a hook ball as compared with those who learned with a straight ball. The spot-aim method of delivery was equally good with the hook or straight ball. Goellner (1956) had his beginning bowlers receive standard bowling instruction; and theories of headpin, spot, and combination bowling were explained and demonstrated to them. Three groups were formed and practiced under each of these methods for six weeks. The investigator reports that the headpin method was best and the spot method poorest. However, further examination of this study indicates the group bowling averages to be fairly close: the pin group had 111.5, the combination group had 110, and the spot group had 105. Since no statistics were used in this study to analyze the data, it is very possible that there were no significant differences in performance between the three groups.

Some devices are utilized to provide the individual with certain information needed to develop skill proficiency. Primarily, this would be the function of the instructor, but sometimes unfavorable teaching conditions do not permit the learner to receive all the assistance he needs. An example of such a device is the Golf-lite, illustrated in Figure 7–2, patented by Mathews and McDaniel (1962). These investigators reported the value of having a small light attached to the shaft of a golf club and powered by a battery placed in the individual's trouser pocket. Supposedly, the light yields a bright spot on the ground during the swing which allows more effective use of the eyes. The learner receives information about his swing, he is benefitted by the after-image effect. In the study reported by these researchers, a skill test given to two groups indicated the group that learned to golf with the aid of the Golf-lite improved more than the control group which received regular instructions and practice.

Beside objects, marks, spots, and devices, films and pictures are other visual aids used to assist the learner in obtaining motor skill. In fact, they are an integral part of many teachers' lesson plans. Let us now analyze their value, as revealed by research.

Visual Aids. Visual aids, in various forms, have been experimentally investigated for their worth in promoting motor learning. They are represented by motion pictures, force-time graphs, loopfilms, pictured representation of the task, slides, and the use of the tachistoscope. These aids serve such functions

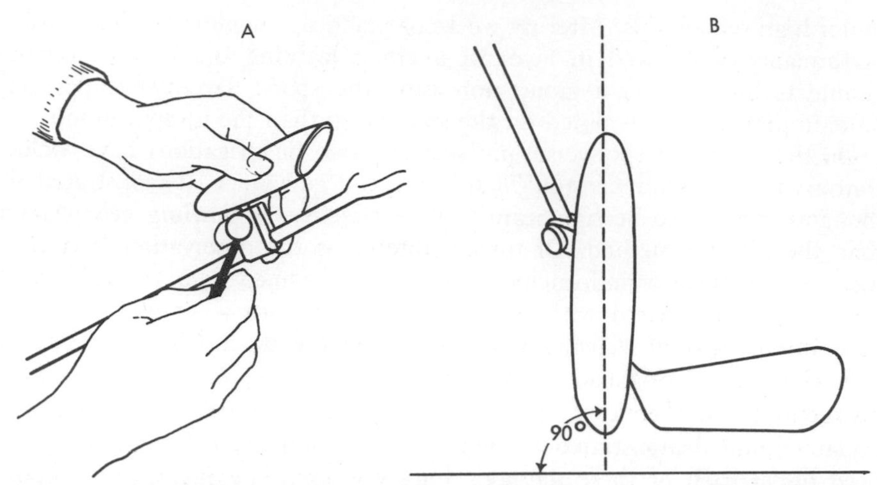

Figure 7–2. **A** Affixing Golf-Lite to shaft of golf club. The universal joint permits easy adjustment in properly positioning the light. **B** Adjusting the Golf-Lite so that the light beam forms a perpendicular line to the ground as one addresses the ball. (From Mathews, Donald K., and McDaniel, Joe. Effectiveness of Using Golf-Lite in Learning the Golf Swing, *Res. Quart.*, 33:488–491, 1962.)

as demonstrating ideal performance (at regular or slow speeds), performance of the subject on the skill, or simple representative images or pictures of the task. The value of visual aids lies in their ability to allow the learner to view the task and critically analyze the task setting and bodily movements involved in skilled movements. This function is especially important if we stop to consider that the problem in executing most motor skills rests not with demands placed on the motor capacity of an individual, but rather in overcoming stimulus complexity in order to react with appropriate movements to particular environmental cues.

Research results, although somewhat favorable, do not indicate the conclusive worth of visual aids. In a study reported by Brown and Messersmith (1948), motion pictures of outstanding tumblers and of the participating group were shown to one group of college subjects. The control group did not witness any films. After seventeen class periods, no significant difference in performance was observed between the groups. Similar results were obtained by Nelson (1958), who used beginning golf students as subjects. The addition of loopfilms to explanation and demonstrations did not improve the skill of the experimental group more than that of the control group.

On the other hand, Lockhart (1944) was quite optimistic about the effects of motion pictures on the skill development of beginning bowlers. She recommends, after an analysis of the data, that the pictures will afford their most value after some practice on the skill. Newer evidence of the benefits of motion pictures is supplied by Watkins (1963). Twenty players from the Iowa State University baseball team served as subjects in his study. Watkins concluded that the baseball players who viewed motion pictures of their batting decreased their batting faults significantly as compared with non-viewing baseball players.

The force-time graph is another means of supplying visual feedback to the learner. Howell (1956) used this device, a pen-drawn graph of force exerted as a function of time, to measure the pressure sprinters applied to the starting block at the start of their sprint. His experimental subjects viewed the graphs immediately following each start and heard them explained. The control subjects learned the sprint start by the conventional method. After ten meetings, the experimental group was rated as performing better than the control group. In skills such as this, where the speed of a complex act makes it difficult to analyze the movement, apparently visual aids can overcome the problem somewhat.

Preliminary training on pictured representations of complex motor acts may help to provide greater insight into these acts. At least one experiment, authored by Gagné and Foster (1949), found this to be the case. Subjects, before learning a discrimination reaction time task, were presented with a paper-and-pencil representation of the task. This procedure was found to be effective in skill acquisition, and more pre-motor practice resulted in better motor performance.

Auditory Aids. Although music may serve as a stimulator, motivator, or relaxer, its exact role as an aid in motor-skill attainment and motor performance has not been determined. Melodies are piped into department stores and supermarkets in order to relax the customers and encourage purchases. Investigations are currently under way to determine the effects of music in general as well as different tempos and tones on sales. The dentist uses earphones with his patients so that the music transmitted may relax his patients and take their minds off the pending pain. Industrial workers have been observed to increase their output when motivated by music.

Because of the success tuneful and rhythmic melodies have had in these areas, it might be hypothesized that similar benefits would be derived in motor learning and performance. It is felt that lively tempos encourage more vigorous practice efforts; slow soft music relaxes individuals who are tense; and highly rhythmic music facilitates rhythmic and coordinated movements desired in the act. Some coaches and physical educators provide music as a background for the performance of skills with these objectives in mind. The difficulty in controlling experimental variables in determining the effects of auditory aids, hence the lack of research permits little more than speculation. In one of the few studies done on the problem at hand, Dillon (1952) reported that her intermediate swimming students taught with music in the background achieved better form and speed than those swimmers taught without music.

Operating under the assumption that more repetitive, monotonous tasks would perhaps be more positively affected by the sound of music, Newman, Hunt, and Rhodes (1966) undertook a project to test this hypothesis.

Workers in a skateboard factory heard four different types of music played on four different days; and no music was played on the fifth day. No difference in output was noted as a result of the type of music played or even in the absence of music. It appears that in routine tasks, tasks in which the performers do not need a high degree of skill, music is not beneficial to performance.

There has been some thought on the relationship between rhythm ability and the ability to perform movement patterns demanded in motor skills. Certain physical educators are of the opinion that by developing a sense of rhythm in children, they will promote the learning of skills, which requires the timing of responses within a period of time. In this case, rhythmic ability is considered to be a more-or-less general factor. Implicit in the assumption is that positive transfer effects are highly probable. Although this concept has not been truly evaluated as yet, Bond's results (1959) shed some light on the matter. Junior high school girls were given a test of rhythmic perception—where rhythmic patterns could be seen, heard, and felt—and five motor-performance tests. Her data yielded low insignificant correlations between the rhythmic test and five motor tests. Further analysis reveals some interesting findings: the correlation between IQ and motor performance was nearly zero whereas the correlations between IQ and rhythm abilities ranged from .24 to .36. These were low positive correlations but significant, nevertheless. Bond suggests that there is a need to analyze the rhythmical components of coordinated performance further if deficits are to be corrected.

Kinesthetic Aids. The role of the kinesthetic sense in skilled movement has already been discussed and emphasized in Chapter 3. A sensitivity to and awareness of body and limb position in movement is naturally an asset to man's performance. Can the kinesthetic sense be sharpened by means other than traditional practice?

An obvious method of attempting to accentuate this sense is to perform the desired act with the eyes closed (if it is a type of activity that can be practiced this way). Concentration is then on the movement rather than its outcome, such as projectile accuracy or distance. Environmental stimuli above and beyond response cues no longer serve as distractions. The eyes-closed or blindfold method of early skill learning has yet to be truly tested as a means of promoting learning. Therefore, at the present time, we must speculate on its effectiveness.

In order to encourage a greater awareness of the physical movement involved in certain acts, a manual manipulation technique is employed by teachers on occasion. The student relaxes as he is guided through a series of movement patterns. This practice serves to activate the receptors associated with the task and provides the learner with the desired movement experience. The manual guidance procedure is based on common sense and not on conclusive affirmative experimental findings; this is another area which needs more intensive research.

A possible manner of activating and sensitizing more proprioceptors is through the use of heavier or lighter equipment. A measurement of transfer of skill would indicate the more desirable procedure. Projectiles of varying weights were thrown by the subjects in a study conducted by Egstrom, Logan, and Wallis (1960). Greater transfer was demonstrated from a light ball to a heavy ball than vice-versa, and the writers reason that the lighter ball sharpened the sensitivity of the receptors and the feedback mechanism. Wright's (1966) experiment in general neither supported nor rejected this conclusion. Young children were tested on physical fitness items and sports skills, and although his results were inconclusive, Wright's evidence suggests that if the children have limited strength motor skills may be learned faster with lighter weight equipment.

Does a player develop a greater sensitivity in basketball shooting if he practices with a larger ball? Weighted baseball bats for warm-up swings and weighted shoes for practice runs and jumps are intended to increase speed, power, and velocity during competition. In these cases and related areas, the research is much too scanty to analyze the effectiveness of such practice procedues. Lindeburg and Hewitt (1965) practiced varsity and junior varsity basketball players with a regulation basketball and a larger basketball. On the tests administered, no difference between groups was observed on foul shots, dribbling ability, and lay-up speed skill. There was a significant difference on the passing test in favor of the group that had practiced with the smaller basketball. Unfortunately, the authors did not test the transference of accuracy from the larger to the regulation basketball.

In motor performance when too much kinesthetic information is withheld, the consequences can be severe. The relative importance of kinesthetic, verbal, visual, and auditory cues in the learning situation will be dependent on the skill in question and the skill level of the individual. All may provide necessary feedback messages, although in many cases they overlap and duplication occurs between the senses and their information. The skilled performer is one who has learned to respond to specific cues and emhasize particular sensory modes at different stages of proficient movement patterns.

Comparison of Cues. There has been an attempt to compare the relative effects of emphasizing or restricting the various cues. Unfortunately, investigations have been based on isolated and unique laboratory tasks. Quite naturally, the results are not consistent from study to study.

Carr (1921), a pioneer researcher, on the basis of his study in which the subjects were tested on a stylus maze, concluded that visual guidance was more important than tactual and kinesthetic experience. He states that "...visual modes of control are much more effective in the acquisition and performance of acts of skill than hitherto suspected." In a comprehensive experiment, Battig (1954) compared performances on the Complex Coordination Test when kinesthetic, verbal, and visual cues were eliminated or emphasized. Six groups of subjects were formed, with all subjects tested on the same task on the first and tenth trials but practiced under different conditions during the middle eight sessions. Standard practice afforded the best results. The sequence of cue importance, after standard practice was determined to benefit skill acquisition, as follows: visual, kinesthetic, and lastly, verbal.

Similar results were obtained in Holding's (1959) investigation. On a tracking task, normally trained and guided groups demonstrated little dissimilarity at the early stages of learning. The guidance group subjects gripped the control knobs, got the feel of the machine tracking itself, and finally had to track themselves. Also noted in the study was that full guidance was better than visual guidance; visual guidance was superior to kinesthetic guidance; and kinesthetic guidance did not yield a significant improvement in performance. The great success of the guidance group indicates the necessary occurrence of correct responses. Holding argues that knowledge of results is not necessary to learning, but the correct movements are, although KR is a means of correcting a response. Knowledge of results is synonymous with error feedback (to many psychologists), but there is no error to feed back if the performance is perfect.

Karlin and Mortimer (1962), using a crank-turning task, found that visual and verbal cues together were more effective than verbal cues alone in learning and retention. Of the cues and combinations of cues examined verbal cues alone were noted to be inferior to all the others.

In general, it would appear that visual cues are extremely important in the acquisition of skill in psychomotor tasks. Kinesthetic cues evidently are of secondary importance in these tasks, whereas in more complex motor skills, e.g., athletic skills, they seem to be more meaningful. Much depends on how and when abilities are measured during skill acquisition. It is possible that different cues are more important at various learning stages, for there is strong evidence that exteroceptive (visual) feedback and spatial orientation ability are related to early achievement in perceptual-motor tasks. Later, at higher skill levels, proprioceptive (kinesthetic) feedback and kinesthetic sensitivity ability is most important. Table 7–1 includes the data obtained by Fleishman and Rich and indicates the relationships between these two abilities in performance on a motor task.

Forty subjects received ten blocks of four trials each on the Two-Hand Coordination Test (THC). They were pretested on a kinesthetic sensitivity measure, the ability to judge the difference between lifted gram weights, and a spatial-visual measure, through the United States Air Force Aerial Orientation Test. An analysis of the data showed the spatial measure to be significantly related to performance on the Two-Hand Coordination Test only early in practice. The kinesthetic measure was significantly related to THC performance only late in learning. It does appear that individual differences in sensitivity to kinesthetic cues may determine *higher* skill levels. Other interesting results of this study point to the fact that both

Table 7–1. Performance During Ten Trials on the Two-Hand Coordination Apparatus with Respect to Obtained Correlations Between Kinesthetic Sensitivity and the Criterion and Spatial-Visual Orientation and the Criterion. As practice continues, the correlations of Two-Hand Coordination (THC) decrease with the spatial ability measure and increase with the kinesthetic sensitivity measure.

THC Trial	Aerial Orientation	Kinesthetic Sensitivity
1	.36**	.03
2	.28*	.19
3	.22*	.15
4	.19	.15
5	.08	.10
6	.07	.09
7	.09	.23*
8	−.05	.28*
9	−.02	.38**
10	.01	.40**

From Fleishman, Edwin A., and Rich, Simon. Role of Kinesthetic and Spatial-Visual Abilities in Perceptual-Motor Learning, *J. Exp. Psychol.*, 66:6–11, 1963.
* $p < .05$, one-tailed.
** $p < .01$, one-tailed.

kinesthetic sensitivity and spatial orientation are necessary to overall performance on the task, as together they correlated .73 with the THC.

For many tasks, conventional practice is not only sufficient but, from the evidence, is often more beneficial than singling out and emphasizing either visual, verbal, or kinesthetic cues. As a final reminder, probably the best advice is to consider the nature of each task and to emphasize equally all sensory cues if the task so demands. Specific cue emphasis should be offered in such cases when one has to react to complex stimuli, execute a complex motor act, or compensate for a weakness in performance.

Training Devices. For various reasons, industrialists, military personnel, and educators have turned to artificial equipment and devices for assistance in facilitating the learning of motor skills. The term *artificial* as used here simply implies that these devices are made especially for training purposes, to simulate to a certain extent the actual performance conditions or, perhaps, to prepare the individual for the actual task via audio-visual or tactile and kinesthetic cues. Technically speaking, we could distinguish these aids by categorizing them as trainers or simulators, although the dichotomy is not always obvious.

A *trainer* is some aid used to promote the learning of a task in the early stages. It could be a film, pictures, or a specially constructed piece of equipment. A *simulator*, on the other hand, is usually a device that more nearly approximates task conditions. It is realistic and provides the performer with concentrated practice when he is at that point of developing a high level of proficiency.

Certain tasks permit more favorable and, indeed, require more frequent usage of these devices if learning efficiency is the desired objective. Consider, for instance, industrial, military, and automobile tasks. The cost of training personnel as well as the inconvenience of activating complex machinery helped to inspire the development of simulators and trainers. Also, there is an element of danger in some tasks, e.g., piloting a plane. Finally, it is not very practical to train a large number of people on tasks which require extreme proficiency on expensive equipment. Because of these factors, various types of aids are used instead of direct practice for the learning of complex motor skills.

Although fake cockpits and automobile controls have been devised for simulating practice flying a plane or driving a car, most athletic skills do not require the usage of such costly and complex equipment. The best practice is afforded by on-the-job tasks or game situations. This is not always practical or possible, although it is certainly more reasonable to expect in educational situations than on military installations or in highly technical industrial work. But, even in education today, where teachers are faced with a greater ratio of students than ever before, training devices have certain advantages over traditional teaching procedures.

These aids allow students to practice skills which otherwise might be impossible to learn under equipment and facility limitations faced by many institutions. Thanks to the initiative of some physical educators, golf can be taught with a certain degree of effectiveness in the gymnasium with the use of plastic or taped balls. These balls do not travel far and are safer than regulation golf balls. The absence of a golf course does not inhibit the teaching of basic golf skills. Similar measures are currently being made so that such sports as water skiing and snow skiing can be simulated in the pool and gymnasium. Although these efforts are probably not as effective as learning the skills under actual conditions, they serve a definite purpose. For instance, Menart (1950) found that a course in dry skiing was advantageous to beginning skiers. An experimental group received one half hour of dry-skiing instruction for six days before being committed to an open slope for ten days of practice and performed significantly better on selected skills than a control group. This does not imply, however, that dry skiing would be as beneficial as actual skiing for the same length of time.

The aids also alleviate the situation where there are too many students for the instructor to provide individual instruction, attention, and direction. Devices that approximate real conditions provide each learner with an immediate knowledge of results, inform him of his performance status, and

Figure 7–3a. Automatic tennis ball machine. The machine consistently tosses ball at a pre-set speed to the player. It provides repetitive stroking and permits the perfection of the strokes. The learner can concentrate on the stroke and not be concerned with unpredictable bounces or the direction of the ball. (With permission from the Ball-Boy Company, Inc., 26 Milburn St., Bronxville, N.Y.)

facilitate his progress. Ball-throwing machines in tennis and baseball are examples of pieces of apparatus that allow individuals to concentrate on hitting techniques. The Ball-Boy Company has manufactured a machine that tosses a ball at a preset speed and a server apparatus which suspends a ball and releases it when contact is made. Both devices eliminate many of the complex factors involved in stroking and serving (see Figures 7–3 and 7–4). Solley and Borders (1965) were interested in determining the effectiveness of the Ball-Boy machine in promoting the learning of tennis skills. After comparing control and experimental groups, the investigators concluded that the machine was very effective. They recommended the procedure of using traditional teaching methods first, followed by the use of the Ball-Boy machine.

Another device which may have value in improving tennis skills is a rebounding net which permits the player to practice his stroking. The Ball-Boy Re-Bound-Net, pictured in Figure 7–5, overcomes a major problem associated with backboards, walls, or other hard surfaces, namely, the ball rebounding too quickly. With the net, a player can hit a ball without reducing stroking velocity since the rebound interval is lengthened. Continuous stroking is thus encouraged.

Figure 7–3b. The automatic tennis ball machine in operation. (With permission from the Ball-Boy Company, Inc., 26 Milburn St., Bronxville, N.Y.)

Figure 7–4. The Server. This apparatus holds a tennis ball at any height, and at contact, the ball is released for a completely normal flight. The Server minimizes some of the complexities of the serve by eliminating the toss. (With permission from the Ball-Boy Company, Inc., 26 Milburn St., Bronxville, N.Y.)

The Golf-O-Tron is an example of a type of equipment invented to facilitate golf learning. This highly technical instrument simulates a golf course and playing conditions and allows the individual to play a round of golf without stepping on the course. Chui (1965) taught two groups to use the 7 iron and then tested transfer skill to the 4 iron. One group was instructed in the conventional method while the other learned with the

Figure 7–5. The Ball-Boy Re-Bound-Net. The net, which can be adjusted for the desired rebound, provides a "set-up ball" that allows the player to continually strike the ball. (With permission from the Ball-Boy Company, Inc., 26 Milburn St., Bronxville, N.Y.)

assistance of the Golf-O-Tron. Positive transfer effects were noted for both groups, with no significant differences between them.

Flotation devices are used in swimming to overcome fear of the water as well as to facilitate the learning of swimming skills. Although there has been very little experimental work scientifically to analyze their effectiveness as teaching devices, Kaye (1965) reported that a group of college beginning swimmers using a waist-type flotation device was able to swim further at the end of his experiment than a group taught without it.

Other devices have been constructed for skill achievement hopefully beyond standard practice methods. In basketball, larger basketballs and smaller rims, to be used in practice, have been developed with the intent of improving accuracy in game situations. One of the few studies on this topic has been completed recently by Takacs (1965), Takacs provided junior high school students with a total of twenty practice periods, with twenty free throw attempts at the basket each period. One group (Group A) shot at a small basket, the other (Group B) shot at a regulation basket. At the end of practice, when tested on the regulation basket, Group A was found to perform significantly better than Group B.

These examples indicate the type of training aids currently being introduced and evaluated in physical education. Since audio-visual materials have already been discussed in this chapter, they have been omitted here. The value of viewing ideal performance or one's self performing should not be minimized, however. A final point to be considered with the use of trainers and simulators and certainly not the least, is their value as motivators. Novel and different methods of instructing serve to elevate motivation. The anticipation, excitement, and challenge of learning under novel conditions can very well be reflected by increased performance scores.

Transfer of Training

Thus far in this chapter, the reader may have realized that there have been many references to the transference of teaching methods and materials to skilled performance. This particular section contains direct reference to the concept of transfer, in theory and practice.

Almost all of learning is based on the concept of transfer. *Transfer* implies the influence of a learned task on one to be learned or the utilization of formed responses in a new situation related to the one in which they were learned. School curricula and educational theory reflect the realization of and need for formal education which will carry over into life's experiences and chosen occupations. Is it not true that the purpose of a general education is to prepare an individual to live more effectively within himself and within society? If we believe in this meaning of education, then we must accept the fact that responses and general behavior patterns may be transferable from one situation to another. In many cases, these occurrences are desirable.

Transfer training may be practiced not only for present use but also for future application. Hopefully, what is learned in one context will be able to be carried over to another context. In a sense, then, transfer training is learning for later situations. Exactly how transfer takes place and what is transferred has been the subject of many investigations and the inspiration for theoretical speculation. Conflicting experimental results and different interpretations of the research confuse the issue but certain principles of transfer are fairly well accepted today.

Measurement of Transfer. Typically, experimental procedures employed in studies of transfer assume two forms. In the first case, an experimental group learns Task A, the control group rests, and both groups are tested on Task B.

	Task A	Task B
Experimental Group	Learns	Learns
Control Group	Rests	Learns

The difference in performance between the groups on Task B, if any, would be due to the effect of learning Task A.

One of the weaknesses in the design in this Table is the possibility that the groups were not evenly equated at the start of the experiment. This problem may be overcome by pretesting the groups on the eventual task to be learned. If too much testing practice is given at this time, there is the danger that the potential influence of one task or a second task will be concealed.

	Task B	Task A	Task B
Experimental Group	Tested	Learns	Learns
Control Group	Tested	Rests	Learns

Transfer from one task to another task or from one situation to another situation will be dependent on the relationship between their stimuli and responses demanded of the individuals. Such psychological terms as stimulus generalization and response generalization are appropriate to this discussion. *Stimulus generalization* explains the condition such that when a particular response is learned to a stimulus, similar stimuli will evoke the same response. In *response generalization,* once a response has been learned to a given stimulus, the stimulus will cause similar responses to be elicited. These terms will be discussed intermittently within the context of the material in this section.

Osgood (1949) has attempted to show stimulus-response relationships and to predict task-to-task transfer effects. Figures 7–6 depicts the Osgood Transfer Surface, a theoretical transfer model. It illustrates that after a specific response is learned to a given stimulus, $S_1 - R_1$, maximum interference, hence negative transfer, occurs when a completely new response has to be learned to that stimulus, $S_1 - R_2$. As the stimulus gradually changes until it is completely different from the first one and the response likewise, $S_2 - R_2$, there is zero transfer. A new stimulus which requires an already learned response, $S_2 - R_1$, results in zero transfer.

Although the Transfer Surface does a good job in explaining and predicting transfer relationships, it does not take into account some potential influencing variables. One of these is the amount of training on the first task, $S_1 - R_1$. More practice yields better transfer effects, for it is observed that little training results in broad generalization transfer and more training in sharper generalization transfer.

The Surface recognizes the possibility of transfer of training effects as being zero, negative, or positive. *Positive transfer* occurs when prior learning promotes present learning, and *negative transfer* infers the inhibition effect of prior learning on immediate learning. *Zero or no transfer* takes place when former learning has no effect on the learning of an immediate task. It would not be difficult for any of us to remember instances where all three conditions

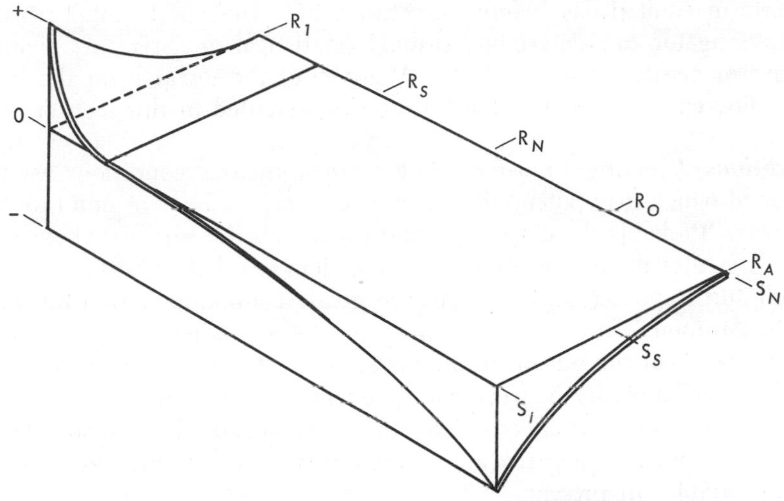

Figure 7–6a. The Osgood Transfer Surface. The medial planes represent effects of zero magnitude, response generalization is represented along the length, and stimulus generalization along its width. R_I original or extremely similar response, S_I original or extremely similar stimulus, R_S to R_A increasingly different responses, S_S to S_N increasingly different stimuli. The Surface may be used to find another task in relation to the original one to predict the extent of transfer as well as the presence of negative or positive transfer. (From Osgood, Charles E. The Similarity Paradox in Human Learning: A Resolution, *Psychol. Rev.*, 56:132–143, 1949.)

have occurred. There is an interesting relationship between amount of transfer, type of transfer, and amount of pretraining. It has already been stated that specific transfer is enhanced by more prior-task training; but, in addition, it is probable that negative transfer will occur with little practice whereas extensive practice will encourage more positive transfer.

Whenever one performs in and reacts to a new situation, to a certain extent his responses will reflect previous experiences. Sometimes it is desirable

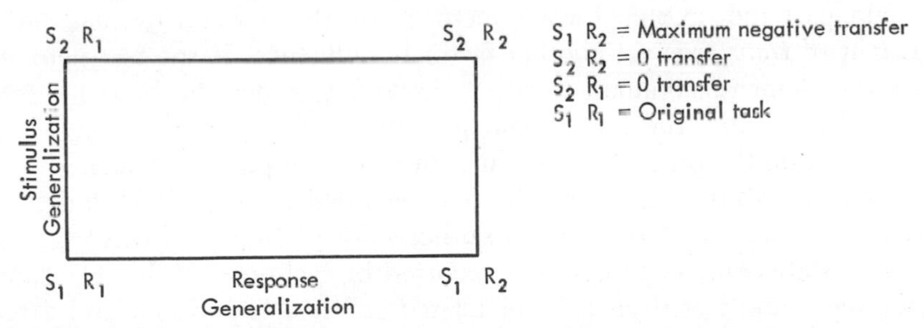

Figure 7–6b. Osgood Surface modified. As the second response R_2 to the same stimulus S_1 becomes more unrelated to R_1, maximum interference occurs. As the stimulus is gradually changed at the same time the response is until the condition S_2–R_2 occurs, less interference is present. When the response remains the same but the stimulus gradually changes until S_2–R_1 is reached, positive transfer effects decrease until no transfer is present.

to perform similarly as before, sometimes not. In experimental situations, the investigator can determine, through statistical analysis, any significant positive or negative transfer effects. A survey of the research on the transfer of training effects on motor skill learning is presented in this section.

Conditions Affecting Transfer. There are numerous conditions associated with, and which may potentially affect, the transfer effects of one task to another task. Probably the most important of these is the *similarity* between the tasks. A greater resemblance between task elements, between their respective stimuli and responses, will result in the greatest amount of transfer. For instance, Ammons, Ammons, and Morgan (1958) trained their subjects on varying speeds of the pursuit rotor. Transfer effects were found to be proportional to the similarity between the speed rates of any two tasks. As in our discussion on this matter, especially the reference to the Osgood Transfer Surface, the probable negative and positive transfer effects are indicated when certain variables are present.

The *amount of practice* on the prior task has already been shown to be related to the amount and nature of transfer expected. *Motivation* to transfer skill or knowledge from one situation to another situation is yet another consideration.

It is also possible that the *method of training* may have some bearing on the transfer effectiveness. In recent years, a few investigators have looked into the matter of whole-versus-part learning methods and their relative efficiency in facilitating transfer. In one experiment, Briggs and Waters (1958), using simulated aircraft control dynamics, found that it was important to practice the whole task if the highest transfer potential is to be realized. Part practice does not integrate component skills. For transfer purposes, the authors recommend that the whole task be simplified rather than fractionalized. Briggs and Naylor (1962) tested their subjects for transfer on a three-dimensional tracking task learned under different practice methods. The whole and progressive part methods were equal and significantly better than the pure-part and simplified whole methods for transfer effectiveness.

Intent of transfer is yet another factor of influence. If the instructor indicates the elements common to two tasks and provides the basis for insight and understanding, the learner will probably make greater use of what he has learned on the prior task when it comes time to perform a related second task. In other words, greater asssistance is provided when skills are taught with the intention of transferring over to other skills. Although this is a generally accepted statement, an exception is reported by Nelson (1957b). His subjects were taught and tested on pairs of related skills: a badminton and a tennis volley against the wall; a volleyball and basketball tap for accuracy; and the track and football starting stances. Nelson concluded that deliberate teaching for transfer was ineffective, as many of the findings were not significant. However, he did note that initial tennis skill learning had some favorable effect on badminton skill as did basketball skill on volleyball skill.

One of the reasons for the lack of positive results in Nelson's study was possibly the simultaneous learning of the skills. He concludes his study by stating that skills and activities involving similar elements and patterns should not be learned at the same time. There is a great concern of physical educators over the effect of one activity on another activity, whether these activities are apparently related or not. Swimming is an activity which has usually been frowned upon during a particular varsity season. Supposedly, its nature is such as to have deleterious effects on other athletic endeavors. In another investigation by Nelson (1957a), one group of subjects learned certain gross motor skills and swam on alternate days while a second group did not swim. No difference was found between the groups in performance on the skills.

Referring back to skills with a certain degree of relationship, it is of interest to speculate if positive or negative effects will occur between such activities as tennis and badminton, baseball and golf, and basketball and volleyball. Let us use tennis and badminton as an example. They are both racket sports involving the striking of a projectile. Eye-hand coordination is extremely important in both sports, as is agility and quickness of movement. It might be hypothesized that outstanding ability in one of these sports should render the individual highly suuccessful in the other sport. However, there are other considerations. Badminton strokes are made with a highly flexible wrist whereas a tennis ball is usually stroked with a firm wrist. A tennis ball has altogether different characteristics than does the badminton shuttlecock. It might, therefore, be argued that high skill in one activity would hinder the learning of the other activity.

Although task similarities encourage related movement patterns, this response generalization is not always desirable. Response generalization promotes initial skill acquisition but it is response distinction that is important at the highly-skilled levels of performance. The precision and accuracy of a given task distinguishes it from that which is required in other tasks. So, in a sense, response generalization is the opposite of skill. Response generalization infers generalized movements common between two tasks whereas skill requires precision movements.

Attempted development of theoretical relationships between sports leaves much to be desired because of the complexity of these activities. When dealing with simple tasks, elements may be identified with much greater ease. Exactly how much transfer occurs from athletic skill to athletic skill is thus difficult to ascertain, especially if the entire context of their usage is considered.

Even the application of mechanical or learning principles to the learning task does not afford expected transfer, as was explained earlier in this chapter. Because of the conflicting experimental results, it is felt that principles may, but need not, transfer. When they are taught specific to certain material, the probability is that transfer will be ineffective. If the situation in which principles are learned is similar to that in which it is to be applied, transfer effects most likely will be more beneficial.

Learning to Learn. Another aspect of the learning function, oftentimes neglected, is the transfer which occurs from merely learning materials similar in nature. When materials or tasks undertaken are alike, improvement results just from learning how to learn them. One has to learn how to take multiple-choice written tests, how to lift weights, or how to solve psychomotor tasks.

Learning how to learn involves learning the technique of attacking a problem of a particular kind. The individual acquires the appropriate *set,* he reduces general stimuli to specific cues. After repeated experience with the same type of tasks, after attentive adjustment is established, greater learning always occurs.

The psychologist most associated with calling this phenomenon to the attention of all those concerned with learning is Harry Harlow. Harlow (1949), working with monkeys, gave them different discrimination problems to solve. At first, the monkeys took a long time to learn the problems, but as they tackled more problems, there was a decrease in solution time. Therefore, learning how to learn something is necessarily a partial explanation of how one task transfers over to another similar task.

Transfer of Responses. There has been considerable evidence that indicates the transference of electrical activity and skilled movements from one part of the body to another. Physiologically, it has been demonstrated that mental activity causes electrical stimulation of the areas of the body being thought about. Mental practice, without any overt practice, can improve motor skill.

The contributions of Cook (1933a, 1933b) to that area of study he calls *cross-education* provided early evidence as to the transfer of a skill learned in one part of the body to another. Transfer was found to be greatest to the muscle group opposite and symmetrical while it was least to the muscle group opposite and unsymmetrical to the practiced limb. Even strength can be transferred from a trained to an untrained limb. Logan and Lockhart (1962) report contralateral transfer of strength from the knee extensors of the trained leg to the knee extensors of the untrained limb.

Thus in any act, there is a tendency for response generalization. Activity that is overt and apparently body specific has an overall effect on the individual. Internal activity is constantly going on during our periods of wakefulness and it appears as if the interwoven complexity of the nervous system permits motor patterns to be learned from practiced to unpracticed limbs.

Task Difficulty. If the ultimate objective is skill in a particular activity, the physical educator may proceed in teaching his class in one of three ways. He may guide his students from easy to more complex steps, thus providing the learners with initial success and satisfaction in the activity. He may teach the given skill(s) directly. Or, he may proceed in having the learners overcome the extreme difficulties of the task(s) before undertaking the precise task(s), thus operating under a complex-to-easy task procedure.

Theoretically, it makes good sense to build up to a particular objective, to master simple skills before learning more difficult ones and to gain the satisfaction which is supplied with successful attempts. Obviously, a person should be able to show the greatest achievement when attempting simple tasks. Contrarily, theoretical support could be mustered for the teaching of skills from the complex to the simple. When one confronts the more difficult task first, if it is not unreasonably complex, a progression to the easier tasks should bother the learner very little since the harder task contained all the elements of the simple ones. It appears as if there might be a conflict as to the desirability of introducing simple skills as opposed to complex ones when teaching for transfer. There is yet another alternative to the problem. If achievement on a particular skill is wanted, and perhaps it is of mediocre difficulty, should it be taught directly? Because of the specificity nature of skill learning, transfer from skill to skill, no matter how related they are, may not occur in the most efficient manner.

Skinner, as we have noted is one of the leading promoters of the teaching machine, and he has introduced the theory of shaping behavior. It is actually based on the concept of transfer of training from the simple to the more difficult. A sequence of events leads to the desired outcome, with the progressive transfer system increasing the probability of a correct response. The theory will be discussed at greater depth in Chapter 8.

As to the actual research related to the problem of transfer and task difficulty, inconsistent results have been obtained among the investigations. Barch and Lewis (1954) trained 230 airmen on the Iowa Pursuit Apparatus. Four tasks were involved: the standard, first-learned task, two intermediate tasks, and one difficult task. The experimenters found a greater positive transfer from a simple to a difficult task than from a difficult task to a more difficult task or from tasks of equal difficulty.

Lordahl and Archer (1958), in two pursuit rotor experiments, varied task difficulty by manipulating target rotation speed or the radius of the target orbit. Direct practice was better than transfer practice. There was slightly more positive transfer when training from the simple to the complex than vice versa in one of the experiments, whereas there were no differential transfer effects from an easy or more complex task in the other experiment.

Baker, Wylie, and Gagné (1950) had subjects follow a signal on a target by turning a crank handle. Response rates were changed for each of four tasks. Training on a faster rate of speed produced more transfer to perform at the slower rate than vice versa. The investigators therefore concluded that a greater amount of transfer occurs when Task I is relatively difficult and Task II relatively easy. Gibbs (1951), utilizing a handle-winding task and a steering task, declared that the greatest transfer from a difficult to an easy task occurred when the same kind of ability was required in both tasks. However, he warns that an increase in task difficulty will not necessarily cause the most rapid rate of learning, as there is an optimum range of task difficulty.

As Day (1956) points out in summarizing the studies concerned with the effect of the difficulty of initial and final tasks on transfer training, there are inconsistencies from study to study in defining difficulty and discrepancies among experimental results. Difficulty of a task can be affected by manipulating stimulus or response variables. With regard to the response situation, Day concludes that there is a greater degree of transfer from a difficult to an easier condition than the reverse.

Singer (1966) designed an investigation using archery skill to study this problem with physical education activities. Three classes of students were practiced under different conditions: Class A learned and practiced archery at the ten-yard line; Class C began at the forty-yard line; and Class B started at the twenty-five yard line. The three groups were then tested on the twenty-five yard line. When testing for transfer, no significant difference was observed in the transfer effects from practice on an easier task (Class A) as compared to the transfer effects of a more difficult task (Class C) in comparison to precise distance practice (Class B). The data are presented in Table 7–2. Ultimate success, as measured by the Columbia Junior Round, indicated no significant difference between the groups—task proficiency was not affected by the initial learning technique.

The matter of what level of skill to begin with is hard to resolve. Immediate reward and satisfaction are certainly important, but so is the time element. It appears as if many present-day writers are in favor of learning a more difficult skill directly rather than through lead-up activities. Many also favor progression from the more difficult to the simple rather than the opposite way. Perhaps the teaching method should reflect the teacher-student objectives. If what is desired is the development of a perfected act (in a stable stimulus environment), then possibly complex skills should be practiced first. If the technique is not as important as being aware of relevant cues and understanding the situation (in a changing environment), possibly, as Knapp (1964) suggests, the learning should progress from the simpler situation.

Theories of Transfer. The transfer effect of learning certain skills or matter precludes the learning of anything new. Actually, nothing a person learns is truly completely new to him. Everything he undertakes he has seen and done before, only in different forms and shapes. What we learn and the speed of acquisition is dependent on positive and negative transfer situations and their interaction effects.

Examine, for instance, the situation in which a person learns the sport of tennis for the first time. He does not really start with a so-called carte blanche, or white card. His past experiences, such as in batting, catching, or throwing a ball will transfer over to this activity. Previous experiences in racket games, examples of which are ping-pong, squash, and badminton, will influence tennis skill acquisition. Experiences in games requiring quick and sudden movements, depth perception, alert reactions, strategy, and the like, will also have an effect.

How can we explain and predict through theory the nature of transfer?

Table 7–2. *Data representing Archery Skill acquired under different transfer situations*

Classes		Yard Lines					Columbia Junior Round			
		10	20	25	30	40	20	30	40	Total
A	$\overline{X}$	177.65	121.50	99.45	79.60	58.30	143.95	102.40	69.95	315.30
	SD	14.34	30.48	26.48	27.10	23.17	26.87	26.29	21.95	69.62
	period	6	7	8	9	10	14	14–15	15	
B	$\overline{X}$	183.10	132.20	107.00	83.75	62.00	139.05	89.05	66.55	292.44
	SD	15.45	19.03	29.92	22.47	20.60	16.93	22.10	24.39	45.17
	period	12	10	8	9	11	14	14–15	15	
C	$\overline{X}$	189.55	123.85	106.55	73.35	50.65	143.50	96.80	74.80	315.60
	SD	12.15	16.59	20.49	27.40	20.89	17.83	27.47	25.03	61.40
	period	10	9	8	7	6	14	14–15	15	

From Singer, R. N., Transfer Effects and Ultimate Success in Archery due to Degree of Difficulty of Initial Learning, *Res. Quart.*, 37:532–539, 1966.

Class A learned at the 10-yd. line.
Class B learned at the 25-yd. line.
Class C learned at the 40-yd. line.

How is the above-accepted concept of transfer, as well as the abundant research evidence to date (only partially reviewed in this chapter) to be incorporated into a theory?

Perhaps the first theory of transfer, which was in existence for many years prior to the twentieth century, is the *Formal Discipline Theory*. It no longer has any support from educators who have even casually reviewed the research evidence. At one time the transferability of mental functions was considered to be wide in scope. The faculties of the mind were supposedly developed through specific courses, and these courses were not taught for their content but for their general mind-strengthening ability. It was felt that such mental functions as logic, concentration, reason, and memory could be developed in this manner.

Through the efforts of the great pioneer psychologist Thorndike in the earlier part of this century, the Formal Discipline theory was discredited. One cannot train the mind in a general sense from particular courses or training. Course-work abilities do not necessarily transfer over to practical situations. Instead, Thorndike proposed the *Identical-Elements Theory*, based on his belief in learning by association (S-R theory). To Thorndike, transfer between two tasks or situations was only as effective as the number of elements common to them. The definition of an element is a question continually raised. When the term element is narrowly interpreted, it leads to more rejection of the theory; and contrarily, more generalized interpretation results in greater acceptance.

Compare the theory to one termed *Generalization Theory*. In contrast to consideration for specific stimuli or specific information, Generalization Theory encompasses the transferability of principles and problem-solving situations. As we now know, evidence conflicts as to the validating of this theory. However, classroom teachings are often based on the premise that an individual can transfer matter learned in these ways to other situations. This theory is probably most consistent with educational philosophy. It, like the Identical-Elements theory, has its proponents and doubters.

Among the other theories proposed is the *Transposition Theory* by the Gestaltists, but this and others need not be presented here. Suffice to say that the numerous theories in existence to describe learning phenomena indicate at least some experimental support. Research findings may often be interpreted in various ways, thus resulting in the possible formulation of a number of theories from the same data.

Social Influence and Motor Performance

A question often raised is whether performance is improved, worsened, or remains the same when it occurs in a social context. The situation may involve competition, working together in a form of cooperation, or performance in front of people. These are examples of social situations in which the individual is not performing solely for his own satisfaction, but rather with the involvement of others. Actually, activity which involves social interaction is quite typical of our endeavors.

Competition. Competition can assume many forms: competing against established norms, against one's own record, or against one or more individuals. It is the latter area that we are concerned with here. Numerous investigations and empirical observations lend support for the contribution competition makes to performance. Typically, performance levels improve when the situation is a competitive one, especially if the task is not so complex as to cause the individual to falter under the stress. Well-learned skills should either be performed with usual or higher-than-usual proficiency.

However, there is some concern as to the over-all beneficial effects of subjugating children and young men and women to constant competitive situations. Although many circumstances in life foster competitiveness, by the same token, many require cooperation. When working with or against people, performances are obviously subject to change. Many educators favor motor skills taught primarily in a cooperative situation rather than in a situation fostering extreme competitiveness.

Cooperation. Invariably, experiments have indicated the superiority of competitive and cooperative ventures over a no-incentive situation. Since so many conditions contain both competitive and cooperative elements, it is not easy to decide which one is more effective in facilitating learning. In team sports and partner games, the performer has to learn how to play cooperatively as well as to express a desire for defeating the opponents. It would appear that pure competitive measures are more effective than cooperative ventures in motivating performance.

This is especially true with younger children. Competition is more of a basic or primitive instinct; cooperation involves greater degrees of maturation and intellectual involvement. Striving to "beat" someone is almost a natural urge. Joint ventures presuppose a sublimation of some personal drives and desires and, with children, require that certain understandings be transmitted to them. When comparing group versus individual performance, there is evidence that cooperative efforts may be more efficient. Weyner and Zeaman (1956) analyzed data obtained from groups of two and four subjects run as teams and individual efforts on pursuit rotor performance. It was found that by numerically increasing the team members, better performances were attained.

Another investigation further supports the idea of group interaction being a more powerful positive influence on performance than an individual effort. Abel (1938) found that a group of boys and one of girls did better on a paper and pencil maze when working in pairs than alone. An implication for the teaching of physical education skills is that working in small groups provides a pooling of learnings which, in turn, more readily benefits performance. Also, merely performing tasks in the presence of others serves as a social motivator. An example of the small-group approach lies in the teaching of swimming skills where students could be paired off to mutually assist each other.

There are other advantages in working in groups. The subjects in Johnston's (1966) experiment had to execute coordination skills demanded in a simulated radar-controlled aerial intercept task. No difference was found if the skills were individual or team taught, but the investigator suggests that the tasks in his study required much more teamwork than those used in other studies. Most physical education activities do not require such deeply involved participant interaction. In apparent agreement with the sentiments expressed throughout this book on the importance of practice conditions closely resembling game conditions is the conclusion to Johnston's report: ". . . when transfer is characterized by team activity, it would appear desirable to train potential team members in a team context rather than individually in order that the necessary team skills may be developed."

The lack of transfer and predictability from skills performed alone to those performed in a group is further demonstrated in a series of studies published by Comrey (1953, 1954). Subjects were tested individually and in pairs on hand-manipulating tasks associated with the Purdue Pegboard Assembly Task. Less than half of the group performance variance could be predicted from individual performance on a similar kind of task. Evidently, individual skill alone is not enough to predict success in a group task, for there are variables to be considered. A warning from the results of these studies is that people should not be paired up on the basis of individual abilities since group performance is not dependent on individual scores.

Presence of Spectators. It has been nearly everyone's experience to know individuals who can demonstrate a high degree of skill proficiency when performing alone or in the comfortable confines of a practice situation but who disintegrate during actual competition and in front of an audience. By the same token, there are those people whose performance improves under this circumstance. Because of the complexity of the human organism and the degree to which a skill may have been learned, the presence or absence of spectators will oftentimes have unpredictable effects on different people.

Contradictory results on the effect of social presence on skill acquisition are presented within the same study reported by Noble and his co-workers (1958). Two motor tasks were learned under social and isolated conditions. Learning individually resulted in a significant decrease in performance on a discrimination reaction time task whereas no difference in performance was found with a pursuit rotor task. Figure 7–7 presents the learning curves derived from the data acquired on the discrimination reaction time task.

Generally speaking, excluding such factors as skill complexity, degree of skill attainment, and the person's anxiety level, the presence of others is usually found to have a stimulating effect on performance. When simpler

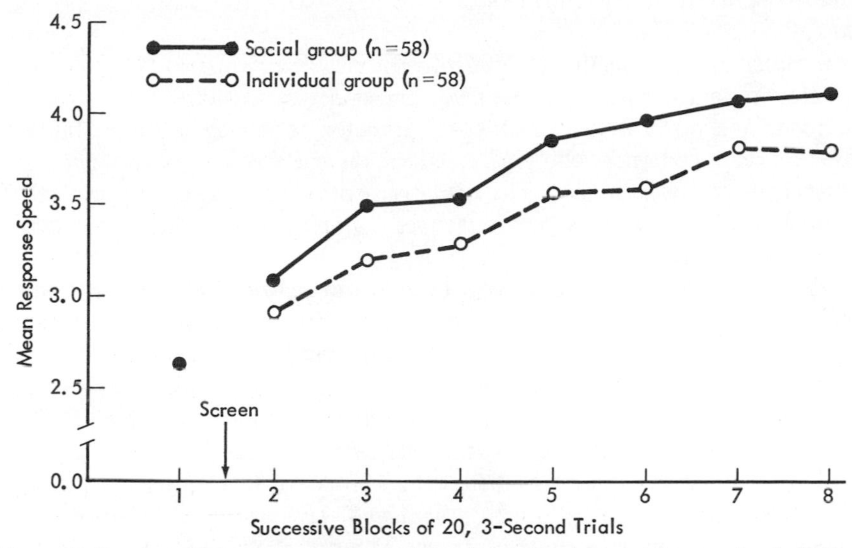

Figure 7–7. Acquisition curves of speed in discrimination reaction under individual (partitioned) versus social (nonpartitioned) conditions of practice. (From Noble, C. E.; Fughs, J. E.; Robel, D. P.; and Chambers, R. W. Individual vs. Social Performance on Two Perceptual-Motor Tasks, *Percept. Mot. Skills*, 8:131–134, 1958.)

processes and abilities are taxed, social influence will be relatively slight. If the skill, especially if it is difficult, is in the stage of being learned, there are some indications that the presence of others might prove to be detrimental. A skill well learned and demonstrated for viewers should be executed in a consistent and stable manner. Highly developed skills are less prone to distractions.

The performer's anxiety level interacts with audience presence or absence, producing a number of possible outcomes. Some aspects of this problem have been discussed already, e.g., under the headings of "Tension," "Anxiety," and "Stress" (Chapter 3); "Level of Aspiration" (Chapter 4); and "Motivation" (Chapter 6). Further evidence is reported in a recent investigation by Cox (1966). The effect of only the experimenter, mothers, teachers, peers, and strangers on primary grade children of varying anxiety levels performing a marble-dropping task was studied. Low-anxious boys showed better performances in general and high-anxious boys poorer performances in the presence of people. Interestingly enough, when only the experimenter was present, low-anxious boys showed response decrements while the high-anxious group improved.

One of the outstanding attributes of the superior athlete is his ability to perform his specialty skills in a consistent, highly-skilled manner apparently disregarding the tension-filled atmosphere associated with stadiums or gymnasiums full of spectators. Is this performance trait transferable to other situations? Are these individuals, after learning entirely new skills in privacy, able to perform in the same efficient manner, with the same success, before an audience?

In order to provide some insight into the problem, Singer (1965) attempted to determine the effect of spectator presence on athletes and nonathletes performing a novel motor task. A stabilometer, requiring balance ability, was the task practiced on by the subjects alone on one day and in front of a group of spectators the next day. The athletes represented various sports at Ohio State University and were acknowledged as being among the better athletes at that university.

The nonathletes were observed to perform significantly higher than the athletes in front of the audience. Apparently, there was no positive transfer effect for the athletes who were used to displaying their motor abilities before spectators. Possibly, athletes are more sensitive to people watching them perform and feel uncomfortable demonstrating before a group a skill at which they are not extremely competent. Even when practicing alone, the athletes did not show superior balancing ability. In fact, although not significant, the nonathletes generally displayed superior performance to the athletes throughout the practice trials. The specificity with which we learn appears to be verified by the inability of the athletes to transfer the balance needed and developed for their particular sports to the task used in this study. Figure 7–8 contains the performance curves of the two groups, alone and before spectators. Thirty-second time trials were administered to the subjects and a decline in the curves indicates better performance.

The social influence on motor performance is certainly an area needing extensive research. Because of the many confounding variables acting on any situation involving the learning and performing of skills in a social context, many researchers have avoided attacking the various aspects of the problem. Since we usually do not learn or perform our skills in an isolated situation,

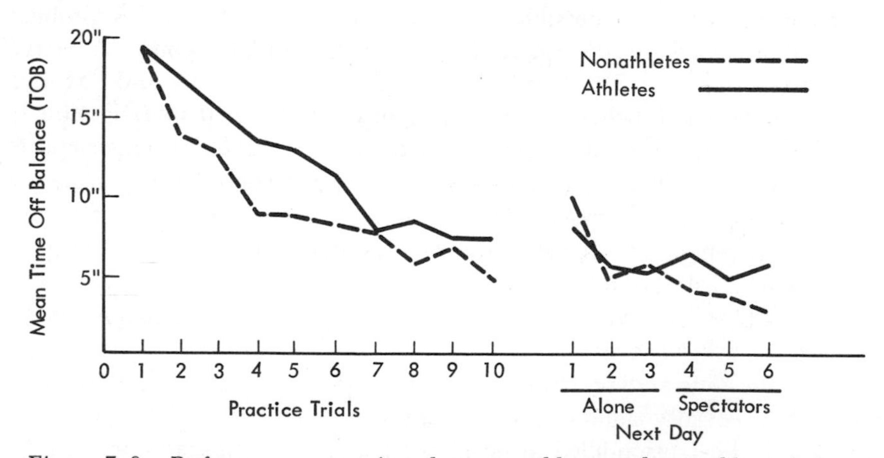

Figure 7–8. Performance comparison between athletes and nonathletes before and during presence of spectators. (From Singer, Robert N. Effect of Spectators on Athletes and Nonathletes Performing a Gross Motor Task, *Res. Quart.*, 36:473–482, 1965).

any learning principles must be modified to consider the individual with his unique emotional qualities and dominant personality features as well as the environment surrounding the activity.

Summary

Instructional techniques range along a spectrum of assorted possible approaches to the teaching of motor skills. The teacher, by merely introducing and/or emphasizing certain factors singularly or in combination, may facilitate the learning process.

Whether to teach skills as wholes or fractioned into parts is not a simply-answered problem. Consideration must be given to the nature of the task, its organization and complexity, and the nature of the learner. Motor skills can be learned without the benefit of actual physical practice. Mental rehearsal of the skill to-be-learned, although not as effective as physical practice, is usually found to be more beneficial than no practice at all. Rather than practice activities artificially, such as slowing down the responses demanded, practice should approximate desired movement patterns as nearly as possible. Psychologists have usually found the beginning and terminal materials of a learned series to be best retained, but the lack of research on gross motor skills discourages the belief that skills learned in a series will be retained in similar manner.

Although drill is satisfactorily used as a means for strengthening certain acts, a problem-solving approach may have much potential for the learning situation, especially in reaching objectives unattainable under the drill method. Teaching machines and programmed learning texts have been successfully employed in industry and education. Their potential has yet to be realized in physical education.

There are many ways in which teacher cues and teaching aids may promote learning. Oral directions and written material assist the learner in reaching his goals. Although it makes logical sense that an understanding of mechanical principles as applied to motor acts should benefit these acts, experimental results are inconsistent in their findings. Perhaps this is because researchers have used various definitions of what a principle is, modes of presentation of these principles have differed, and diverse tasks have been employed.

Visual cues, whether of the usual type or man-constructed, have usually been of great service to individuals learning motor skills. There are certain skills which might be more effectively acquired without the distraction of visual stimuli, but with emphasis on the kinesthetic sense or sense of feel instead. The probability exists that different cues are more important at various learning stages, for visual and spatial orientation abilities have been found to be important early in practice, but proprioceptive abilities are more important when higher skill levels are attained. The influence of such auditory aids as musical sounds and tempi on motor performance has yet to be scientifically verified. Many training devices have been developed to supplement teacher instruction, and although sparse the research on the various pieces of equipment indicates the value of some over and beyond usual teaching procedures.

Practically all of learning is based on some form of transfer. Everything we do is influenced by previous experiences, and in a given situation, positive, negative, or zero transfer may occur from prior to present learnings. Stimulus similarity, response similarity, learning how to learn, task difficulty, and other factors reflect transference potentiality of one task to another task. Social situations, e.g., audiences, competition, and cooperation, will usually positively affect performances of individuals. Exceptions may be found, especially when examining anxiety levels, task complexity, skill level achieved, and other aspects of the performer and the task.

References

ABEL, THEODORA M. The Influence of Social Facilitation on Motor Performance at Different Levels of Intelligence, *Amer. J. Psychol.*, 51:379–388, 1938.

AMMONS, R. B.; AMMONS, C. H.; and MORGAN, R. L. Transfer of Skill and Decremented Factors Along the Speed Dimension in Rotary Pursuit, *Percept. Mot. Skills*, 11:43, 1958.

ANDERSON, THERESA. A Study of the Use of Visual Aids in Basket Shooting, *Res. Quart.*, 13:532–537, 1942.

BAKER, KATHERINE E., and WYLIE, RUTH C. Transfer of Verbal Training to a Motor Task, *J. Exp. Psychol.*, 40:632–638, 1950.

BAKER, KATHERINE E.; WYLIE, R. C.; and GAGNÉ, R. M. Transfer of Training to a Motor Skill as a Function of Variation in Rate of Response, *J. Exp. Psychol.*, 40:721–732, 1950.

BARCH, A. M., and LEWIS, D. The Effect of Task Difficulty and Amount of Practice on Proactive Transfer, *J. Exp. Psychol.*, 48:134–142, 1954.

BARTON, J. W. Smaller Versus Larger Units in Learning the Maze, *J. Exp. Psychol.*, 4:418–429, 1921.

BATTIG, WILLIAM F. The Effect of Kinesthetic, Verbal, and Visual Cues on the Acquisition of a Lever-Positioning Skill, *J. Exp. Psychol.*, 47:371–380, 1954.

BATTIG, WILLIAM F. Transfer from Verbal Pretraining to Motor Performance as a Function of Motor Task Complexity, *J. Exp. Psychol.*, 51:371–378, 1956.

BOND, MARJORIE H. Rhythmic Perception and Gross Motor Performance, *Res. Quart.*, 30:259–265, 1959.

BRIGGS, GEORGE E., and BROGDEN, W. J. The Effect of Component Practice on Performance of a Lever-Positioning Skill, *J. Exp. Psychol.*, 48:375–380, 1954.

BRIGGS, GEORGE E., and NAYLOR, JAMES C. The Relative Efficiency of Several Training Methods as a Function of Transfer of Task Complexity, *J. Exp. Psychol.*, 64:505–512, 1962.

BRIGGS, GEORGE E., and WATERS, LAWRENCE K. Training and Transfer as a Function of Component Interaction, *J. Exp. Psychol.*, 56:492–500, 1958.

Brown, Roberta. A Comparison of the "Whole," "Part," and "Combination" Methods of Learning Piano Music, *J. Exp. Psychol.*, 11:235–247, 1928.

Brown, H. Steven, and Messersmith, Lloyd. An Experiment in Teaching Tumbling With and Without Motion Pictures, *Res. Quart.*, 19:304–307, 1948.

Carr, Harvey. The Influence of Visual Guidance in Maze Learning. *J. Exp. Psychol.*, 4:399–417, 1921.

Chui, Edward F. A Study of Golf-O-Tron Utilization as a Teaching Aid in Relation to Improvement and Transfer, *Res. Quart.*, 36:147–152, 1965.

Clark, L. Verdelle. Effect of Mental Practice on the Development of a Certain Motor Skill, *Res. Quart.*, 31:560–569, 1960.

Colville, Francis H. The Learning of Motor Skills as Influenced by Knowledge of Mechanical Principles, *J. Educ. Psychol.*, 48:321–327, 1957.

Comrey, Andrew L. Group Performance in a Manual Dexterity Task. *J. Appl. Psychol.*, 37:207–210, 1953.

Comrey, Andrew L., and Deskin, Gerald. Group Manual Dexterity in Women, *J. Appl. Psychol.*, 38:178–180, 1954.

Cook, Thomas W. Studies in Cross-Education. Mirror Tracing the Star-Shaped Maze, *J. Exp. Psychol.*, 16:144–160, 1933a.

Cook, Thomas W. Studies in Cross-Education. Further Experiments in Mirror Tracing the Star-Shaped Maze. *J. Exp. Psychol.*, 16:679–700, 1933b.

Corbin, Charles B. Effects of Mental Practice on the Development of a Unique Motor Skill, *Coll. Phys. Educ. Assoc. Proc.*, 69:100–102, 1966.

Cox, F. N. Some Effects of Test Anxiety and Presence or Absence of Other Persons on Boys' Performance on a Repetitive Motor Task, *J. Exp. Child Psychol.*, 3:100–112, 1966.

Cross, Thomas J. A Comparison of the Whole Method, the Minor Game Method, and the Whole-Part Method of Teaching Basketball to Ninth Grade Boys, *Res. Quart.*, 8:49–54, 1937.

Day, R. H. Relative Task Difficulty and Transfer of Training in Skilled Performance, *Psychol. Bull.*, 53:160–168, 1956.

Deese, J., and Kaufman, R. A. Serial Effects in Recall of Unorganized and Sequentially Organized Verbal Material, *J. Exp. Psychol.*, 54:180–187, 1957.

Dillon, Evelyn K. A Study of the Use of Music as an Aid in Teaching Swimming, *Res. Quart.*, 23:1–8, 1952.

Egstrom, Glen H.; Logan, Gene A.; and Wallis, Earl L. Acquisition of Throwing Skill Involving Projectiles of Varying Weights, *Res. Quart.*, 31:420–425, 1960.

Fulton, Ruth E. Speed and Accuracy in Learning Movements, *Archives of Psychol.*, No. 300, 1945.

Gagné, Robert M., and Foster, Harriet. Transfer to a Motor Skill from Practice on a Pictured Representation, *J. Exp. Psychol.*, 39:342–354, 1949.

Gibbs, C. B. Transfer of Training and Skill Assumptions in Tracking Tasks, *Quart. J. Exp. Psychol.*, 3:99–110, 1951.

Goellner, William A. Comparison of the Effectiveness of Three Methods of Teaching Beginning Bowling, *Res. Quart.*, 28:386–394, 1956.

Goodenough, Florence L., and Brian, Clara R. Certain Factors Underlying the Acquisition of Motor Skill by Pre-School Children, *J. Exp. Psychol.*, 12:127–155, 1929.

HARLOW, HARRY F. The Formation of Learning Sets, *Psychol. Rev.*, 56:51–65, 1949.

HOLDING, D. H. Guidance in Pursuit Tracking, *J. Exp. Psychol.*, 57:362–366, 1959.

HOWELL, MAXWELL L. Use of Force-Time Graphs for Performance Analysis in Facilitating Motor Learning, *Res. Quart.*, 27:12–22, 1956.

JOHNSON, G. O. Generalization (Transfer of a Principle) in Comparative Studies of Some Learning Characteristics in Mentally Retarded and Normal Children of the Same Mental Age, Syracuse: Syracuse University Research Institute, 1958, as reported in KIRK, SAMUEL A., and WEINER, BLUMA B. (eds.), *Behaviorial Research on Exceptional Children*, N.E.A., The Council for Exceptional Children, 1963.

JOHNSTON, WILLIAM A. Transfer of Team Skills as a Function of Type of Training, *J. Appl. Psychol.*, 50:102–108, 1966.

JONES, JOHN GERALD. Motor Learning without Demonstration of Physical Practice under Two Conditions of Mental Practice, *Res. Quart.*, 36:270–276, 1965.

JUDD, C. H. The Relations of Special Training to General Intelligence, *Educ. Rev.*, 36:28–42, 1908.

KARLIN, LAWRENCE, and MORTIMER, RUDOLF G. Effects of Visual and Verbal Cues on Learning a Motor Skill, *J. Exp. Psychol.*, 64:608–614, 1962.

KAYE, RICHARD A. The Use of a Waist-Type Flotation Device as an Adjunct in Teaching Beginning Swimming Skills, *Res. Quart.*, 36:277–281, 1965.

KIMBLE, G. (ed.); HILGARD, E. R.; and MARQUIS, D. M. *Conditioning and Learning*, New York: Appleton-Century-Crofts, Inc., 1961.

KITTELL, JACK E. An Experimental Study of the Effect of External Direction During Learning of Transfer and Retention of Principles, *J. Educ. Psychol.*, 48:391–405, 1957.

KNAPP, BARBARA. *Skill in Sports: The Attainment of Proficiency*, London: Routledge and Kegan Paul, 1964.

LINDEBURG, FRANKLIN A., and HEWITT, JACK E. Effect of an Oversized Basketball on Shooting Ability and Ball Handling, *Res. Quart.*, 36:164–167, 1965.

LOCKHART, AILEENE. The Value of the Motion Picture as an Instructional Device in Learning a Motor Skill, *Res. Quart.*, 15:181–187, 1944.

LOGAN, GENE A., and LOCKHART, AILEENE. Contralateral Transfer of Specificity of Strength Training, *J. Amer. Phys. Therapy Assoc.*, 42:658–660, 1962.

LORDAHL, D. S. and ARCHER, E. J. Transfer Effects on a Rotary Pursuit Task as a Function of First-Task Difficulty, *J. Exp. Psychol.*, 56:421–426, 1958.

MCGUIGAN, F. J., and MACCASLIN, EUGENE F. Whole and Part Methods of Learning a Perceptual Motor Skill, *Amer. J. Psychol.*, 68:658–661, 1955.

MATHEWS, DONALD K., and MCDANIEL, JOE. Effectiveness of Using Golf-Lite in Learning the Golf Swing, *Res. Quart.*, 33:488–491, 1962.

MENART, WALTER A. An Analysis of the Value of Dry-Skiing in Learning Selected Skiing Skills, *Res. Quart.*, 21:47–52, 1950.

MILLER, ROBERT B. *Handbook on Training and Training Equipment Design*, AF WADC TR 53–136, U.S. Air Force, Dayton, Ohio, 1953.

MOHR, DOROTHY R., and BARRETT, MILDRED E. Effect of Knowledge of Mechanical Principles in Learning to Perform Intermediate Swim Skills, *Res. Quart.*, 33:574–580, 1962.

MOSSTON, MUSKA. *Teaching Physical Education*, Columbus, Ohio: Charles E. Merrill Books, Inc., 1966.

NAYLOR, JAMES C., and BRIGGS, GEORGE E. Effects of Task Complexity and Task Organization on the Relative Efficiency of Part and Whole Training Methods, *J. Exp. Psychol.*, 65:217–224, 1963.

NEIMEYER, ROY. Part Versus Whole Methods and Massed Versus Distributed Practice in the Learning of Selected Large Muscle Activities, *Coll. Phys. Educ. Assoc. Proc.*, 62:122–125, 1959.

NELSON, DALE O. Effect of Slow-Motion Loopfilms on the Learning of Golf, *Res. Quart.*, 29:37–45, 1958.

NELSON, DALE O. Effect of Swimming on the Learning of Selected Gross Motor Skills, *Res. Quart.*, 28:374–378, 1957a.

NELSON, DALE O. Studies of Transfer of Learning in Gross Motor Skills, *Res. Quart.*, 28:364–373, 1957b.

NEWMAN, RICHARD I.; HUNT, DONALD L.; and RHODES, FEN. Effects of Music on Employee Attitude and Productivity in a Skateboard Factory, *J. of Appl. Psychol.*, 50:493–496, 1966.

NOBLE, C. E.; FUCHS, J. E.; ROBEL, D. P.; and CHAMBERS, R. W. Individual Versus Social Performance on Two Perceptual-Motor Tasks, *Percept. Mot. Skills*, 8:131–134, 1958.

OSGOOD, C. E. The Similarity Paradox in Human Learning: A Resolution, *Psychol. Rev.*, 56:132–143, 1949.

PERRY, HORACE M. The Relative Efficiency of Actual and "Imaginary" Practice in Five Selected Tasks, *Archives of Psychol.*, 243:1–76, 1939.

RAWLS, JAMES R.; PERRY, OLIVER; and TIMMONS, EDWIN O. A Comparative Study of Conventional Instruction and Individual Programmed Instruction in the College Classroom, *J. Appl. Psychol.*, 50:388–391, 1966.

SCHRAMM, WILBUR. Programmed Instruction Today and Tomorrow, in FOSHAY, ARTHUR, et al. (eds.), *Programmed Instruction*. Washington, D.C.: Office of Educ., U.S. Govt., 1964.

SINGER, ROBERT N. Effect of Spectators on Athletes and Non-athletes Performing a Gross Motor Task, *Res. Quart.*, 36:473–482, 1965.

SINGER, ROBERT N. Sequential Skill Learning and Retention Effects, *Res. Quart.*, 39:185–194, 1968.

SINGER, ROBERT N. Transfer Effects and Ultimate Success in Archery due to Degree of Difficulty of the Initial Learning, *Res. Quart.*, 37:532–539, 1966.

SKINNER, B. F. Teaching Machines, *Scientific American*, 205:90–102, 1961.

SOLLEY, WILLIAM H. The Effects of Verbal Instruction of Speed and Accuracy upon the Learning of a Motor Skill, *Res. Quart.*, 23:231–240, 1952.

SOLLEY, WILLIAM H., and BORDERS, SUSAN. Relative Effects of Two Methods of Teaching the Forehand Drive in Tennis, *Res. Quart.*, 36:120–122, 1965.

SORENSON, WAYNE W. Test of Mechanical Principles as a Suppressor Variable for the Prediction of Effectiveness on a Mechanical Repair Job, *J. Appl. Psychol.*, 50:348–352, 1966.

START, K. B. Intelligence and the Improvement in a Gross Motor Skill After Mental Practice, *Brit. J. Educ. Psychol.*, 34:85, 1964.

SUMMERS, DEAN. Effect of Variations of Delivery and Aim on Bowling Achievement of College Women, *Res. Quart.*, 28:77–84, 1957.

TAKACS, ROBERT. A Comparison of the Effect of Two Methods of Practice on Basketball Freethrow Shooting, unpublished Master's thesis, Arkansas State College, Jonesboro, 1965.

TRAVERS, ROBERT M. *Essentials of Learning,* New York: Macmillan Co., 1964.

TRUMBO, DON; ULRICH, LYNN; and NOBLE, MERRILL E. Verbal Coding and Display Coding in the Acquisition and Retention of Tracking Skill, *J. Appl. Psychol.,* 49:368–375, 1965.

TWINING, WILBUR E. Mental Practice and Physical Practice in Learning a Motor Skill, *Res. Quart.,* 20:432–435 1949.

TWITMEYER, E. M. Visual Guidance in Motor Learning, *Amer. J. Psychol.,* 43:165–187, 1931.

WATKINS, DAVID L. Motion Pictures as an Aid in Correcting Baseball Batting Faults, *Res. Quart.,* 34:228–233, 1963.

WEYNER, NORMA, and ZEAMAN, DAVID. Team and Individual Performance on a Motor Learning Task, *J. Gen. Psychol.,* 55:127–142, 1956.

WHILDEN, PEGGY P. Comparison of Two Methods of Teaching Beginning Basketball, *Res. Quart.,* 27:235–242, 1956.

WICKSTROM, RALPH L. Comparative Study of Methodologies for Teaching Gymnastics and Tumbling Stunts, *Res. Quart.,* 29:109–115, 1958.

WICKSTROM, RALPH L. In Defense of Drills, *The Physical Educator,* 24:38–39, 1967.

WRIGHT, EDWARD J. Effects of Light and Heavy Equipment on the Acquisition of Sports-Type Skills by Young Children, Paper presented at the annual Amer. Assoc. Health, Phys. Educ., Rec. Convention, Chicago, Illinois, 1966.

Annotated Student References

METHODS OF INSTRUCTION

EGSTROM, GLEN H. Effects of an Emphasis on Conceptualizing Techniques During Early Learning of a Gross Motor Skill, *Res. Quart.,* 35:472–481, 1964.

Well-organized investigation and good theoretical discussion on mental versus physical practice.

FULTON, RUTH E. Speed and Accuracy in Learning Movements, *Archives of Psychol.,* No. 300, 1945.

Investigates the problem of whether early training on motor skills should emphasize speed or accuracy.

LUMSDAINE, A. A., and GLASER, R. (eds.). *Teaching Machines and Programmed Learning,* Washington, D.C.: National Educ. Assoc., 1960.

A description of the development of self-testing devices, techniques of instruction, and their impact on education.

MOHR, DOROTHY R. The Contributions of Physical Activity to Skill Learning, *Res. Quart.,* 31:321–350, Part II., 1960.

Briefly summarizes much of the research on instruction and skill learning.

NAYLOR, JAMES C., and BRIGGS, GEORGE E. Effects of Task Complexity and Task Organization on the Relative Efficiency of Part and Whole Training Methods, *J. Exp. Psychol.*, 65:217–224, 1963.

Goes beyond the usual whole-versus-part training approach and raises new considerations on the problem.

TEACHING CUES AND AIDS

ADAMS, THURSTON. Motion Pictures in Physical Education, *Teach. Coll. Contr. Educ.*, New York: Columbia University, 1939.

Indicates why to and how to employ motion pictures for supplemental instruction.

BATTIG, WILLIAM F. The Effect of Kinesthetic, Verbal, and Visual Cues on the Acquisition of a Lever-Positioning Skill, *J. Exp. Psychol.*, 47:371–380, 1954.

The role of several cues on skill acquisition were determined by emphasizing and eliminating certain ones.

COLVILLE, FRANCIS H. The Learning of Motor Skills as Influenced by Knowledge of Mechanical Principles, *J. Educ. Psychol.*, 40:321–327, 1957.

The ineffectiveness of teaching mechanical principles related to physical education activities is demonstrated in this novel and well-designed study.

GAGNÉ, ROBERT M., and FLEISHMAN, EDWIN A. *Psychology and Human Performance*, New York: Henry Holt and Co., 1959.

Interesting presentation of materials, devices and other supplemental training equipment and techniques.

MILLER, ROBERT B. *Handbook on Training and Training Equipment Design*, AF WADC TR 53–136, U.S. Air Force, Dayton, Ohio, 1953.

Although geared for military training, many of suggested training procedures are quite applicable to all types of motor learning.

TRANSFER OF TRAINING

DEESE, JAMES. *The Psychology of Learning*, New York: McGraw-Hill Book Co., Inc., 1958.

Presents a comprehensive overview on all aspects of transfer of training.

McGEOCH, JOHN A. *The Psychology of Human Learning*. New York: David McKay Co., Inc., 1961.

Contains an extensively footnoted chapter on the topic of transfer, with material ranging from basic considerations to theoretical implications.

NELSON, DALE O. Studies of Transfer of Learning in Gross Motor Skills, *Res. Quart.*, 28:364–373, 1957.

One of the few attempts at determining the transfer effects between related physical education activities.

OSGOOD, C. E. The Similarity Paradox in Human Learning: A Resolution, *Psychol. Rev.*, 56:132–143, 1949.

A theoretical treatment of stimulus and response relationships and transfer effects.

SOCIAL INFLUENCE

SINGER, ROBERT N. Effect of Spectators on Athletes and Non-Athletes Performing a Gross Motor Task, *Res. Quart.*, 36:473–482, 1965.

An attempt to research some of the problems related to the social effect on performance.

THOMPSON, GEORGE G. *Child Psychology*, Boston: Houghton Mifflin Company, 1962.

Contains a chapter concerning the social interaction with performance and behavior, with an enlightening review of the literature on cooperative and competitive ventures.

8

Learning Theories and Their Application to Physical Education

Psychologists during this entire century have been formulating and modifying theories of learning. Extensive research has been the basis for these theories as well as a means for questioning them. Although learning theories are far from fully developed and clearly defined, they, just as philosophies, can offer much to the physical educator. Familiarity with learning theories should encourage intellectual stimulation and thought, provide better understanding of learning phenomena and the laws regulating them, as well as promote a method of teaching consistent with scientific evidence.

Physical education, like all the disciplines in the educational sphere, is concerned with the most effective teaching methods. A theory provides the guidelines within which one may work. It suggests a frame of reference, a means of obtaining objectives. Basically, a theory deals with a particular area of knowledge in which large collections of facts and information are explained and interpreted in a limited number of words. It is an ordered and formal presentation of data. The theory explains relationships within the body of knowledge and permits deduction of new relationships or new facts.

Scientists interpret data, whereas theorists use these facts to formulate theories. Facts alone do not satisfy many individuals; hence, the need for a theory to organize the data into meaningful and unifying systems. Systems of laws explain the regularity of events surrounding us, and a theory integrates these laws. A few facts do not constitute a theory in themselves, for the quality and acceptability of a theory is determined by the scope of the scientific facts it represents.

Scientific inquiry, based on the search for the truth, serves as the foundation for theory formulation. With the accumulation of facts, laws are constructed which pertain to and govern isolated events. The explanation of many events allows us to interpret and predict behavior in given situations

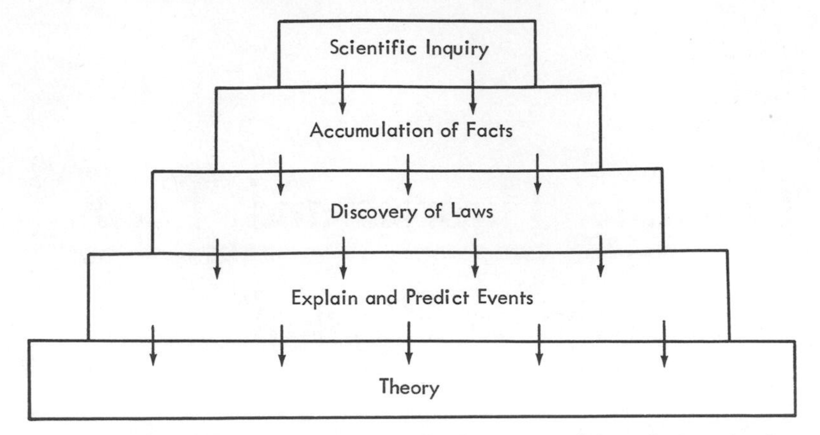

Figure 8–1. Scientific inquiry leads to the development and formulation of a theory.

and the final result is a system of laws or theory. This state of transition in theory construction is depicted in Figure 8–1.

There are two levels in science: the observable, or empirical relationships, which contain most psychological research; and the theoretical, or inferred relationships. The implicit assumption in theory construction is that it is formed as a basis of scientific activity and stimulates further activity. The fruitfulness of theory is that it enables a person to deduce a large number of empirical relationships. Facts should support theory, which in turn should generate research and new hypotheses, resulting in a reformulation of theory.

Actually, theories should arise after the relevant variables have been studied extensively. Because it is debatable whether psychologists have met this responsibility, Skinner (1965) questions whether we are ready for learning theory yet. He states that we may best understand learning from research not designated to test learning theories.

One of the major criticisms of earlier learning theories is that they attempted to explain all of learning on the basis of fragmentary facts. Another problem arose and still persists that is associated with the conflicting results obtained with different learning materials when investigating certain learning phenomena. Theories have also presented problems in communication. Note in this chapter how some theories have been written in clear language while others are represented by sign language. Actually, theorists may talk about the same thing in different ways, a practice which serves to confuse the issue. Mathematical models and cybernetics are examples of sign language theories. Other variables have led some individuals to probe into the meaningfulness and practical application of theories.

Beyond their limitations, theories, if based on the scientific approach, serve a number of purposes. A scientific system meets the following criteria:

1. Material is presented in a systematic and orderly fashion. It is not a haphazard collection of statements or facts.

2. Material is essentially based on the most accurate scientific information present at the time. There is evidence or proof for existence of statements.
3. Material is such that it allows us to understand behavior better. It explains and predicts behavior in all its forms in relatively few principles.
4. Material is offered in a conceptual form. It allows a person to generalize over a series of related events as to expected occurrences.
5. Material is pertinent to given situations; it allows for predictions in these situations.
6. Material is of such nature that it encourages further research.
7. Material is applicable to practical situations.

The last criterion, practical application, holds the greatest meaning for the average physical educator. Unfortunately, as of the present time, it must be frankly stated that the present stage of theory development does not permit an easy transition from theory to practice. Theories disagree on certain points, although many theories are actually reconcilable on the larger issues. Theory can be helpful in governing teaching practices, but a number of problems still cannot be handled because of the lack of many well-established principles. Nevertheless, some theories appear to apply to certain situations better than others, and this chapter contains the highlights of particular theories as well as examples of potential applications to physical education. Unfortunately, because of the difficulties and dangers in applying psychological learning theory to physical education, very few articles on the topic exist in the literature (see, for example, Singer, 1966).

Modern theory no longer explains performance solely through simple conditioning. There is a tendency to go to miniature or mathematical systems in place of the broad theories, and thus to a more fine-grained analysis of particular areas of interest. Besides this, clinical and social psychologists, tired of seeing rats representing human behavior, have formulated their own theories to explain learning and behavior.

Older Theories

Of the many theories attempting to explain and predict learning and behavior, some have unique differences but have still managed to remain in existence in spite of the scrutiny of researchers. Although earlier theories have usually been modified in later years because of certain contradictions from more controlled and extensive research, they should be studied for a number of reasons: (1) for their contribution toward bettering general teaching methods; (2) for the impetus to research which would at a later date, uphold or refute these theories; (3) for an understanding of how theories have developed through the years and the direction in which they are going; and (4) for any possible direct application the physical educator might be able to make to his specific teaching situation.

At the beginning of this century, the Behaviorists led by Watson battled against the idea that behavior was caused by preformed connections called instincts. Behavior, according to this group, was accounted for by stimulus-response conditioning. No other factors, including reinforcement, were thought to be important except that the S-R occur together (contiguity).

From this start, the reinforcement theorists exerted great influence on education and psychology behind the leadership of Thorndike. The necessity of some form of reinforcement occurring after the response was thus recognized. Many theories were formed in the 1930's and 1940's, from Gestalt (cognitive and field) theory, to Tolman's sign-learning theory, to Hull's drive-reduction theory, to Skinner's operant-conditioning theory. The earliest theories did not account for mentalistic actions (intervening variables) as they were based on the S-R conditioning made so famous by Pavlov and Watson. With more research and greater consideration for human as well as environmental conditions, theorists have tended to become more aware of factors besides an S-R occurrence.

Considering the various types of learning situations, one may ask if these different categories of learning demand separate and unique theories. Some theorists firmly state that their laws and postulates can encompass all aspects of the learning process; others have deliberately attempted to deal with specific types of learning. Because of the disagreement in psychology as to the nature of learning, Melton (1964) has designated seven categories of learning: short-term memory and incidental learning, probability learning, perceptual-motor skill learning, verbal learning, problem solving, classical and operant conditioning, and concept forming. Even here there is no total agreement, but a taxonomy (classification) of human learning promotes a more comprehensive understanding of the forms of human learning and how they interact. Theories can then be tested more accurately as to specific or general values in describing and predicting behavior. The reader should keep these categories of learning in mind as he scrutinizes the older theories, for each theory has been formulated primarily to treat learning comprehensively and in general rather than a "type" of learning as specified by Melton.

For convenience, the traditional theories have been classified as being *connectionist* (S-R) or *cognitive* (Gestalt). Some theorists believe in intervening variables occurring between the S-R, others do not. Still other theorists have combined elements from both types of theories. Gestalt and S-R theories as well as the term *intervening variable* will be discussed in following sections. There is agreement that S-R theories are more exacting and lead to greater research, whereas cognitive theories are more general and elusive, emphasizing the perceptual and intellectual processes.

In this chapter, which contains a few of the more prominent earlier learning theories and later theories and an indication of current theory direction, the theories are presented first with brief explanations and later in relation to physical education. The learning theories primarily to be examined in this section of the chapter include one stimulus-response theory (Thorndike), two varieties of stimulus-response behaviorism (Guthrie and Skinner), and the Gestalt or field theory. Other related theories are briefly noted for their significance.

Stimulus-Response Connectionism and Trial and Error Theory. For many years, Edward L. Thorndike (1931) was the leader in the formulation of learning theory. He was the forerunner in stimulus-response or S-R psychology of learning, and his theory has been termed *association theory, bond theory,* or *connectionism.*

These terms simply imply that there are no intervening ideas between the stimulus and response, that the connections are strengthened automatically when they occur. Thorndike gave much impetus to knowledge in the area of problem solving and contributed his famous laws of readiness, exercise, and effect. Even though many of his laws had to be revised in later years because of research findings that contradicted his theory, his laws are still acknowledged for their impact on education.

For example, his original *law of exercise* stated that during repetition the S-R connections were strengthened and the probability of the desired response was increased. However, studies have shown many instances where mere repetitions of an act were not enough to demonstrate learning. Thorndike modified his position and stated that for more effective learning the desired connection should be rewarded by praise, knowledge of right or wrong, food, or some other means.

The *law of effect* is another example of a famous Thorndike postulate, modified in his later years. Generally speaking, this law is concerned with what happens after an act. If the response is followed by a satisfier, i.e., it is pleasant and rewarding, the tendency is for that response to be strengthened. When an annoyer such as punishment occurs the response is weakened. At first Thorndike felt that both conditions had an equal effect on the individual, but later he adjusted this law to give greater importance to satisfiers than annoyers. He was among the first to emphasize the value of reinforcement, for this is what the law of effect is concerned with.

Of interest to physical educators is Thorndike's belief that learning takes place through trial and error. In other words, the learner when faced with a problem does not suddenly perceive the solution but rather gradually, through random behavior, learns the correct response. Motivation is extremely important, and the laws of readiness, exercise, and effect were utilized by Thorndike to explain how learning was promoted. With repeated responses, a problem is solved because of a diminishing of incorrect responses and a fixation of the correct response.

Physical educators might consider the importance of reinforcement as well as acknowledge that practice alone does not make perfect; and, in addition, consider the readiness of the individual to learn. Physical educators might also observe whether their classes contain situations that are trial and error by nature. Are the learners being taught? Are there too many trials and too many errors before success is achieved? It will be interesting for the reader to note Skinner's thinking on this matter of learning and how he would "shape" behavior.

In some situations, behavior does seem to be random and thus of a trial-and-error nature. Instead of selecting this type of learning, it would seem wiser to replace chance success with directed strivings and an understanding of relations.

Another part of Thorndike's learning theory dealt with transfer, and it is referred to as the *identical-elements theory of transfer*. Basically, he states that all learning is specific and may appear to be general only because the new situations or acts contain elements similar to elements of old situations or acts. It is in this area of transfer that Thorndike made one of his most significant contributions to education. He attacked the then popular belief in the generalized theory of transfer (logic, memorization, reasoning, and the like transferred from specific school subjects to everyday life's experiences) and emphasized specific training and education for desired behavior.

It is important to remember that in trial-and-error theory the emphasis is on the learner and his motives, readiness, and needs. Also considered are the rewards and effects which "stamp in" or imprint the portions of a random activity which bring chance success. All parts are regarded singularly and as isolated. This emphasis is in contrast to Gestalt theory, as will be seen later. Finally, the theory stresses the importance of the need or intention to learn. To learn well, the learner must participate actively; to do that, he must have drive.

Contiguous Conditioning. Edwin R. Guthrie (1935) attempted to remain true to the basic S-R theory. His was the simplest and probably the most ingenious of all the learning theories because of this simplicity.

Guthrie's theory can be summarized through his four postulates:

1. Postulate 1, the Principle of Association states that any time a response is made to a stimulus, that same stimulus becomes a direct cue for that response. There is no notion of reward, cognition, or motivation. According to Guthrie, any one of these conditions changes the stimulus.
2. Postulate 2 states that a stimulus that accompanies two or more responses becomes conditioned only to the last response. For example, when a baby is presented with a bat, he may respond by saying "Dada." The bat is kept there and the baby says "Cookie"; and finally the baby says "Bat."
3. Postulate 3, the Principle of Response Probability states that the more frequently the same stimulus situation is presented, the better the chance that the desired response will occur.

4. Finally, Postulate 4 is concerned with the dynamic nature of the stimulus situation: that the stimulus pattern often changes as a result of boredom, fatigue, hunger, sickness, and other similar factors.

Let us see how this simple theory would apply in general to the learning of an athletic skill. The basketball player desires a foul shot which he can score with a great deal of consistency. If his environment, body position, and body movements are similar during each trial, the probability of success is increased. For instance, his feet are aligned in the same manner during each attempt. He bounces the ball twice preparatory to shooting. Hopefully, the follow-through is executed in the same manner with each attempt at the basket. Even the addition of a breath while shooting changes the stimulus environment. The presence or absence of players along the foul lanes or of spectators in the gymnasium creates an altered environment.

The more practice a player has, the greater the probability that he will exhaust the pool of stimuli which by chance might occur in that situation. Hence, familiarity with varying circumstances encourages a greater chance for a successful foul shot. Theoretically, according to Guthrie, if there are no competing stimuli—if the succeeding situation is *exactly* like the preceding one—there should be an S-R association and the response should be duplicated. However, stimuli vary from trial to trial, causing a response variation.

If there is an undesired movement or response to a stimulus and another is desired, it is necessary to attach a competing response to this stimulus. On breaking in a horse, the process can be gradual or sudden. Beginning at a weak stimulus level the horse is not allowed to run or buck. A saddle is placed on him. Eventually and gradually the horse learns the desired response through associated and less–desired responses, until he finally allows the rider to ride him.

The rider can also break in the horse by not permitting any undesired responses. He may suddenly jump on the horse's back and cling while the horse runs until exhausted. In the end, the rider (stimulus) obtains the desired response from the horse—the last one made—walking quietly and obediently.

Physical education skills are primarily taught in a gradual manner. In archery, the goal may be for the participant to score accurately from the forty-yard line. He learns first from the ten- or twenty-yard stripe, moves back to the thirty yard, and when achieving a reasonable degree of skill, goes still further back to the forty-yard line. Rarely, if ever, does a beginning archer first learn the sport shooting from the forty-yard line.

Other implications for the teaching of skills may be evident from Guthrie's theory. As was stated previously, the theory is simple and is used more to explain behavior than as a predictor. The gradual acquisition of a skill is described through stimulus sampling and the contiguous association of the stimulus and response. To a certain extent, the theory may be considered a perception theory, as the learner has to obtain knowledge of the environmental stimuli. He has to perceive in order to react successfully.

Operant Conditioning. Of all the psychologists prominent in the field of learning in this century, B. F. Skinner has had the most impact on our culture. He is interested not only in predicting behavior but also in controlling it—an idea objected to by many people.

Among other contributions, Skinner is the author of *Walden Two*, a novel on the development of a Utopian society made possible by controlling human behavior. He invented the Skinner Box, where animal behavior could be observed and data produced visually and made readily comprehensible. He developed the "baby box," an enclosed compartment in which the baby lives and the temperature is maintained. Skinner's promotion of the teaching machine has caused the method of programmed instruction to gain wide theoretical and practical acceptance and has had an enormous impact on industry and education.

Skinner's (1938) theory of operant conditioning contrasts with respondent conditioning (S-R standard theory, e.g., Pavlov's works). In respondent behavior, the subject has to respond in a certain way to a given stimulus. Standard laboratory experiments demonstrate such specific S-R connections, which are also called reflexes. Operant learning is reflected by behavior emitted by the organism instead of by stimuli. Most human behavior is of the operant kind, for example, playing in sports, and Skinner is mainly concerned with responses instead of stimuli.

Perhaps Skinner's theory can best be represented by the widely used *shaping concept*. If there is a response desired and the possibility of occurrence is quite remote, the chance for success would increase if the act were reinforced in some way whenever it occurs. However, there is an alternate possibility. The desired response should be thought of as in the larger domain of behavior. Therefore, reinforcement should be made for a general response in the direction of the desired response. This is the procedure followed by animal trainers.

For example, the desired response might be for a novice bowler to execute a four-step approach and roll a hook ball into the 1-3 pocket. He should be reinforced (verbal reward) increasingly as he approaches the ultimate goal. According to Skinner, the effect of reinforcement is extremely important. The bowler, instead of achieving the desired movement by chance in trial-and-error performance, is channeled into the correct groove through constant verbal encouragement. Concern would first be focused on the skill in the approach and ball release, later on accuracy and score.

The teaching machine apparently is an extension of this shaping concept and perhaps has great implications for physical educators. The teaching machine discourages any wrong response throughout the learning of a subject. It shapes learning from the simple to the complex. If a child is learning to read he must first know about forms. Matter becomes more complicated as the child learns about forms, letters, simple words, more complex words, and finally sentences. He is not permitted to continue until he has mastered all the information presented up to that point. He never has to go back because he was not permitted to learn errors along the way, as incorrect responses were rejected, requiring these responses to be repeated.

Physical education academic courses, physiology of exercise and kinesiology, for instance, might be taught this way satisfactorily. Teaching machines are used in other academic areas. The machines allow students to move at their own speed while the teacher assists those students having difficulties.

Then again, perhaps the entire concept of the teaching machine can be applied to the teaching of physical education skills. When learning a skill (hitting a tennis ball with a forehand stroke, as an example) each element of the movement is taught and correctly executed before advancing to additional or more complex movements. The student learns the correct stance, the correct movement, and, in a stationary position, strikes a ball thrown from a machine. He does not begin hitting balls on the run until this act is performed successfully.

The tennis student learns to hit balls accurately when running sideward, then forward, then backward. It is important to remember that complex movements are building on simpler ones. No advancement is allowed until mastery is shown at a particular level of skill. No errors are accepted. Later on in the course there will be no competing responses (wrong and right) for only the right ones have been learned.

How many of us as youngsters learned a sport skill incorrectly? Trying to execute that skill in good form later in life presents a difficulty. The situation is a consequence of the effect of competing responses. Is it not easier to learn a skill correctly for the first time than to undo past error-filled experiences?

Skinner is a firm believer in the power of reinforcement in promoting learning, advocating the principle that a response followed by reinforcement increases the probability of the occurrence of that response. His classification of reinforcement manipulations, or the schedule of reinforcements—concerning *ratio* and *interval, fixed* or *variable*—has permitted a better understanding of reinforcement and the relative values of the different kinds. Skinner states that behavior is determined by law, not chance. Behavior is related to environmental manipulation, and as teachers we can manipulate the movement patterns of students. How much behavior and performance can and should be controlled is a matter of conjecture. Perhaps time, knowledge, and experience will tell.

Gestalt Theory. The Gestalt movement had its greatest impact on American learning theories in the 1930's, and is usually associated with the names of Max Wertheimer, Wolfgang Kohler, Kurt Koffka, and Kurt Lewin, all of whom fled to our shores from Hitler's Germany. The German word *gestalt* means form or shape. Gestalt theory indicates that the learner perceives meaningful relationships in his environment and gains insight into the understanding and solving of problems.

Hilgard (1956) elaborates on the effect of Gestaltism on learning theory and on its development as an alternative to Thorndike's trial-and-error theory. Gestalt psychology came into prominence as educators, primarily because of the Dewey influence, were more concerned with the individual and his own ability to determine outcomes in a situation. To these educators, Thorndike was too mechanistic and his theory too laboratory oriented. Gestaltists believe that learning is not random and accidental, but instead, a result of organized, meaningful, and perceived experiences. The learner perceives the environment as a whole; he constantly reorganizes his experiences, and eventual insight is inevitable. The theory goes beyond the simple S-R explanation of learning. Whereas S-R theorists are concerned with overt behavior, the Gestalt theorist is more interested in the cognitive process, in what the learner understands. A greater understanding of Gestalt psychology may be obtained by reading *The Principles of Gestalt Psychology* by Koffka (1935).

Perhaps one of the greatest contributions of gestalt theory to education is the concept of emphasizing the holistic manner of teaching material as contrasted to an atomistic relationship of parts. Putting it another way, the whole method of teaching would be advocated by Gestaltists over the part method.

Many physical education teachers introduce a skill in its entirety first and then break it down into its components. The learner understands what he is attempting to achieve and constantly re-evaluates his experiences until finally he is able to put into action that which he perceives as being the desired act. He strives to make sense of each task, to search for significant relationships between tasks, until progressive change occurs through the discovery of insightful wholes. The gestaltist physical educator believes that the learner, once he gains insight in shooting a basketball from ten feet in front of the basket will be able to transpose this experience so that it leads to skill in shooting from fifteen or twenty feet away from the basket.

A discussion of the gestalt approach to learning as opposed to Skinner's shaping of behavior, Thorndike's trial and error, and Guthrie's contiguity conditioning is presented later in this chapter. Basically, it is important to comprehend the gestaltist belief that during practice changes go on within repetition, not as a result of repetition. Also, transfer from one skill to another takes place not because of identical elements but, rather, because of similar patterns.

Other Theories. Although it would be impossible in this chapter to do justice to all the earlier theories of learning, others worth mentioning, at least briefly, for their significance are those of E. C. Tolman and C. L. Hull.

In the 1930's, psychologists revolted against the physiological explanation of behavior, and one of the leaders of this revolution was E. C. Tolman. He insisted that psychology could study performance at the purely behavioral level as contrasted with a physiological explanation. He incorporated ideas of the gestalt school and S-R theorists in his explanation of learning and behavior in rats.

In later years Tolman introduced the concept of the *intervening variable,* stating that something occurred between the antecedent condition (S) and the behavior (R). Finally, he (Tolman, 1949) offered the possibility that there are six kinds of learning, one of the six being the learning of motor patterns. He accepted Guthrie's explanation for the learning of motor movements. There are many modern theorists who would hold that different theories are needed to explain the various types of learning. Tolman raised the interesting question as to whether one general theory could explain and predict all learning and behavior; he thought perhaps a theory of motor learning might well prove to be different in many ways from theories of memorization and the learning of written matter.

Clark L. Hull (1943) followed Tolman in influencing learning theory. He developed many postulates and definitively described the effect of intervening variables on behavior. For example, Hull's theory of a performed act would be described by the symbols $S^{\dot{\bar{E}}}R = (S^{H}R \times D \times K \times V) - (^{I}R + S\ ^{I}R) - S\ ^{O}R - S\ ^{L}R$. Interpreted in an overly-simplified manner, this means that the momentary affective reaction potential is equal to the number of reinforced trials × drive × incentive × intensity of stimulus – (reactive inhibition + conditioned inhibition) – the fluctuation of the individual from moment to moment – reaction threshold.

Hull's theory was one of the most formal, precise, and elaborate of all behaviorist theories to be proposed. He mathematically arrived at figures which were used as constants and helped to quantify his postulates. Hull talks mainly in terms of needs and drives, and his theory has been often referred to as a drive-reduction theory. His efforts encouraged much research and his most famous disciple, Spence, has continued his work.

An important consideration of Hull's theory for physical educators is the effect of mere practice on performance. Hull demonstrated that repetitious practice led to what he termed *inhibition,* a sort of depressant variable that is built up during nonreinforced trials and which offsets the strength of the performance. Reactive inhibition dissipates with rest. This would explain why a basketball player who attempts 100 consecutive foul shots would most likely perform best in the middle trials and worst nearing the termination of the trials. Yet the following day he is able to begin again at a greater skill level than he had at the end of the previous practice session. This is a perfect example of the effect of practice on performance rather than learning. Obviously the performance level of the participant can be raised or hindered, depending on the manner in which skills are practiced. However, the true extent of learning may be disguised.

Application of Learning Theories to Physical Education

A difficulty in accepting and applying a particular learning theory is that each theory discussed here emphasizes a different aspect of learning, either problem-solving, the nature of the stimulus, perception, the nature and effect of intervening variables, or any one or combination of a number of factors.

Functionalism. A possible idea would be to follow the eclectic point of view described by Hilgard (1956) as *functionalism.* A leading representative of functionalist theorists is Judd (1939). The functionalist gathers all the facts and theories and incorporates the most plausible and acceptable parts of the theories into one theory. He is ready to adjust to changing conditions, and his theory is therefore loosely constructed. One may criticize an eclectic point of view, for when you have a little of everything you sometimes end up with nothing. Also, there is a lack of consistency of thought within the theory.

Because of the manner in which this theory is formed, there are some who hold that functionalism should be considered a position rather than a theory. In either case, a functionalist approach may have the most meaning for the physical educator at the present because of the apparent weaknesses in each of the more prominent theories. An even better reason for its acceptance is that all the learning theories have been developed mainly on the strength of research completed on human learning of prose, nonsense syllables, mazes, and pursuit rotors, and animal learning in the Skinner Box, on mazes, and in discriminatory situations. Relatively little research may be found on the learning of motor skills,— athletic skills specifically.

A simple S-R explanation might not be enough to describe the learning of motor skills. True, the stimulus, whether it be an isolated object or a particular situation, must be understood and controlled to a certain extent if the desired response is to be made. The relative complexity or simplicity of the stimulus and the type of response to be made are important considerations in the learning situation. Maintaining a constant uncomplicated stimulus is most necessary, especially during the early trials of learning a new skill.

The tennis instructor might avoid having beginning tennis players hit the ball back and forth in every manner and position conceivable hoping that they would learn the correct movements. Instead, each player would stand constantly in the same position on the court, the ball being tossed to him at the same rate of speed and distance from the body, and he would hit forehands over and over until he had mastered the technique somewhat. The stimulus situation is stable and relatively simple. It becomes more complex as player improvement necessitates the progressive change.

This method of teaching might not be the best nor the most practical. Perhaps, when a student learns a new skill, he should initially be allowed to explore, to feel his way about, to be permitted to practice the skill in a trial-and-error method. The student should have observed the ultimate desired skill via film or demonstration so as to have an idea what is expected of him. After some exploratory trials, a more controlled learning situation might be followed in which desired responses are shaped whenever possible. The learner who is in danger of fixating an error that is giving trouble must be interrupted and the significant parts isolated and related to the whole. By means of appropriately timed guidance and emphasis, the teacher can direct the conditioning process so that the proper cues are reacted to and the conditions reinforce the desired response.

These two opposing learning methods are concerned mainly with the stimulus environment. But the learning of one skill or all skills in tennis or any sport probably is determined by factors in addition to the isolated stimulus and response. The roles of perception, motivation, stress, and other variables relevant to learning must also be considered.

In order for the student to perceive, to structure his environment, past experiences relevant to the new skill to be learned are necessary to promote this process. Insight is best achieved when understanding is present. A foreign soccer player, unfamiliar with squash, may have great difficulty in learning this sport. The tennis player would probably have much greater success with squash because of similarities between these two sports. The tennis player perceives the object of the game, its movement, style, and manner. The soccer player questions the value of a sport enclosed by four walls, utilizing a racket and a small hard ball. He cannot conceive of this being a sport; he has trouble visualizing its goals, purposes, techniques, and strategy.

This does not mean that insight will not occur eventually. The point made here is that the teacher must consider the background of his students, their familiarity and past participation in various sports, in order to determine the success they will have learning a particular sport. The growth of skill is affected by the learner's perceptions of the relationship between cues. It is not enough to have the cues and their relations present. They must be interpreted and activate responses.

Gestalt and S-R theories have a basic difference in educational purpose and application. Whereas Gestaltists have demonstrated interest in the individual, his personality and cognitive processes, S-R theorists have attempted to develop learning principles after studying group behavior. In reality, the lack of ideal teacher-learner situations in education has encouraged many teachers to follow behaviorist practices. However, the revolt against mechanistic theory has been strong in education, and physical educators should be aware that both theories contain elements of merit. Drill and problem-solving approaches may both be employed effectively when teaching motor skills.

Dual Theory for Motor Skill Learning? Although physical skills differ considerably from one another in nature, it is possible to classify them into two main categories. Disastrous, perhaps, but nevertheless possible. An interesting concept is the further possibility that perhaps two theories are necessary to best describe the type of learning going on primarily in either category.

For example, as Knapp (1964) interestingly points out, skills might be classified as predominantly perceptual or predominantly habitual. Such sports as tennis, basketball, and fencing would be perceptually oriented whereas diving, putting of the shot, and trampolining would be habitually oriented. In other words, in some sports and activities, the prime concern of the performer is the potential changing environment. His reaction cannot be fixed but, rather, depends on the circumstance. Other skills require repetitious practice until the act can be performed as a habit; perceptual need is minimized and the ability to reproduce the same act continuously and consistently is emphasized.

Habitual Skills and Learning Theory. Habitual skills, those requiring a fixed response to a given situation, appear to be learned best under Stimulus-Response theory. The stimulus environment is relatively stable. Desired response can only be achieved through constant practice, and the performer's attention is to the act itself. With successful practice, skill sets in, and the individual may execute the skill as if automatically, without any direct concern over the intricacies of the act.

The diver's environment consists of a diving board and a pool, with the board a certain height over the pool. This condition is constant, wherever he goes to compete. True, things are never quite the same day to day or place to place, but then again, no skill is purely habitual or purely perceptual. Elements of both are necessary for successful skill execution, but emphasis on each is dependent on the nature of the skill. Difference in diving-board structure, pool temperature, and spectators present, among many other factors, will contribute to an altered stimulus environment. In some cases, the diver must perform the same regardless of this change, e.g., not pay attention to the crowd of people. In other situations, such as the board having more or less spring than the diver is accustomed to, he must use his perceptual mechanisms and adjust his dive accordingly.

But basically, the dive is an example of an habitual skill. Guthrie's theory of contiguous conditioning as well as an S-R learning theory might apply very well to this learning and performing situation. The act is to be repeatedly performed under the condition in which it must ultimately be demonstrated for success to be probable. Any sport where the participant initiates the action rather than having to respond to thrown objects or moving players can be identified as primarily habitual by nature.

Perceptual Skills and Learning Theory. The Stimulus-Response theory appears to have limited value in team sports as well as in many individual and dual sports where perceiving a changing environment is necessary. Gestalt theory appears to be more appropriate for this situation. However, the initial learning of the basic skills underlying a sport might very well be conditioned, using the S-R approach. Common sense would dictate that a skill must be learned well under stable conditions before the individual will be able to execute it regardless of circumstances that may be unpredictable.

But a fixed response is of no use to the performer reacting under varying conditions. The emphasis later would be on the environment, understanding relationships and patterns, utilizing Gestalt methodology. A tennis player might have beautiful form and execution when hitting against a ball-throwing machine. A game situation, however, requires much flexibility in response, for the ball now comes to the stroker at varying speeds, with curves and slices, and with indiscriminate bounces. Now he needs to demonstrate his awareness of spatial relationships and an ability to perceive and react according to changing stimuli. In team sports, the same condition exists. The basketball player must consider not only his own developed skill but also his position on the court with regard to fellow and opposing players. It is not enough merely to assume a definite response pattern each time a specific situation is present. The player who mistakenly fixates an offensive or defensive move, who reacts in an unflexible manner to given stimuli will certainly be discovéred shortly and advantage will be taken of these conditioned patterns. It is much more desirable to have skills developed to be called into play at any time, regardless of the situation.

Most motor acts require more than a conditioned reaction. Their complexity requires an understanding of many facets of the learning process on the part of the teacher and performer in order that skill might be more effectively demonstrated. Therefore, the physical educator should be aware of the nature of both habitual and perceptual learning, and know how an emphasis on one or the other might better facilitate the desired outcome. Certainly both S-R theory (in its many forms) and Gestalt theory have much to offer the physical educator.

Newer Theories

It perhaps does an injustice to those theories already presented and those to be discussed arbitrarily to classify them as "older" and "newer." There is no doubt that the older theories are in existence today, only modified to be more consistent with our latest knowledge. Many of the newer theories have their roots in traditionally accepted psychological laws and principles.

However, the theories described in this section have used different approaches to describe and predict behavior than the standard S-R and perceptually oriented theories. Their prominence and impact on education may be traced back only ten to twenty years, and therefore may be categorized as recent. One can readily perceive unique terminology, methodology, and intent of application, as well as some resemblance to the standard and well-known theories. To be presented here are the following: neuropsychological theory, mathematical models, information theory, cybernetics or feedback theory, and some theories that are lesser known.

British researchers have had a great impact on recent theory development.

Whereas the traditional behavioristic-type theories, which are American-oriented, emphasize response, contiguity of stimulus-response, and reinforcement, Adams (1964) writes that the sensory theory of learning, with impetus from the British, is currently being intensively investigated. New language has been introduced; humans are compared to machines. Behavior is ascribed with sensory input channels as mechanisms for processing stimuli that are interacting with feedback from past experiences to affect responses. Theory development stresses (1) the temporal-expectancy mechanisms governing the timing of responses and (2) the concept of a one-channel decision mechanism that permits the attending of one event at a time. Notably there is a completely different vocabulary, at least context-wise, than we might be accustomed to. First Hebb's neuropsychological theory and an overview of statistical theories will be described. Then an explanation of greater depth (although still a superficial treatment) will be advanced about theories employing such terminology.

Neuropsychological Theory. Although physiological theories explaining learning were briefly outlined in Chapter 2 on the nervous system, neither they nor the purely psychological theories have mutually satisfied psychologists and physiologists. Few attempts have been made to bridge the gap between the two disciplines. Lashley, through his extensive writings and research, encouraged the interaction of knowledge from both areas. He, in turn, inspired D. O. Hebb to construct a neurological model, consistent with neurological and psychological evidence. Hebb (1949) received great acclaim for his contributions, first enunciated in his book, *Organization of Behavior.*

Hebb emphasized the role of neural action in learning and described changes due to maturational development and learning experience. It is no wonder that his theory has been widely accepted by developmental psychologists. Hebb suggests that as a result of experience, such structural changes as a closer physical contact of the neurons occurs. Although not verifiable, he hypothesizes the growth of end bulbs on the dendrites as a result of learning which allow them to fire (eject impulses) more easily and more quickly. The closer proximity of the neurons at the synapse causes an act to be performed skillfully, for when something is well learned, the same neural pathways are constantly invoked (aroused and stirred up).

According to Hebb, maturation, or the result of aging, causes changes in the nerve cells and cell assemblies. A *cell assembly* is a series of neurons that provides a circular type of circuit for the nerve impulse. An effective response can only appear if all the assembly units are at a state of maturity. An elaboration of many cell assemblies has been termed a *phase sequence* by Hebb.

In comparing different species, he describes why (1) more complex tasks can be learned in higher species at maturity, (2) simple relationships are learned equally well in high and low species, and (3) the first things to be learned in the higher species are learned more slowly than in the lower species. The ratio of association (A) fibers to sensory (S) projection fibers in the brain determines the primary learning period. A longer learning period occurs when there are more A's than S's. A larger number of A's yield a larger number of alternate pathways, and a human organism demonstrates a tremendous variability in response and takes so long to learn (compared with lower animals) because of the many alternate pathways for different responses.

Hebb, in describing learning and synapse changes, calls his theory *a recruitment theory*. Neurons are recruited for a particular circuit and usually are not used in a competing circuit. This primary law of first come, first served, is used by Hebb in conjunction with the maturation and readiness of cell assemblies concept to explain what occurs during critical learning periods. Once past a critical period, the particular cell assemblies have to be re-recruited, a difficult task for the body. As was pointed out earlier in the book, it is important to determine the state of readiness to learn various skills. Practice prior to the optimal period is wasted, and later practice has to be concentrated in order to be effective. Indeed, it may never result in the same learning as practice which occurs during the critical learning period.

Hebb also handles the problem of injury to the nervous system in a plausible manner. With repeated stimulation, cells in the cell assemblies increase and overlap in function. Damage to a portion of the critical sensory area later in life has little effect because alternate routes, previously built up, can work to do the desired acts. Early brain damage is thus worse than later-in-life brain damage.

One weakness in Hebb's theory is that much of it is not experimentally verifiable. However, it does provide promise in handling that area of learning theory so often neglected by other theorists: growth and development. In particular, stages of readiness and effects of maturity and experience are confronted in Hebb's work. His approach to learning is unique and refreshing.

Mathematical Statistical Models. It is probably evident in reviewing the theories of learning presented thus far that a great deal of precision is lacking in their formulation. The interest of mathematically-oriented people in theory construction produced a new wave of statistical models about 1950. This emergence of more specific, restricted theories has solved many problems but created others.

The use of mathematical equations actually dates back to an earlier portion of this century with Thurstone as one of the primary contributors. There were attempts to deduce curves of learning mathematically, to fit the best curve to data already available. The learning function via the learning curve was analytically defined on the basis of simple probability theory and differential equations. How a measure of performance improved with practice was mathematically described.

Hull was the first proponent of formal theory, and he pioneered in mathematically translating certain learning phenomena. However, his primary concern was with mean performances, not other details of learning data. The efforts of Estes, Bush and Mosteller, and Miller and Frick have resulted in models successful in demonstrating the great impact of mathematics on psychology and learning. Models are not as complete as theories; they do not attempt to deal with all aspects of learning.

The present models predict the shape of learning curves, but have limited value since they cannot describe all learning situations. However, they do treat all that can be known from the data recorded. Most present efforts encompass the process of acquisition, of how something is learned in a choice situation. They try to answer the question of why a certain response is made in a given situation and how long it takes before the response is stabilized. Probability theory is important here and is applied to the stimulus population in a given situation. The number and nature of stimuli associated with an act is of central importance to model formulators such as Estes. The present mathematically-inclined theorists are mainly disciples of such famous behaviorist theoreticians as Guthrie and Hull and have tended to fit their loosely stated postulates in precise statistical form.

For instance, Restle (1964) building on Guthrie's concept of one-trial learning, contends that learning is a single all-or-none event. Performance supposedly stabilizes that which has been learned. Equations are based on probabilities and the supposition is supported through mathematical deductions. The concept of repetitions being unnecessary for learning and contiguity being most important has also been discussed convincingly by Rock (1958).

Estes (1959) also accepts Guthrie's theory and has probably formulated the most widely accepted statistical model. He has constructed a probabilistic response model, and his approach is better understood when one realizes that his definition of learning is a systematic change in response probability. Unfortunately, most statistical models appear to describe the acquisition of verbal material better than motor-skill learning; and, indeed, the concern of most psychologists has been in the former area. Because of this, other models and theories have been developed, especially by those interested in industrial and military performance. Although the resultant works, information theory and feedback theory, are constructed on certain mathematical bases, their differences from statistical models entitle them to be analyzed as separate categories.

Modern Theories of Performance. The dissatisfaction of industrial engineers and psychologists as well as military psychologists with the traditional theories of learning, i.e., S-R (Stimulus-Response) and cognitive (Gestalt), has been evidenced by the new approaches taken to theorize about the learning of motor skills. World War II brought about a great involvement of psychologists in assisting the armed forces to develop better training devices and techniques. The revolution in industry, advancing the most sophisticated of computer models, has promoted an interest in comparing machine methods of operation with human operational techniques. Industry as well as the military encourages the maximum efficiency on motor tasks.

These operational and theoretical factors have caused departure from theories geared mainly to describe verbal learning or rat performance to others intended to explain and predict human performance in the motor-skill area. It should be realized that the motor skills considered in these newer theories are of positioning or tracking type, not the athletic skills so familiar to physical educators. However, it does appear that physical education activities might have more in common with the military and industrial tasks than with verbal learning or rat performances.

The concept of *signal detection* or *vigilance,* which is involved with perceiving above threshold events during a period of time, is of interest to military personnel. After all, rare events are important to detect during war. Contributors to research and theory in this area include Mackworth, Adams, Broadbent, Jerrison, and Baker. A vigilance situation is very boring, because of infrequent signals and silence, and psychologists disagree as to why performance decrements occur during vigilance.

The practice of athletic skills to a high level of proficiency can often be repetitious and monotonous. According to Frankman and Adams (1962), vigilance is the attentiveness of a subject and his capability of detecting changes in stimulus events during a lengthy period of observation. Although vigilance does not apply directly to the performance of most athletic skills, the concern for maintaining motivation and perceptibility is certainly there. Evidently, motivation and vigilance are decreased very little if (1) the task is complex, (2) knowledge of results are provided, (3) many cues are present, (4) the period of involvement contains some break or recess and (5) the stimuli are of greater intensity and longer duration.

Four leading theories extended to explain vigilance include inhibition theory (Mackworth), filter theory (Broadbent), expectancy theory (Deese), and activationist theory (Scott). Broadbent's (1958) *filter theory,* which is actually an attention theory, attempts to explain more than just performance decrements. He states that there is a *filter* at the entrance of the nervous system that permits some classes of stimuli to pass but not others. The priority of selection is given to stimuli that are physically intense, of greater biological importance, and which are novel. Decrements in performance are attributed to competition of the stimuli.

According to Broadbent, the person is selective in what he takes in from the environment. He absorbs some stimuli and leaves out others, and the selection varies from time to time. The uniqueness of signals or cues will result in attention; but after a long time period attention is lost with the absence of a unique signal. With practice on a task fewer cues are needed and the capacity required for performance is reduced, freeing neural mechanisms for other tasks.

Broadbent's theory in its entirety is actually a communication or information theory. The S-R approach of simply considering the presence or absence of particular stimuli is not satisfactory to information theorists. They feel that the whole ensemble of stimuli have to be considered as well as the coding of input into output. Patterns, situations, and temporal sequences of stimuli rather than simultaneous patterns are central to information theory. The evolvement of information theory and its characteristics are described somewhat later.

The *detection theory* (Swets, 1964) provides a framework for human behavior in a variety of perceptual tasks and has been popularized by Blackwell, Swets, Tanner, and Birdsall. Statistical decision theory has been translated into signal detection theory. The detection or perceptual process is based upon the observer's detection of the goal and the information he has about probabilities and values concerning it. He does not merely passively reflect environmental events, but makes a substantial contribution to what he perceives. A decision or detection process depends on the stimulus condition as well as the instructions to the observer.

The concept that a human samples stimuli from his environment in a predictable manner is, of course, relevant to military warfare and possibly to athletic competition. Theoretically, if you have sufficient data on an enemy or opponent, you can know his cut-off point for making a decision or executing an act. Thus far, though, the theory has had limited application for all types of behavior and has been restricted mainly to visual experiences.

This theory, which is concerned with the decision-making process, contradicts previous theories which advocated that stimuli were only detected where a certain threshold level was present. Perceptual decisions, which usually preclude motor acts, are based on rewards and expectancies according to the signal detection theory. In other words, a person makes a decision after considering his pay-offs from the possible outcomes of his responses as well as estimating the actual stimulus. Perhaps an example in sport will serve to demonstrate the theory in actual practice.

Consider the batter in a baseball game. He can perceive any pitch to be a strike or a ball, and in fact, the pitch may be a strike or a ball. There are two kinds of possible mistakes in this situation: (1) if the pitch is a strike and the batter does not swing, or (2) if the batter swings when a pitch is not a strike. The batter is actually faced with several alternatives. See Table 8–1:

Table 8–1. The Decision-Making Process as Faced by the Baseball Batter, Showing the Outcome of Responses

Event	Swing	No-Swing
Strike	Possible hit	Possible strike out
Ball	Possible strike out or badly hit ball	Possible walk

The respondent has to weigh the possible pay-offs of his response in terms of rewards and penalties. Past experiences and the present situation will influence expectations and pay-offs. Although the precise methodology for predicting signal detection will not be discussed here, the signal detection theory does permit specific predictions on stimuli detection and behavioral responses.

Information Theory. *Information theory,* also called *communication theory,* is another example of probability theory serving as a basis for a model. Shannon and Weaver are given credit for its development in 1948 and their recent publication (1962) describes the formulation of the theory and latest contributions to it. This descriptive and quantitative theory has been used mainly for verbal learning, with visual displays, and tracking, but it is inviting to speculate on its application to gross motor skills.

The capacity to transmit information is determined by assigning numbers to various magnitudes of stimuli. Uncertainty and information are terms used interchangeably, for the more uncertainty in a situation, the greater information can be of assistance. In other words, information removes or reduces uncertainty. Miller (1956) compares variance to amount of information, since greater variance indicates more uncertainty. In any communication system, man or machine, there is a great deal of variability of what goes in and what comes out. Naturally, a good system will show some relation between input and output. The amount of overlap between input and output, whether expressed as variance or amount of information, is illustrated in Figure 8–2.

The binary digit (two possibilities—yes or no), a bit, is the unit used in the measurement of information and uncertainty. The object, then, is to determine the number of bits (the power to which two must be raised to equal the number of alternatives) needed to solve a particular problem.

Attneave (1959) presents the simple illustrative case where, of sixty-four square cells in a large square, the reader must guess the predesignated cell. With the formula $M = 2^H$, where M = number of alternatives and H = binary possibilities, we substitute $64 = 2^6$ for the example. Six questions, or six bits, are needed to find the cell in question. The first question might be if the cell is in the right thirty-two cells. (1) Yes. Is it in the upper half? (2) No. Is it in the right lower half? (3) Yes. In this line of questioning,

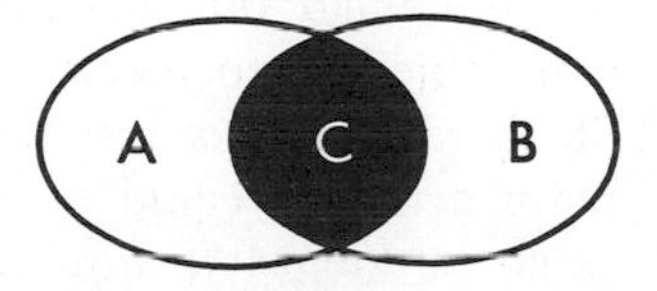

A-Input, Stimuli
B-Output, Response
C-Overlap, Transmitted Information

Figure 8–2. The relationship of output to input.

the correct cell could be discovered in six statements. One bit of information is needed to make a decision between two alternatives, two between four alternatives, four between sixteen alternatives, and six bits for sixty-four alternatives.

We often talk about the uncertainty in stimuli and responses. How much can we remember in a given situation; how many objects or words can be recalled after a short exposure to them? Information transmission is another way of talking about accuracy, and Figure 8–3 serves to represent the information processing system. The sensory processes encode the stimuli, it is then transmitted in the organism, and decoded and translated into muscle movements. No mechanism is perfect; *noise* (amount of uncertainty) may be present anywhere—in the encoder, decoder, or in the transmission where processing takes place. Therefore it is a rarity when the response will equal the stimuli.

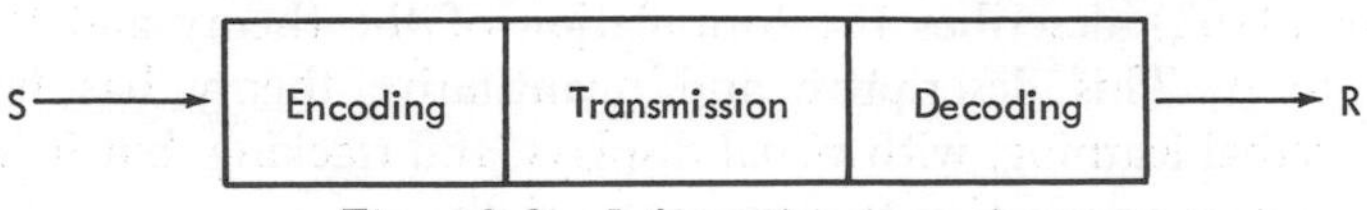

Figure 8–3. Information processing.

Every person has a *channel capacity* above which information cannot be transferred. This capacity can be determined by increasing the input and measuring it with the responses, for if the material can be handled accurately, there will be few errors. With too much of an increase, more errors are expected. Greater input results in increased output, to a point, as there is an asymptotic value for every channel. For example, it is not difficult to distinguish among a few tones. When more tones are presented to the observer, he will be able to recognize and distinguish a limited number of them.

It has been found that 2.5 bits is the average channel capacity of the typical listener making judgments in pitch. This number of bits is equal to about six alternatives. In other words, if an infinite number of alternate pitches are presented, the average listener can only distinguish about six of them. Other studies indicate that unidimensional judgments, for individual sensory attributes, 6.5 bits is average. More dimensions increase the total channel capacity but decrease accuracy for any particular variable. In this case the person makes rough judgments.

Studies have shown that an individual can increase the amount of information he can store. When the object is to memorize a series of numbers, more can be remembered if these numbers are recoded. If the channel capacity of the learner of motor activities could be determined, the appropriate amount of material would be taught to him at one time. Too much material would be wasted and not monitored, too little would not promote maximum use of the time allotted. The search for the number of bits which could be transferred in a motor-learning situation certainly is worthwhile.

In the *discrete information process* a person not only recognizes a stimulus but does something about it. For example, a subject makes one of several responses on a choice reaction time test. The concern for channel capacity and how it affects reaction and movement times has been mainly expressed by Welford (1960). He forwards the *single-channel* hypothesis, that the central mechanisms can handle only one signal or set of signals at one time. If a second signal occurs right after a first signal, response to the second one takes longer, as it has to wait until the central mechanisms are free.

The three major mechanisms needed for information processing are described previously in Chapter 6 in the section entitled "Motivational Factors —Knowledge of Results." To review, the *perceptual mechanism* perceives and identifies information sent from the sense organs; the *translation mechanism* decides the choice of action; and the *central effector mechanism* coordinates and phases the action. *Feedback* from the central effector controls information in the perceptual-transmission process.

Welford theorizes that movement time is determined more by central processes controlling movement than by any factors of muscular effort involved. Choice reaction time is primarily affected by the translation mechanism. Performance is limited by the phasing and coordinating movement of the central mechanism.

Information Processing for the Continuing Case is usually represented by research on compensatory and pursuit tasks. A pursuit task in tracking consists of the subject's attempt to maintain a stylus on a disc rotating on a turntable. A compensatory task is exemplified by an individual trying to maintain a constant reading on a car speedometer, hence the same speed whether traveling on level road or up a hill.

On a pursuit task, there are two elements: a target, which moves on its own, and a follower (cursor). The subject has to perceive the difference and minimize it. There is only one moving element in a compensatory task—a needle—and when it departs from the desired reading, compensation must be made by manipulation. There is more information in the pursuit task since there are two moving elements, hence it is easier to attain greater proficiency under pursuit conditions than under compensatory conditions.

Tracking error is equal to the input error minus the output signal. Performance in tracking is, according to Adams (1961), influenced by task and procedural variables. Task variables are machine-centered and concern the nature of the input signal, the nature of the display, and so on. Procedural variables are man-centered, having to do with instructions, number and length of practice trials, and motivational techniques. In order to understand man's motor skill in tracking, he is compared to a machine as a control unit.

Man-machine Dynamics (*Cybernetics*). The idea that man and machine might be compared on the basis of their activities and means of functioning is by no means new. However, it took the work of Wiener in 1948 to crystallize the relationship and formulate a new science: *cybernetics*. Cybernetics, formally defined, is the study of control processes and mechanisms in machines and human organisms. Human beings are thought of as complex machines. A recent publication of Wiener (1961) contains the theory in its original presentation as well as recent developments in this area.

The cybernetic viewpoint considers biological evidence in terms of mathematical precision; it cuts across many disciplines namely biology, psychology, communication, engineering, mathematics and physiology. Actually, the origin of the word cybernetics is Greek: it is based on "kybernetes" meaning steersman, one who operates a ship and has to keep it on course. The human brain and machine computer are both types of control systems, hence the descriptive term to describe and compare them. Cybernetics deals with control and communication, an analogy to which is the human and his behavior and the electronic transmission system and transmitted events. The digital computer contains an input and output system, a control, and a storage system. The human organism receives stimuli, responds, has a brain as a controlling process, and a storage system in the form of memory.

George's cybernetic theory (1962) provides a conceptual framework for experimental psychology. His easy-to-follow analysis of cybernetics as well as his proposed theory will well reward the interested reader. Cybernetic theory operates under the principle of feedback. *Feedback* occurs when some of the output is isolated and fed back into the machine as input. The principle of feedback is characteristic of all organisms and closed-loop control systems.

Another name for the feedback mechanism is *servomechanism.* A servosystem is a closed-loop control system operating on the principle of feedback. Information, in the form of errors, is sent back to the device controlling the output, the input is then modified, and the output is corrected. Every human organism must know or see his results; otherwise, he will not improve. In a skilled act, responses cause sensations from the proprioceptors, eyes, and other sense organs, and this feedback or knowledge of results tells the person how he is doing. When errors in movement are made, feedback informs us as to the nature and extent of the correction needed. Motor skills with which the physical educator are concerned may be thought of as continuous closed-loop system interactions between performance and the sensory effects of each performance. Activity is controlled and regulated by means of this sensory input.

Adaptive behavior is modified through experience. George (1965) suggests that feedback brings about simple adaptation whereas complete adaptation is the outcome of learning. The typical example of a device that operates on the principle of feedback is the thermostat. This is a self-controlling, self-regulating device, for temperature itself controls the change of temperature. When the temperature is low, the thermostat turns on the heating unit, causing the temperature to rise. When the temperature reaches the desired level, the thermostat turns off the unit, the temperature will eventually fall, and the process will be reversed. Room temperature is the input, furnace activity the output, and the difference between the thermostat and the room temperature is fed back into the system as input.

Theoretical approaches in cybernetics emphasize different areas of interest, but there is no doubt that these theorists display dissatisfaction with traditional learning theory. Namely, they question whether learning is a sequential process, conditioned by reinforced ideal responses to given stimuli. Of great concern to these theorists are the spatial and temporal factors in behavior; more specifically, the feedback mechanism which affects temporal and spatial behavior.

The study of delayed sensory feedback and organized motion in man has led to what Smith (1962) terms a *neurogeometric theory.* This theory is formulated on the premise that all significant behavior is space-structured and based on the sensory feedback process. In Smith's (1964) words:

> The main human factors in the learning and training of motions in man accordingly are not those of stimulus or reward reinforcement but of the dimensions and conditions of relative space displacement of the dynamic efferent-afferent interactions between sensory and motor system.

The justification for studying sensory feedback lies in the fact that man, in most of his behavior, reacts to stimulus changes that are caused by his own actions. Sense receptors feed back information on his movements and provide a check on their precision.

Smith distinguishes sensory feedback which involves intrinsic body mechanisms, from reinforcement which is a part of external stimulus relationships. Learning situations, writes the author, are dependent on space-time patterns of motions. Basic bodily movements are space-structured, and learning is a process of establishing new spatial relationships in patterns of motion. The human organism is not a "victim" of his environment responding passively to environmental stimuli, but rather dynamically with the resultant activity processed in the form of feedback for control and guidance. Smith, with his interest in realistic learning problems and a concern for motor patterns and skills learned outside the laboratory, has demonstrated but another of the recent attempts to move away from an S-R viewpoint of learning which he calls artificial and restricting to our acquisition of knowledge on the learning process. His theory shows much promise for education in general and physical education in particular.

Perhaps cybernetic theory in general has done more for promoting interest and providing information in motor-skill learning than any other type of theory. Gyr and his co-workers (1966) are critical of research utilizing computer simulations of perceptual processes because it has been sensory as opposed to a sensorimotor or active process. They feel that the tasks are artificial. Although the point is a valid one, the relative contributions of this mode of research to other types in creating a new approach to analyzing the learning process certainly cannot be denied. What of the criticism, then, of rat experimentation or nonsense syllable learning as a means of constructing learning principles for human behavior? Fitts (1964) is of the opinion that the development of control and communication mechanisms, in theory and practice, has been very fruitful in providing information on human motor behavior.

This chapter is an attempt to familiarize the reader with the development of learning theory throughout this century. Theories ranging in all directions are surveyed. Where possible, application is made to motor learning. What of theories devoted strictly to the learning of physical education activities or to motor learning in general? Unfortunately, the few theories attempting to handle phenomena related to the learning of motor skills are quite new and therefore lack ample research support as well as elaborate formalized structures.

Motor Learning. Dissatisfaction with general learning theories and miniature models has led to the formulation of tentative motor-learning theories. The word tentative is used, for no doubt these theories will be restructured and elaborated upon with further research. Observations and experimental research have led to theories for handling performance in industrial work, psychomotor tasks (tracking, movement positioning tasks, and so on), and athletic skills.

Although Poulton's (1957) model is geared for predictions in industrial work, it is certainly applicable to the learning of physical education skills. He distinguishes skills as being either closed or open. A *closed skill* depends on internal feedback, i.e., the kinesthetic feedback from the execution of the skill. There are no external requirements; no reference to the environment is needed for the performance of a closed skill. Requirements of the act are therefore predictable, for the concern is for the body's operation in a fixed environment. Such skills can be performed with the eyes closed.

Closed skills are probably similar to the *habitual* athletic skills discussed earlier in this chapter. Fundamental skills involved in diving and gymnastics are basically dependent on the organism's own efforts and independent of the environment.

Poulton describes an *open skill* as one performed either in an unpredictable series of environmental requirements or in an exacting series, predictable or not. However, these skills usually occur in unstable environments. Feedback comes from external and internal sources when open skills are performed, and these skills may be likened to the *perceptual skills* which were discussed in context with habitual skills. Most team and dual activities transpire in environments which are changing unpredictably.

Poulton would probably include advanced gymnastic and diving skills, which require extremely exacting movements, in the category of open skills. Usually associated with closed skills are repetitive, monotonous tasks that demand little, if any, perceptability. Obviously, different requirements are placed on the performer with closed skills than with open skills. These two categories of skills may be divided even further, encouraging more specific consideration for the requirements imposed by different types of tasks.

There are greater barriers to success in skills performed in unpredictable situations and/or skills composed of precision movements. According to Poulton, smooth movements in open skills can be made if (1) the requirements are not too exacting; (2) requirements are presented to the individual before he is ready for them; and (3) the requirements are not separated by inactivity. These considerations are not only basic to industrial work, but athletic performance as well.

Fitts (1964) favors an approach to studying motor-skill learning that contains a framework of three types of theoretical models. These models, already outlined in this chapter, have been termed by Fitts as *communication, control system,* and *adaptive system* models. Communication models deal mainly with *information processing* and *coding;* control system models, or servomechanisms, with *feedback* and the *transfer function* of input to output; and adaptive system models with memory, or *information storage,* and *hierarchical processes,* which handle different levels (higher-order, lower-order) of programs.

Within the general framework of the composite of these three models, it is easier to deal with more concepts and events associated with skill learning. However, Fitts is concerned primarily with tracking tasks and computer operations. His own experiments and the research he chiefly quotes from is far removed from typical physical education research. As such, his approach serves to re-emphasize the wide assortment of tasks that demand motor skill for their successful completion. Perhaps we have reached the point where a general theory of motor-skill performance will not suffice—but rather specific models for specific categories of skills.

Henry (1960) has proposed a Memory Drum Theory of Neuromotor Reaction, that deals with various aspects of motor performance. This theory has been reviewed in essence in Chapter 4; therefore, it need not be treated here. Because Henry is a physical educator, his theory is of interest to others in the profession. Although Henry's own research supports his theory, the theory is limited to concepts related to reaction time, movement time, and the nervous system in general.

The latest attempt at formulating a theory to explain the nature of perceptual-motor learning has been made by Bryant J. Cratty (1966), author of the book, *Movement Behavior and Motor Learning.* He, like Henry, is a physical educator. Their theories are therefore more sensitive then psychologically-oriented theories to the problems faced by physical educators in their teaching situations.

Cratty has incorporated in his theory three levels of factors which presumably influence learning and performance. Level one is represented by general factors in human performance, including level of aspiration, task persistence, and ability to analyze task mechanics. This level contains attributes associated with a wide range of perceptual-motor and cognitive tasks.

Specific ability traits associated with success in perceptual-motor performance are presented in level two. Examples of these abilities are trunk strength, arm-leg speed, and extent flexibility. At the third and highest level are found factors specific to the given task, such as practice conditions, past experience, and the unique movement patterns required by the task.

Cratty calls for the teacher to be aware of all three levels and their interactional effects on skilled performance. General and specific factors operate in the learning of all tasks, according to Cratty's schematization. Although this is no doubt true, one might question why Cratty's second level, which he calls perceptual-motor ability traits, appears to include only abilities that are primarily physical in nature. In fact, the traits he lists have been proposed by Fleishman as representing physical proficiency.

There are other abilities that may account for performance levels, and Fleishman has extensively researched these possibilities as well. From his experiments, he suggests ten psychomotor factors (Fleishman, 1967) that seem to appear consistently in the tasks he utilizes. Their labels are manual dexterity, control precision, multilimb coordination, reaction time, arm-hand steadiness, wrist-finger speed, aiming, speed-of-arm movement, response orientation, and rate control. Certainly, psychomotor abilities should be considered along with physical proficiency measures as important to the attainment of skill.

The theories reported here by no means exhaust those proposed to describe motor learning. Rather, they have been presented in brief form to indicate the directions which motor learning theories are apparently taking.

Summary

The science of psychology is a relatively recent development and consequently theories of learning are in their initial stages of formulation. Although these theories are constantly being revised and new ones emerging because of extensive and intensive research, they have in the past and are in the present offering guidelines which educators might follow in practice.

Theories overlap or are distinguished by emphasis on unique features. For Guthrie, it is the contiguity of the correct response to a given stimulus. Skinner is associated with reinforcement, the Gestaltists with perception and cognition, and cybernetic theorists with spatial-temporal patterning of responses. Theories differ in vocabulary. Stimulus-response, input-output, reinforcement-feedback, and other terms serve to distinguish methods of analyzing the learning process.

Learning theories exhibit many questionable features, and these must be clarified before they will meet with more acceptance in education. The problem areas in the leading theories are as follows: (1) generalizations beyond actual scientific evidence; (2) selective use of facts, interpretation for convenience; (3) social problems not usually considered; (4) impractical and unrealistic application to everyday life; (5) too broad in scope; (6) disregard for developmental factors; and (7) too much concern for mass behavior rather than individual behavior.

Both generalized and specific theories have their respective values. The more general theories provide general laws of learning, consistent over a wide assortment of learning materials. Specific theories are concerned with particular situations and therefore apply to those unique problems associated within the area of interest more adequately. Learning theorists have been primarily interested in verbal learning and classroom methodology. More recent developments indicate trends in which dissatisfaction with traditional theories has resulted in the theories of communication and control. Although tracking studies are the basis for much in the formulation of these theories, at least tracking is a form of perceptual-motor behavior. Without a theory to turn to which physical educators can call their own, they must apply that which appears to be most relevant from the available theories. However, in recent years, a few physical educators have attempted to formulate models for describing motor learning;—a promising note, indeed, and hopefully a trend.

References

ADAMS, JACK A. Human Tracking Behavior, *Psychol. Bull.*, 58:55–79, 1961.

ADAMS, JACK A. Motor Skills, *Annual Rev. Psychol.*, 15:181–202, 1964.

ATTNEAVE, FRED. *Applications of Information Theory to Psychology*, New York: Henry Holt and Co., 1959.

BROADBENT, D. E. *Perception and Communication*, London: Pergamon Press, 1958.

CRATTY, BRYANT J. A Three Level Theory of Perceptual-Motor Behavior, *Quest*, Mon. VI, 3–10, 1966.

ESTES, W. K. The Statistical Approach to Learning Theory, in KOCH, SIGMUND (ed.), *Psychology: A Study of a Science*, Vol. II, New York: McGraw-Hill Book Co., Inc., 1959.

FITTS, PAUL M. Perceptual-Motor Skill Learning, in MELTON, ARTHUR W. (ed.), *Categories of Human Learning*, New York: Academic Press, 1964.

FLEISHMAN, EDWIN A. Development of a Behavior Taxonomy for Describing Human Tasks: A Correlational-Experimental Approach, *J. Appl. Psychol.*, 51:1–10, 1967.

FRANKMAN, JUDITH P., and ADAMS, JACK A. Theories of Vigilance, *Psychol. Bull.*, 59:257–272, 1962.

GEORGE, F. H. *The Brain as a Computer*, London: Pergamon Press, 1962.

GEORGE, F. H. *Cybernetics and Biology*, San Francisco: W. H. Freeman and Co., 1965.

GUTHRIE, E. R. *The Psychology of Learning*, New York: Harper and Brothers, 1935.

GYR, JOHN W.; BROWN, JOHN S.; WILLEY, RICHARD; and ZIVIAN, ARTHUR. Computer Simulation and Psychological Theories of Perception, *Psychol. Bull.*, 65:174–192, 1966.

HEBB, D. O. *The Organization of Behavior*, New York: John Wiley & Sons, 1949.

HENRY, FRANKLIN M. Increased Response Latency for Complicated Movements and a "Memory Drum" Theory of Neuromotor Reaction, *Res. Quart.*, 31:448–458, 1960.

HILGARD, E. R. *Theories of Learning*, New York: Appleton-Century-Crofts, Inc., 1956.

HULL, C. L. *Principles of Behavior*, New York: Appleton-Century, 1943.

JUDD, CHARLES H. *Educational Psychology*, Boston: Houghton Mifflin Co., 1939.

KNAPP, BARBARA. Skill in Sport: *The Attainment of Proficiency*, London: Routledge & Kegan Paul, 1964.

KOFFKA, K. *The Principles of Gestalt Psychology*, New York: Harcourt, 1935.

MELTON, ARTHUR W. (ed.). *Categories of Human Learning*, New York: Academic Press, 1964.

MILLER, GEORGE A. The Magical Number Seven, Plus or Minus Two: Some Limits on our Capacity for Processing Information, *Psychol. Rev.*, 63:81–97, 1956.

POULTON, E. C. On Prediction in Skilled Movements, *Psychol. Bull.*, 54:467–478, 1957.

RESTLE, FRANK. The Relevance of Mathematical Models for Education, in HILGARD, ERNEST R. (ed.), Theories of Learning and Instruction, *Sixty-Third Yearbook of the National Society for the Study of Education*, Chicago: The University of Chicago Press, 1964.

ROCK, IRVIN. Repetition and Learning, *Scientific American*, 199:68–72, 1958.

SHANNON, CLAUDE E., and WEAVER, WARREN. *The Mathematical Theory of Communication*, Urbana: The University of Illinois Press, 1962.

SINGER, ROBERT N. Learning Theory as Applied to Physical Education, *Coll. Phys. Educ. Assoc. Proc.*, 69:59–66, 1966.

SKINNER, B. F. *The Behavior of Organisms*, New York: Appleton-Century, 1938.

SKINNER, B. F. Are Theories of Learning Necessary?, in GOLDSTEIN, HENRY; KRANTZ, DAVID L.; and RAINS, JACK D. (eds.), *Controversial Issues in Learning*, New York: Appleton-Century-Crofts, 1965.

SMITH, KARL U. *Delayed Sensory Feedback and Behavior*, Philadelphia: W. B. Saunders Co., 1962.

SMITH, KARL U.; GOULD, JOHN; and WARGO, LYNN. Sensory Feedback Analysis in Medical Research, *Amer. J. Phys. Medicine*, 43:49–84, 1964.

SWETS, JOHN A. (ed.). *Signal Detection and Recognition by Human Observers*, New York: John Wiley & Sons, Inc., 1964.

THORNDIKE, E. L. *Human Learning*, New York: Century, 1931.

TOLMAN, E. C. There Is More Than One Kind of Learning, *Psychol. Rev.*, 56:144–155, 1949.

WELFORD, A. T. The Measurement of Sensory Motor Performance: Survey and Reappraisal of Twelve Years' Progress, *Ergonomics*, 3:189–230, 1960.

WIENER, NORBERT. *Cybernetics*, New York: The M.I.T. Press and John Wiley & Sons, Inc., 1961.

Annotated Student References

George, F. H. *The Brain as a Computer*, London: Pergamon Press, 1962.

The history, scope, and application of cybernetics to human behavior is written with the uninitiated in mind.

Hilgard, Ernest R. *Theories of Learning*, New York: Appleton-Century-Crofts, Inc., 1956.

One of the finest books dealing with theoretical developments throughout the century—a "must" for any student of learning.

Hilgard, Ernest R. (ed.). Theories of Learning and Instruction, *Sixty-Third Yearbook of the National Society for the Study of Education*, Chicago: The University of Chicago Press, 1964.

A comprehensive analysis of theories of learning; their structures, scope, and practical application to education.

Hill, Winfred F. *Learning: A Survey of Psychological Interpretations*, San Francisco: Chandler Publishing Co., 1963.

Interprets learning theories with clarity and simplicity, offering distinctions and comparisons for those in education.

Koch, Sigmund (ed.). *Psychology: A Study of a Science*, Vols. I and II, New York: McGraw-Hill Book Co., Inc., 1959.

Contains the systematic formulations of the leading psychologists, prepared especially for these volumes by the same psychologists.

Luce, R. Duncan (ed.). *Developments in Mathematic Psychology*, Illinois: The Free Press of Glencoe, 1960.

Surveys three of the extensive mathematical developments in psychology: the discrete theory, statistical models, and models handling manual tracking.

Miller, George A. The Magical Number Seven, Plus or Minus Two: Some Limits on Our Capacity for Processing Information, *Psychol. Rev.*, 63:81–97, 1956.

Geared for the uninitiated on information theory, the article is written simply, clearly, and interestingly.

Wolman, Benjamin B. *Contemporary Theories and Systems in Psychology*, New York: Harper & Brothers, Publishers, 1960.

A comprehensive picture of contemporary psychological theory.

9

Sociopsychological Factors

To view man's behavior as being dependent only on environmental manipulations and a simple conditioning process of responses to stimuli is inconsistent with contemporary thoughts on the matter. Man is presently viewed as an organism that responds totally when stimulated. With reference to the learning and performing of motor skills, interest and success will certainly depend on motor abilities, educational methodology, and emotional and personality attribute measures.

Man's performance is thus potentially affected by many factors. How he reacts in a given situation is reflected by sociopsychological influences. His activity is social-oriented when the performance occurs with, against, or in front of others. Social presence is a usual experience in everyday activities, and its effect may be one of motivation or anxiety, facilitated or inhibited performance, depending on the personality structure of the organism.

An individual's personality, his characteristic way of behaving, is the result of learning and experiences in life. Heredity sets limits and predisposes the person to react in certain ways to environmental events. One's actions and feelings are the result of previous experiences; and the interaction of many traits, some more modifiable than others, determines his particular uniqueness. Personality may be viewed from two vantage points. One, the effect or impact an individual has on other people usually results in his evaluation on a social basis. For instance, is he pleasing and popular? Besides this so-called *external* personality, another type may represent the *real* him. Personality, according to most experts in this area, should be defined in terms of the way a person really is, not necessarily the way others see him. Other people may not see the real him. In determining an individual's personality, a difficult endeavor indeed, an indication of his behavioral patterns and actions is also uncovered. When we know an individual's personality, we understand him better. To know someone's personality, then, is to be able to predict his behavior.

The prime concern of this chapter is to analyze the role of personality in activity interests and athletic success, as well as how it is affected by sports participation. Cultural and group impact on behavior and other aspects of the sociopsychological area are either omitted or summarily treated because of space limitations.

Personality

Composition of Personality. This book does not undertake to delve into the many diverse interpretations of personality theories offered as to how personality develops and affects behavior. We are more concerned with a basic understanding of the term *personality,* in order to make it easier to discuss the inter-relationships between personality and motor activity.

Let us accept Guilford's (1959) view that personality is composed of a unique pattern of traits. He groups these traits in classes called modalities, and a diagram of the modalities of traits which interact to compose personality is found in Figure 9–1. He distinguishes modalities pertaining to the following features: soma, motivation, aptitude, and temperament.

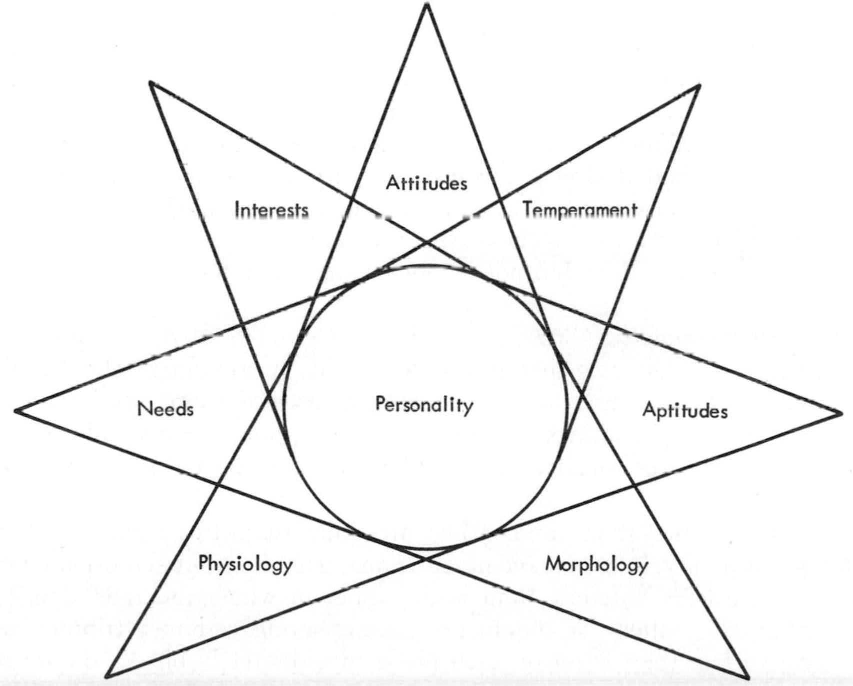

Figure 9–1. Modalities of traits representing different aspects of personality. (From Guilford, J. P. *Personality,* New York: McGraw-Hill Book Co., Inc., 1959.)

The *somatic* modality includes physiological and morphological traits. The former concerns organic functions and the latter physical structure, such as height and weight. Three traits—needs, interests, and attitudes—are encompassed in the *motivational* modality. The *aptitude* modality includes one's abilities to perform at given tasks. Finally, the *temperament* modality refers to those traits that make up a person's disposition.

Rather than observing most traits, we observe acts that represent traits. These acts, indicating the nature of one's traits, serve to remind us that traits differ as to degree, not in kind, from person to person. The above traits (and perhaps many more) interact in such a way as to represent a distinct individual. Since most traits are modifiable, in varying degrees, personality can be looked upon as a general characteristic which also may be adapted. Perhaps this is one of the leading concepts guiding physical educators in believing that their organized programs will have beneficial effects on the participant's social, emotional, and personal behavior. The process of change though, is a slow tedious process. The true personality develops gradually. A quiet sensitive person does not become an outgoing, devil-may-care individual overnight. An emotionally unstable person took many years to get that way; it will take a lengthy period of time for him to learn socially-desirable qualities. Certain traits are relatively stable throughout life whereas others are modified with new experiences.

This discussion leads to another problem. How do we know what type of personality one has? How do we measure it? A reference to personality type infers the relative arrangement of a large segment of general behavioral characteristics. Without general classifications, it can be stated that everyone has a different personality type. Therefore, it is quite convenient to categorize individuals according to predetermined criteria. Typically, personality-measuring techniques and devices are concerned with the motivational modality (needs, interests, and attitudes) and the temperament modality. There are many methods of measuring these aspects of personality, each of which contributes to our knowledge but not without being prone to severe criticism.

Measuring Personality. Since personality is viewed from diverse points of view, it is understandable that approaches for its measurement should, likewise, range in many directions. Personality is assessed from (1) interviews, (2) observation, (3) ratings, (4) projective tasks, and (5) psychological inventories. Defined personality types will be dependent on the evaluative tools used.

Interviews, observations, and ratings are quite subjective means of determining personality. Interview and observational techniques are self explanatory; ratings are usually obtained from rating scales in which the rater develops a number of questions or statements for measuring certain attributes and proceeds to rate the subject on each phase, not discretely but to the degree that it pertains to the subject. Ratings may be on a 1 to 5 basis, with 1 indicating little relevance to the subject and 5 indicating extreme relevance.

In any case, a scale is formulated in order that the attributes may be measured in degrees rather than absolutes.

Projection-type tests are primarily used as clinical tools and they should be administered and evaluated by clinically-trained psychologists. These tests contain unstructured stimulus objects, and as such, the subject is encouraged to respond freely to certain stimuli and thus reveal his true personality. Probably the two most popular and widely-used instruments are the Rorschach ink-blot test and the Thematic Apperception Test (TAT). The Rorschach test consists of a series of cards, each containing a complex ink blot about which the subject is asked to interpret and orally express himself. Ambiguous situations concerning people are represented by the TAT pictures. The person is asked to relate a story concerning each picture orally. In all projection tests, it is hoped that the subject will project himself in his interpretations.

By far the most frequently used technique for obtaining information on a person's personality is through the personality inventory. This may be verified by merely glancing at the completed research on personality in psychology, education, and physical education. Inventories usually contain questions or statements concerning personal feelings, attitudes, and interests, and are designed to measure various aspects of one's personality. As such, they are easy to score (although validity measures may be questioned), permit group testing, and do not require an exceptional amount of administration time or clinical background on the part of the examiner.

They have been criticized on various fronts, namely: falsifications on the part of the respondent, willful or otherwise; the questions are interpreted differently by different people; the individual may not know himself well enough to respond accurately; and the test items are questionable in terms of what they are supposed to be measuring.

Here are some of the more popular instruments for making personality inventories.

1. *The Minnesota Multiphasic Personality Inventory* (*MMPI*). This is probably the most clinically oriented, and is used extensively in research. It was designed to diagnose pathological conditions, not for discriminating individuals from a normal population, yet it is amazing how often it is employed in the latter case in published research.
2. *The Cattell 16 Personality Factor Test.* This is another popular instrument. Through the factor analysis method, Cattell obtained 16 independent scales representing aspects of the personality.
3. *The California Test of Personality* (*CPI*). This has been designed with four variations, for four different age groups from elementary school to college.
4. *The Edward's Personal Preference Schedule* (*EPPS*). This test is based on needs and is scored in such a way as to determine one's need to achieve, to be dominant, to affiliate, and the like. It is one of the few instruments that employs the forced-choice technique; that is,

the interviewee is faced with paired descriptions (each unrelated) of himself for each question, and he must select the one that best represents him.

There are many other personality inventories currently in use, but those mentioned here probably are most frequently utilized for research purposes. Many references to these instruments appear in the research reported in all sections of this chapter. Although personal reports are to be viewed with caution, the instruments and the experimental data obtained from them do provide insight into some of the personality-sport problems.

Personality and Motor Activity

By our definition of personality everything we do will have an effect on us. By the same token, our behavior will be determined by unique personal characteristics. There have been numerous investigations and articles depicting relationships between participation in motor activities and personality, social status and athletic achievement, and in general a combination of social and personal factors with proficiency or interest in physical activities.

To date many of these studies have merely scratched the surface as to the interrelationship of the above variables. The lack of well-validated scientific measuring instruments, precise research methodology, and cause-and-effect experiments, leads to generalized assumptions in this area. In a sense however, perhaps we are no worse off here than in any other aspect of the study of motor learning and performance. Previous chapters of this book have presented representative investigations of various dimensions of motor learning, investigations which, by the limitations of their scope, are better controlled and therefore less resistant to questioning than research pertaining to social and personality factors. Even so, inconsistent findings from experiment to experiment measuring similar variables have, in many cases, permitted nothing more than very general statements of learning principles.

Therefore, the evidence described in this chapter should be weighed, not for its limitations, but rather for the insight it provides in better understanding sociopsychological problems associated with motor performance. Perhaps these studies may be classified according to those concerned with (1) activity interests and personality; (2) the effect of sports participation on personality; (3) success in sport and personality; and (4) social status and athletic accomplishments.

The first two areas are directly related. There is general agreement on the concept that participation in sports can and does affect the individual's social interactions and personal qualities either favorably or unfavorably. Less thought has been given to an alternate supposition. An individual with certain personality traits might select sports in which to participate that satisfy his unique needs. It is extremely probable that people choose particular sports because of their personalities as well as change them because of experience in these activities. How to determine the relative effect of each condition is a perplexing problem indeed, especially since typical studies on this topic have merely determined the relationship between personal, social, and activity participation variables. In other words, the obtained correlations indicate existing relationships, not factors that contributed to or resulted from participation.

The possible interaction between tendencies toward participation and effects of participation has been diagrammed by Fraleigh and is located in Figure 9–2. The circular relationships of skill and achievement in physical education activities to social and personal adjustment may be observed. It is probable that better adjustments accompany athletically developed skill and better adjusted individuals tend to participate in such activities.

Activity Interest and Personality. It appears that particular activities attract certain types of individuals. Although far from conclusive, research evidence on the personality nature of athletes representing different sports indicates that athletes may be distinguished by sport on personality-measuring instruments.

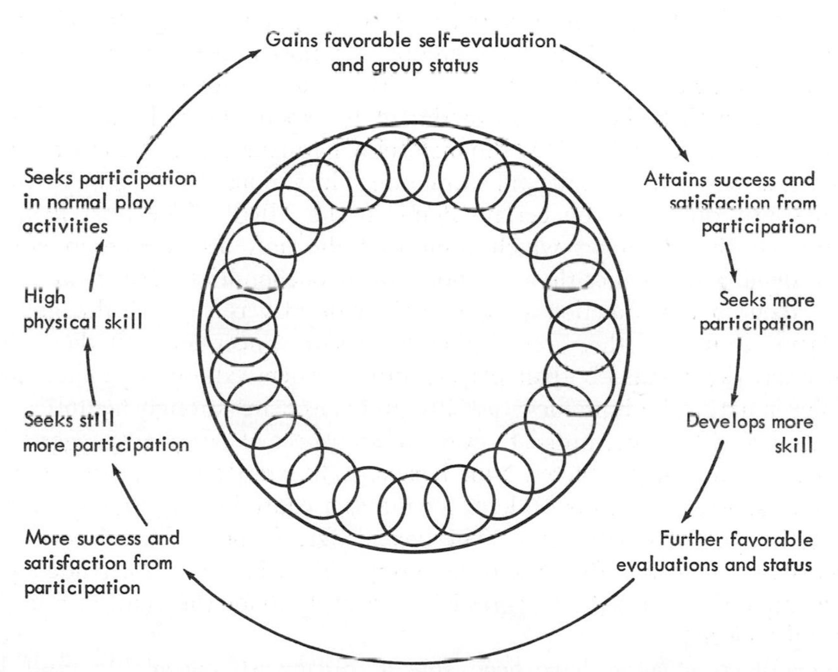

Figure 9–2. A theoretical explanation of the relationship between greater skill and achievement in physical play activities and better social and emotional adjustment. (From Fraleigh, Warren. The Influence of Play Upon Social and Emotional Adjustment, with Implications for Physical Education, *Coll. Phys. Educ. Assoc. Proc.*, 59:268–273, 1956.)

Weight-lifting is quite different in nature from most sports; hence it is not surprising that researchers should find weight-lifters to have distinguishable personality types. Thune (1949) and Harlow (1951) are in agreement although they employed opposing personality measuring devices on separate samples of weight-lifters. Thune compared 100 YMCA weight-lifters to 100 athletes who were not weight-lifters on personality and attitude measures. He noted that weight-lifters were shy, lacked confidence, and were very concerned with their appearance. In conclusion, he stated that the sport of weight-lifting appeals to individuals differing in needs, interests, and personality from other types of people.

Harlow utilized two similar though smaller groups of subjects. He administered two projective personality tasks to them, the Thematic Apperception Test and the Sentence Completion Test, and found a significant difference between the groups on thirteen of eighteen variables. Among the distinguishing qualities, weight-lifters were observed to have greater feelings of masculine inadequacy, more homosexual tendencies, more of an inability to cope with the environment, more narcissistic feelings, and stronger feelings of dependency. The author reasons that weight-lifters go into their specialty to compensate for feelings of masculine inadequacy and inferiority.

Evidence distinguishing other types of athletes is not quite as clear cut. Isolated studies have found differences between groups of athletes, although applying particular labels to these groups is almost impossible, primarily because measurable personality traits vary with the instruments used and consistency in research findings from experiment to experiment is lacking. Slusher (1964) administered the MMPI to high school athletes representing wrestling, basketball, baseball, football, and swimming. The various athletic groups scored significantly differently on certain items in the MMPI. The least neurotic group was the swimmers which comprised the only athletic group not to score significantly higher than the norm on hypochondriasis (worry and concern about bodily functions). The basketball players showed the greatest deviation from the other groups; they were very concerned with themselves and easily depressed. Football players and wrestlers exhibited profiles quite similar in nature; both profiles were interpreted as being strongly neurotic.

Husman (1955) attempted to evaluate an aspect of personality, aggression tendencies, in college athletes. Nine boxers, eight wrestlers, nine cross-country runners, and seventeen nonathletes serving as a control group were given two projective-type personality tests. The boxers were found to have less over-all intensity of aggression than the other groups. They had less of a tendency to be extrapunitive, to express aggression outwardly, than the runners and the control subjects.

Not all investigators have been able to distinguish personality traits between athletic groups. Keogh (1959) obtained data from 167 college students on the Larson Motor Ability Test, the Athletic Participation Index, and the California Personality Inventory (CPI). An analysis of the data yielded no significant relationships between motor ability or athletic participation and eighteen scales of the CPI. Lakie (1962) selected five scales of the Omnibus Personality Inventory—Complexity of Outlook, Social Maturity, Social Introversion, Liberalism, and Aggressive Activity—and administered them to 230 athletes from different colleges. The athletes represented such sports as basketball, football, golf, tennis, track, and wrestling. No significant differences on the scales were found between the sport groups.

However, interestingly enough, athletes from the various institutions of higher learning differed on some of the personality scales. Athletes at a private college scored significantly higher on Social Maturity than the athletes representing the other colleges. There is the possibility that certain schools attract different kinds of people.

The preceding investigations have dealt with varsity athletics and therefore have limited application to our problem of determining the relationship between personality traits and activity interests. Flanagan (1951) was interested in the personality factors contributing to choice of activity in the college physical education program. Students were studied from six classes: fencing, basketball, boxing, swimming, volleyball, and badminton. A personality inventory, constructed from other instruments, was used to measure such traits as masculinity-femininity, ascendance-submission, extroversion-introversion, and emotional stability-emotional instability.

A number of traits were found to distinguish the groups. For instance, fencers were more ascendant, higher in dominance, than basketball players, volleyball players, and boxers. Fencers were also more feminine than basketball players. Badminton players were found to be more extroverted than volleyball players and of all the groups, volleyball players were noted to be the least emotionally stable. Because of the differences in personality of the groups of individuals selecting the various activities, Flanagan concludes that personality must play a role in activity selection.

In summary, then, although empirical evidence and common sense would lead us to believe that activity interest and participation is based on numerous factors, one of which is needs as defined by our unique personality structures, the research completed thus far confirms only a few hypotheses. Better personality assessment tools, better experimental methodology, and longitudinal studies will provide more concrete data as to how personality traits interact to influence activity selection.

Athletic Versus Nonathletic Participation. There have been many approaches undertaken to determine personal and social qualities associated with athletic participation as contrasted with nonparticipation. The difficulty in ascertaining personality differences due to participation as contrasted with the effect of certain personal characteristics on attracting individuals to particular activities has already been mentioned. In most cases, personality changes as an effect of athletic participation are inferred rather than proven. Therefore, it must be with great reservation that we assign any personality adjustment values for participants in programs of physical education. Research as it fits into the context of this discussion is presented to provide information on athlete and nonathlete similarities and differences in the personality area.

Effect of Sports Participation on Personality. We in physical education claim that student participation in our programs causes certain favorable personality changes to occur. If this concept could be substantially verified, the belief in the psychological and social contributions offered by our profession to participators in our programs would be greatly enhanced.

Some evidence for the benefits of athletic experience is offered by Sperling (1942). He compared athletes, intramural participants, and nonathletes on certain personality measures. Varsity and intramural players scored significantly higher on ascendance, extroversion, and motivation for power than nonathletes; but more importantly, the athletes with more experience had better adjustment scores than individuals with less athletic experience. A rather interesting finding was that those athletes representing group and individual sports did not differ from each other on the personality items measured. Individual sports members were more similar to the nonathletic group than were team sports members.

Cattell (1960) offers further evidence on the effect of extensive athletic experience. Former Olympic champions were significantly different from the average population on four personality factors as measured by the Cattell 16 PF Inventory. The athletes scored (1) greater in ego strength, i.e., they were less neurotic; (2) higher in dominance; (3) higher on being more outgoing; and (4) lower on worrying. Once again there is the problem of explaining these differences. Either certain psychological attributes predetermine success or athletic success modifies certain personality qualities.

The results of a study by Skubic (1956) implies the benefits to be derived from participation in little league and middle league baseball. Boys in the leagues were rated as being better emotionally and socially adjusted than nonplayers. Another investigation of little league participants, completed by Seymour (1956), raises some interesting questions. Little leaguers were studied before and after the baseball season, and the results listed when comparing little league participants to nonparticipants were (1) the needs and problems were no different between the groups and (2) little leaguers scored higher *before* and *after* play on personality traits and social acceptance.

Longitudinal studies more extensive than Seymour's study are needed to clarify the situation. However, his results do point to the fact that participants on athletic teams may very well be better adjusted individuals prior to their organized athletic experiences. Nevertheless, let us review a few more representative cross-sectional investigations in this area. Booth (1958) compared 141 college athletes to 145 nonathletes and found some differences in personality measures between athletes and nonathletes and participation in individual, team, and team-individual sports. As an example, varsity athletes scored lower on anxiety than other groups measured.

Finally, Cassel and Childers (1963) offer evidence that suggests little difference between high school football players, the student body of that school, and the norms of the country on leadership patterns, social insight, and personality tension needs.

The effects on personality development of participation in varsity athletics and programs of physical education may be favorable, detrimental, or unnoticeable. The traits which comprise one's personality, especially as they relate to social experiences, are learned; they are not inborn. Obviously, the physical educator and coach have the opportunity to influence the behavior and values of the participants favorably.

If more concrete evidence could be offered on the benefits of participation in organized physical activity, the value of athletics would be acknowledged. More important, there is the possibility of prescribing certain physical education activities for personality remedial purposes. Even as exercises are prescribed for those low in physical fitness, desired changes in a person's personality and social attitudes might require the utilization of particular physical education activities. For example, we might wish the quiet, shy, introverted youngster to become more socially conscious in order to relate better to his peers. Participation in well-organized team sports might be the answer. The unconfident and socially rejected person might need to develop skill in an individual sport. Achievement in this endeavor could possibly result in greater security and acceptance.

Hazelton and Piper (1940) studied the social values of a team game and of two individual sports as judged by the attitudes of freshman college women. The authors hypothesized that social values could be attained from a team game more surely and easily than from individual sports. Questionnaires were given to groups of students who had participated in speedball, tennis, and archery. The percentage of girls in speedball was compared for each attitude with the percentage of students in tennis and archery responding to that attitude. The authors concluded that students who had taken speedball (a team game) developed more in certain social traits than did students taking archery and tennis (individual sports).

The sore loser and poor winner might learn sportsmanship when entering into teacher-guided team, individual, and dual sports. A sense of values and ethics might also be cultivated, and this possibility is mentioned with particular reference to juvenile delinquents. The individual with a strong need to succeed and excel has an outlet and a means of expression in sports. The hypotheses could continue indefinitely. Unfortunately, the absence of confirming studies is a thorn in the side of physical educators. Whether specific sports develop certain personality patterns is a controversial issue since there is a discrepancy in the findings of the investigations concerned with this issue.

Some of the aspects of personality favorably affected by experience in physical activities have been conjectured by Steinhaus (1966) in the following statements.

Self-confidence is important for winning in sports and for effectiveness in daily life. No doubt the earliest experiences with physical activities in the home have much to do with this. A child that is permitted to enjoy success in activities that have an element of risk in them will gain self-assurance which an over-protected child that is forbidden to try dangerous activities, will never attain.

The success-related feeling of self-worth, self-respect, and self-acceptance which is essential to a high level of fitness takes form early in life, at a time when big muscle activity is virtually the only way the child has of expressing itself. The direction taken in this early beginning may well determine the direction for life. Equally if not more important is the fact that one can have no real confidence or respect for others if he does not have confidence and respect for himself. Positive attitudes toward self and others are basic to a social structure that places worth on an individual, as in a true democracy. The earliest feelings of confidence in self no doubt come to the child from success in the performance of large muscle activities.

Success in Sports and Personality. Skills are extremely important in athletic achievement. Physical characteristics and developed motor patterns contribute to success, but so does that intangible something—the urge to win, the need for achievement, the willingness to suffer and forego pleasures during training. The psychological factors that interact within an individual to push him just a little further in his endeavors have only recently received the attention they deserve.

During the Olympics at Tokyo in the fall of 1964, many scientists studied various physiological, anatomical, sociological, and psychological aspects of the participating athletes. In an effort to distinguish champion athletes from nonchampions, psychological traits were compared between these groups as well as among the athletes within each sport. Preliminary reports indicated that male champions tend to be more introverted and sensitive than lesser competitors, although these leaders generally seem to have more than average emotional stability otherwise. It would seem reasonable to expect that a person who is introspective, who constantly evaluates his performance, and who is rarely satisfied with his efforts, would perform more consistently with his motor capacity in a given sport. Proficiency in sports is a result of the interaction of physiological and psychological variables.

Another personality quality of apparent importance is the need or desire to achieve. High drive for success is a tremendous motivational factor, often distinguishing the best from the almost best. An experiment by Johnson, Hutton, and Johnson (1954) serves to demonstrate the relationship between such personality measures as this and ultimate success in athletic performance. These investigators measured certain personality variables of twelve outstanding athletes from different sports on two projective tests, the Rorschach and the House-Tree-Person (H-T-P) Test. Compared to test norms, the athletes showed extreme aggression, a lack of emotional control, high anxiety, high self-assurance, high levels of aspiration, and in general, a strong need to achieve.

Another interesting aspect of the personality is its ability to adapt to given situations. In other words, the immediate sense of athletic competition may bring out certain personal tendencies not usually revealed. Another investigation by Johnson and Hutton (1955) would tend to indicate this. Eight college varsity wrestlers were given a projection personality test before the wrestling season, four to five hours before the first match of the season, and the morning after competition. The data indicated increased aggressive feelings and neurotic signs on the part of the wrestlers before the event and a return to their original condition the following morning.

Returning to the problem of winners versus almost winners, of starters versus bench warmers, and similar comparisons, oftentimes it is felt that the difference is not merely one of demonstrated skills. There is some evidence to support the contention that better athletes display different personality patterns than poorer athletes. Unfortunately, these differences are not always favorable to the superior athletes. Consider, for example, Schendel's (1965) study, in which he administered the California Personality Inventory (CPI) to ninth grade, twelfth grade, and college subjects. Although he was also concerned with athlete versus nonathlete personality differences at these stages of education (and specific differences were found), let us examine the data relevant to outstanding athletes, regular players, and substitute athletes. No contrast in personality was observed between these groups in the ninth grade, but the highest-rated twelfth grade and college athletes demonstrated less desirable personal-social psychological characteristics than athletes with a lower rating.

The findings in an investigation by La Place (1954) apparently contradict those mentioned in the Schendel study. La Place chose to compare professional baseball players from the American and National Leagues, designated because of this status as being successful athletes, to Class D league baseball players, labeled as unsuccessful athletes because of their lower status. The MMPI distinguished the major leaguers, minor leaguers, and general population on certain personality items. Profiles of the two baseball groups are illustrated in Figure 9–3.

Major league baseball players scored significantly lower on the Schizophrenia Scale than minor leaguers and the general population. In fact, the minor leaguers scored significantly higher than the general population on this scale. On the Psychopathic Deviate Scale, which measures unacceptable social values such as a tendency to lie and cheat, the major leaguers were found to be significantly lower than the minor leaguers. In general, it was concluded that both groups of baseball players had the same strong drives but the minor leaguers had other traits detrimental to their personalities. Whereas the minor leaguers lacked self-discipline, the major leaguers were better adjusted.

Other findings of the study are in line with previous ones discussed in this

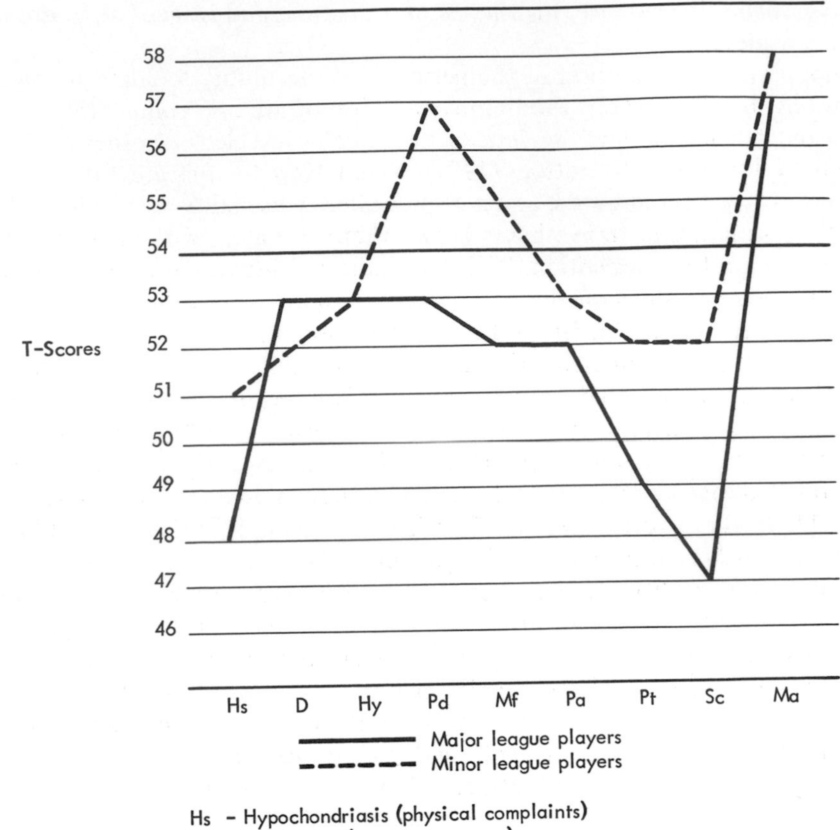

Figure 9–3. MMPI profiles of major league and minor league players. A T-score of more than T54 indicates a significant profile score over the general population. The major leaguers scored higher in Hypomania (strong aggressive drive) and the minor leaguers had significant scores on the Psychopathic Deviate, Femininity of Interests, and Hypomania scales (associated with behavior-problem individuals). (From La Place, John P. Personality and Its Relationship to Success in Professional Baseball, *Res. Quart.*, 25:313–319, 1954.)

section. The successful players scored significantly greater than the general population on the Depression Scale, the tendency to worry, to be sensitive. Both major and minor league groups were higher than the general population on the following scales: Hysteria (frankness, worry), Hypomania (strong drive, ambition), and Interest (sensitivity).

At the present time, it is surprising to note that very few researchers are devoting their energies toward the discovery of the psychological make-up of athletes as a group of selected individuals and the psychological structure of different athletic groups. Fortunately, such psychologists as Ogilvie and Tutko have combined forces to answer some of the individual psychological factors associated with improved athletic performance. After examining numerous professional and amateur athletes representing various sports, they have outlined personality profiles for athletes in general as well as for athletes representing selected sports.

Through their preliminary research, Ogilvie and Tutko (1967) have identified the following tentative factors as being related to outstanding athletic achievement:

1. Need for achievement.
2. Endurance. Ability to apply oneself over a period of time.
3. Resistance to stress. Ability to maintain poise.
4. Dominance.
5. Leadership qualities. But a nonjoiner, socially.
6. Coachability. An openness to learning.
7. Intrapunitive. Ability to bear pain.
8. Self-assertive. Bold.
9. Intelligence. Higher than the college average.

Athletes have been found to be a little higher than average in extroversion and less neurotic than nonparticipants.

As advances are made in understanding general group behavior as well as individual personality differences, coaches and physical educators will be better able to determine psychological potential for success. Each athlete needs to be motivated in a different manner, and a sensitive and informed coach will realize individual differences in personality profiles and will employ techniques of motivating performances consistent with the profile dissimilarities.

It does appear as if superior athletes may be distinguished from lesser athletes on certain personality measures. Whether these differences are due to heredity or caused by experiences in life can only be conjectured. Nevertheless, the personal characteristics already mentioned, namely need to achieve, sensitivity, and personal endurance are strongly related to athletic success.

Social Status and Athletic Achievement

There appears to be no doubt of the positive relationship between athletic success and social acceptance and adjustment, especially with younger children. Proficiency in motor activities is a respected quality in contemporary civilization, and with it comes social status. Social prestige has an important impact on personality, and it is no wonder that we typically expect a more favorable personality development to occur with participation in physical education activities.

The school is responsible for meeting the personality needs of its students. Of a number of recommendations for enacting this objective, Symonds (1948) lists *first* and as being foremost the opportunity for boys and girls to engage in sports competition. The potential value of play actvities and organized forms of athletic competition to personal and social adjustment is beyond question. Numerous investigations have reported similar findings on the relationship between social status and adjustment and athletic participation. A few investigations are examined here.

At the elementary school level, proficiency in motor skills is very important for social acceptance and prestige. For instance, Clarke and Greene (1963) using seventy-eight boys ten years of age found a positive relation between peer status and athletic ability. In another study, Volberding (1949) determined the characteristics of successfully socially adjusted youngsters versus those who were unsuccessful in social adjustment. The better adjusted children were more intelligent, more interested in active play, and interested in play in competitive groups.

Similar results have been obtained with junior high school children. McCraw and Tolbert (1953) studied the relationship of social status to athletic ability with 438 boys. The best liked individuals scored higher on an index of athletic ability, and a moderately high relationship was noted between athletic ability and sociometric status. These investigators interpreted their data as indicating that athletic participation should be encouraged in order that social status might be improved. The importance of an interest in participating in activities to social success was further demonstrated by Bretsch (1952). Six hundred and ninety-six boys and girls were divided into three groups of social status as determined by sociometric techniques. The well-accepted group performed more social skills—many of which were athletic in nature, e.g., tennis, swimming—above average as contrasted with the middle and poorly accepted groups. This top group also displayed more versatility via diversified interests in a wide range of activities.

The same pattern unfolds at the high school level. In Biddulph's (1954) study, two groups of subjects were formed on the basis of their scores on six tests of athletic achievement. The high athletic achievement group was significantly higher in self-adjustment, as measured by the CPI. Although no differences between groups were found on social adjustment when the CPI was used, two other measuring techniques favored the athletic group.

Participation in physical activities may even make the difference between finishing or not completing high school. An analysis of the students in a large Chicago high school revealed some surprising relationships (Thomas, 1954). Not one person who dropped out of school before the end of the third year had participated in even one extracurricular activity, whereas 89 per cent of those who graduated that year had done so. Evidently it was not the number of activities that was important, but rather a question of whether any were engaged in. Of all those factors studied that might contribute to becoming a drop-out, the activity factor was most related to whether a student would graduate from high school. Although this investigation was concerned with all types of extracurricular activities, the implication for programs of physical education is certainly present.

It can be observed through these few representative studies that social status can be greatly enhanced through success in sport. Moreover, interest and participation in many activities lead to and is part of healthy social development. Certain actions of an individual, as reflected by his values, needs, and interests, will also determine his social acceptance. Let us now turn to some of those personal qualities composing a personality that will influence social approval and be influenced by social mores.

Character. A term often used interchangeably with personality or as a component of it is *character*. Exemplified through behavior, character may be conceived, in popular terminology, to be good or strong. Good character refers to moral behavior, to behavior which is acceptable according to social standards and expectations. On the other hand, strong character implies actions that are persevering, consistent, and enduring. Both applications of the term are certainly not independent of each other; both are interpreted in accordance with the standards set up by society.

We usually think of character as relating to morals and value judgments whereas personality is used in a social context to denote popularity. This convenient distinction would be challenged by psychologists. But it does serve the purpose of creating a frame of reference for the usage of each term. Other psychologists would argue that personality and character are synonymous terms or, perhaps, that personality is composed of two parts: temperament and character.

Why does a person exemplify good character? Are character traits generalized over a series of situations or specific to a given situation? In answer to the first question, Stagner (1961) offers five possible reasons for the existence of ideal behavior or integrity: (1) social pressure to conform to accepted practice and desire to establish a good reputation; (2) personal expectancy whereby certain values are developed which the person wants to live up to; (3) impulse control; (4) perceptual differences; and (5) will power. Research on the second question does not yield definite results. There is evidence to favor the specificity of character traits, e.g., a person may cheat in school on written tests but not cheat with money; or the relative generality of these traits, for there are individuals who are relatively consistent and predictable in their behavior.

In order to study the relationship of character development to organized physical activities, it is first necessary to delve more deeply into some of its component parts. It was mentioned before that a reference to one's character is also a reference to his value standards. The overlapping and complex structure of values and attitudes necessitates an examination of their differences as well as the role of physical education in their development.

Values and Attitudes. Our feelings toward something, our dispositions to evaluate and/or act in a certain way to certain stimuli are learned and develop with experience and maturity or even from tradition. These attitudes or ways of regarding something become more pronounced with age. They may be formed because of personal experience with the object or in the situation, rendering favorable or unfavorable attitudes. Complete lack of personal involvement will not hinder the formation of attitudes, for tradition, culture, subculture, and familial attitude formation encourage similar thought patterns in the member. For example, there are many people who have no valid reason for disliking Negroes and Jews, yet do so because of traditional biases. In this case, an attitude is a predisposition to evaluate someone or something as good or bad, as desirable or undesirable.

The importance of the many types of experiences occurring with age in influencing attitudinal patterns has been demonstrated in experiments as well as through empirical observations. Extremely young children do not display the prejudices older children do, and adulthood brings fairly well-established attitudes. With age comes a greater awareness of social expectancies and pressures and a desire to conform to the value system of a culture or subculture.

The introduction of the word *value* in the previous sentence serves to place it in the context of our discussion and to point out its relationship to an attitude. The value system of a society establishes certain standards that provide direction to an attitude and account for its persistence. Attitudes are conditioned by values, they are not inseparable. Our attitude to make a choice from a number of alternatives is mediated by personal values. Some psychologists think of values as generalized attitudes, since attitudes supposedly have fairly specific objects. Regardless of semantics, both have a place in personality formation. The sequence of events leading to a value choice may be thought to occur in the following manner:

Expression of personality → attitudes and values → motivation → choice

Attitudes and values are primarily social in nature but also represent the individualized response. In other words, although social pressure will result in a great amount of conformity, each person perceives situations differently and varies in needs, desires, values, and other characteristics. Not only will individuals react dissimilarly in situations, but the same individuals may not be consistent in their values. The question of whether a person is dominated by a single unitary value system or demonstrates inconsistent values is a debatable issue. Once again, it appears as if people may fall into either category.

An interesting topic is the relationship of established attitudes to learning. If the matter to be learned contradicts these attitudes, possibly learning and retention will be hampered. One of the best examples of this occurrence has been reported by Levine and Murphy (1943) concerning the learning of controversial material. Learning as we have seen is not a simple conditioning process, and even our values and needs affect our perception and ultimately what we learn. This attitudinal effect on learning has been designated as *frame of reference.*

In the Levine and Murphy experiment two groups were formed, one strongly pro-communist and the other strongly anti-communist. All subjects first learned neutral prose material in order to determine their relative abilities at this task, and both groups were rated as being similar. Following this, both groups learned two passages, one pro-communist, the other anti-communist. They studied for four weeks and were tested for retention during a five-week period, and the data are illustrated in the form of curves in Figures 9–4.

Although the pro-Soviet selection did not distinguish the two groups significantly during the learning phase of the study, a significant difference in favor of the pro-communist group was observed during the retention period. A significant marked superiority of the anti-communist group over the pro-communist group on the anti-Soviet selection was found both during learning and retention test intervals. There is a tendency to selectively perceive and recall, to remember that which supports our social attitudes rather than that which conflicts with them.

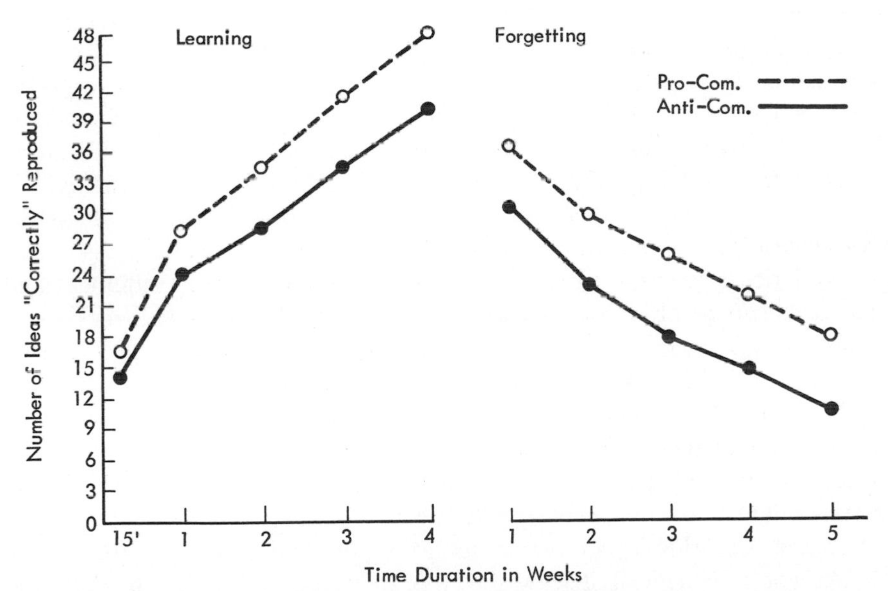

Figure 9–4a. Learning and forgetting curves for "correct" responses for pro-communist and anti-communist groups on the pro-Soviet Union selection. (From Levine, J. M., and Murphy, Gardner. Learning and Forgetting of Controversial Material, *J. Abnorm. Soc. Psychol.*, 38:507–517, 1943.)

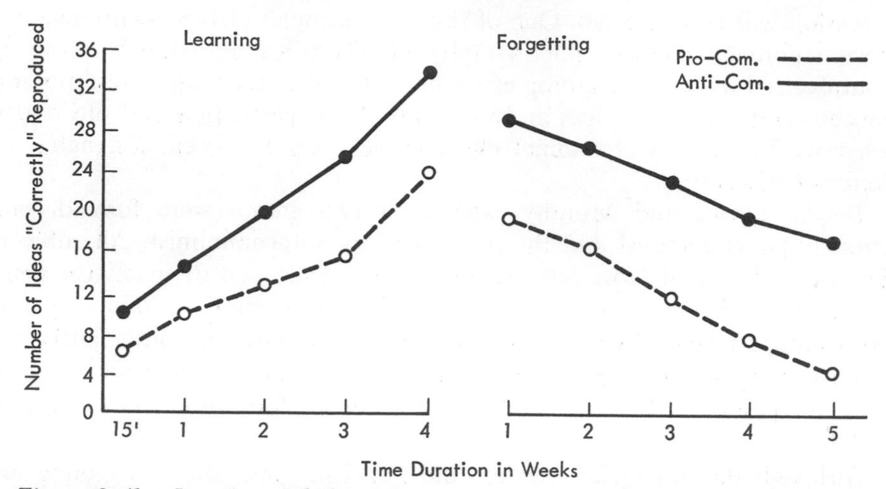

Figure 9–4b. Learning and forgetting curves for "correct" responses for pro-communist and anti-communist groups on the anti-Soviet Union selection. (From Levine, J. M., and Murphy, Gardner. Learning and Forgetting of Controversial Material, *J. Abnorm. Soc. Psychol.*, 38:507–517, 1943.)

An application of this knowledge may be made to the learning of motor skills. If the athlete or student does not respect the coach or teacher or agree with what is being taught, these negative attitudes will suppress learning effectiveness. Many times a person thinks he knows how a skill should be performed, and if he is set in his attitude, his unwillingness to accept a new learning approach will be evidenced in his lack of progress. Perhaps even more serious is the situation whereby the coach or instructor is not respected either as a person or for his seeming lack of knowledge and poor teaching ability. The barrier formed between learner and teacher will be difficult to overcome and certainly will not represent a favorable learning situation.

Sportsmanship. One example of socially desirable values often associated with athletics is good sportsmanship. During competition, the excitement and tense atmosphere often places the participant in the unusual situation of having to make many value choices and display perhaps some of his most inner qualities. Being a good winner and good loser, honesty, fairplay, and the like, are often associated with sportsmanship. Physical educators often state that under their influence sportsmanship qualities are developed in the participants in their programs. It is further hypothesized that these characteristics will carry over to everyday activities.

The role of athletics in the formulation of sportsmanship qualities is perhaps not so beneficial as we would like to think. This is not to deny the potentially favorable impact athletic participation might have on one's value system, but rather to suggest that in a number of cases sportsmanship qualities are not taught at all and unsportsmanship-like behavior is condoned in a few instances. This pessimistic conclusion is based on the results of some recent investigations concerned with athletics and sportsmanlike qualities.

Kistler (1957) noted that high percentages of the college students he queried demonstrated what we might consider to be unsportsmanlike attitudes in sport situations. One of his surprising findings was that college men who had previous varsity experience displayed poorer sportsmanship attitudes than nonvarsity athletes. In another study, Richardson (1962) verified Kistler's results. A sportsmanship inventory was administered to 233 students from fifteen colleges. Because no statistical analysis was employed, the results of this investigation should be accepted with reservation. An overwhelming number of respondents approved of the practice of taking advantage of a sports situation if they would not be caught or penalized. Nonletter winners had a higher degree of sportsmanship than did letter winners, and of these letter winners, subsidized athletes scored lowest. With regard to specific sports, football players displayed the lowest sportsmanship qualities, whereas baseball players, track and field members, and basketball players had the highest scores.

Kroll and Petersen (1965) examined value systems from another point of view. They formulated an interesting experimental design in order to obtain data on three winning and three losing collegiate football teams. Value profiles distinguished the winning teams, which were nationally ranked and represented university, state college, and private church-related institutions, from the losing teams which were sister schools with very poor win-loss records. An analysis of the data revealed that both the nature of the school and the win-loss record were sufficient to discriminate between the teams studied. The social factor (unselfishness, kindness, relating to people) distinguished the teams, for winning teams scored *lower* than losing teams on these items. The university teams scored lowest on this factor, whereas the private schools displayed the highest ranking.

As these researchers indicate, the demonstrated attitudes of winning versus losing teams are inconsistent with our image of athletics, sportsmanship, and high ideals. Perhaps there are inconsistencies within our society's value standards and their application to practical competitive situations. Do athletes who want to win at any cost and are prone to violate moral rules become more successful winning athletes? Are coaches responsible for the value qualities of their players? Do players have these qualities fairly well conditioned before they come under the influence of their coaches? These are some of the questions that have to be answered on a more scientific basis, for we have treated them very lightly, merely assuming a commonsense approach to these problems.

There is some indication of the changes that occur in sportsmanship attitudes during the maturing years. McAfee (1955) administered the Sportsmanship Preference Record to 857 sixth, seventh, and eighth-grade boys. The instrument contains twenty choice situations, with the following as an example.

> It is against the rules to pitch side arm, but you know a way to pitch side arm that is hard to detect. If you pitch side arm you know you could win this game and your team would be school champs. What would you do? (a) Pitch side arm until the umpire catches you. (b) Pitch side arm just when the good hitters are up to bat. (c) Don't pitch side arm at all. (d) Don't pitch side arm unless you start to lose.

McAfee found that the attitudes became progressively lower from the sixth to the eighth grades. Pictured with Kistler's results on college students reported earlier, we get the impression that sportsmanship attitudes become less idealistic and more materialistic with increasing age. Athletes who are faced most often with competitive situations involving the pressures to win perhaps feel the need to moderate and sacrifice their ethics and morals. Whatever the case, there is a definite need to discover the impact athletics and physical education classes have on the participants and on the development of sportsmanship.

Needs and Interests. Educators service the needs and interests of the students through various curricular and extracurricular activities. Interests may be thought of as attitudes we have with respect to certain objectives. Usually, attitudes refer to social or political opinions and feelings, interests to vocational or physical activity preferences. Needs are deeply rooted in biological drives and as such might be thought of as presupposing interests.

Needs determine behavior, for the body is in a state of disequilibrium when a need state is aroused. An individual's personality can be explained through needs, as Murray (1938) has done so successfully. A person's actions are caused by an interaction of his personality needs and the surrounding environmental stimuli but are modified and restricted by social sanctions. In other words, the forces within an organism drive him to search for or react to various environmental objects.

It is commonly thought that needs can best be met through involvement in need-gratifying activities, and athletic participation helps to meet certain needs. Not only this, but the nature of the sport, e.g., team, individual, recreational, body-building, will dictate which needs are best met. The needs of athletes versus those of nonathletes have not been studied at any great depth. One investigation reported by Meyers and Ohnmacht (1963), found no difference in needs between participants in intramurals and interscholastics and nonparticipants. The subjects were junior high school pupils evaluated on a need instrument called the Self-Descriptive Form.

It is often felt and shown to be true that successful athletes have a higher than average need to achieve. Of the many aspects of one's personality though, need to achieve is probably not a sufficiently powerful trait to insure proficiency. There must be an ideal proportion and interaction of the many desirable traits. The relationship of a person's motivation or need achievement and his anxiety level on performance has been investigated by Atkinson and Litwin (1960). Evidently these two variables interact in such a way as to determine predictability of behavior.

These writers ascertained the need for achievement and test anxiety levels of their college subjects who were to perform in a ring toss game. The students were told to stand any distance up to fifteen feet from the wooden peg and attempt to toss a ring over the peg. They thought they were being measured for score, but in actuality it was their chosen distance from the peg that was recorded. Subjects high in need for achievement but low in test anxiety preferred a distance of nine to eleven feet away from the peg—of intermediate range. Those subjects who were low in need for achievement and high in anxiety level took the least number of attempts at the intermediate range; they performed primarily at the extreme distances. The other types of students selected distances somewhere between these two classified groups of subjects. In applying these findings to athletic situations, it would appear that a high need to achieve coupled with a low–test anxiety level results in realistically high levels of aspiration and superior performance. The inhibitive effects of high anxiety on complex test performance has already been discussed in previous chapters.

With regard to student interests, many investigations have been reported through the years as to student preferences in physical education activities. Questionnaire studies of the activity interests of students reveal preferences for the informal or natural program as contrasted with the formal and an increasing student interest in individual and dual sports rather than team games during the college years.

Activity preferences of students are of interest to physical educators responsible for curriculum planning. Data were collected by the writer at a large Eastern university on the physical activities mentioned by the students that they would prefer to take in the required physical education program. Figure 9–5 depicts their fifteen top choices, and special notation is made to distinguish courses offered from those not offered in the program and included in this list. Of 713 students, 301, or 42 per cent, selected bowling as their first choice. Only one team sport was listed among the first five choices, and the other four are considered to be recreational carry-over type activities.

These activity interests reflect the desires and needs of the students at a particular time in their life, in a specific geographic region, and at a point in history. The interests are specific to this situation. College students who feel the social need of approval from their peers want to be able to demonstrate skill in those activities that will provide them with this satisfaction. Recreational, coeducational-type activities are associated with adulthood.

The interests of children would range in a different direction; they desire team, competitive, and body-contact activities. Very often activity interests are nothing more than the desire of people to conform to society's expectations of them to proficiency sports pertinent to a given age level, sex, socioeconomic class, geographical location, and so on. Then too, we often attempt to go beyond social demands and expectations.

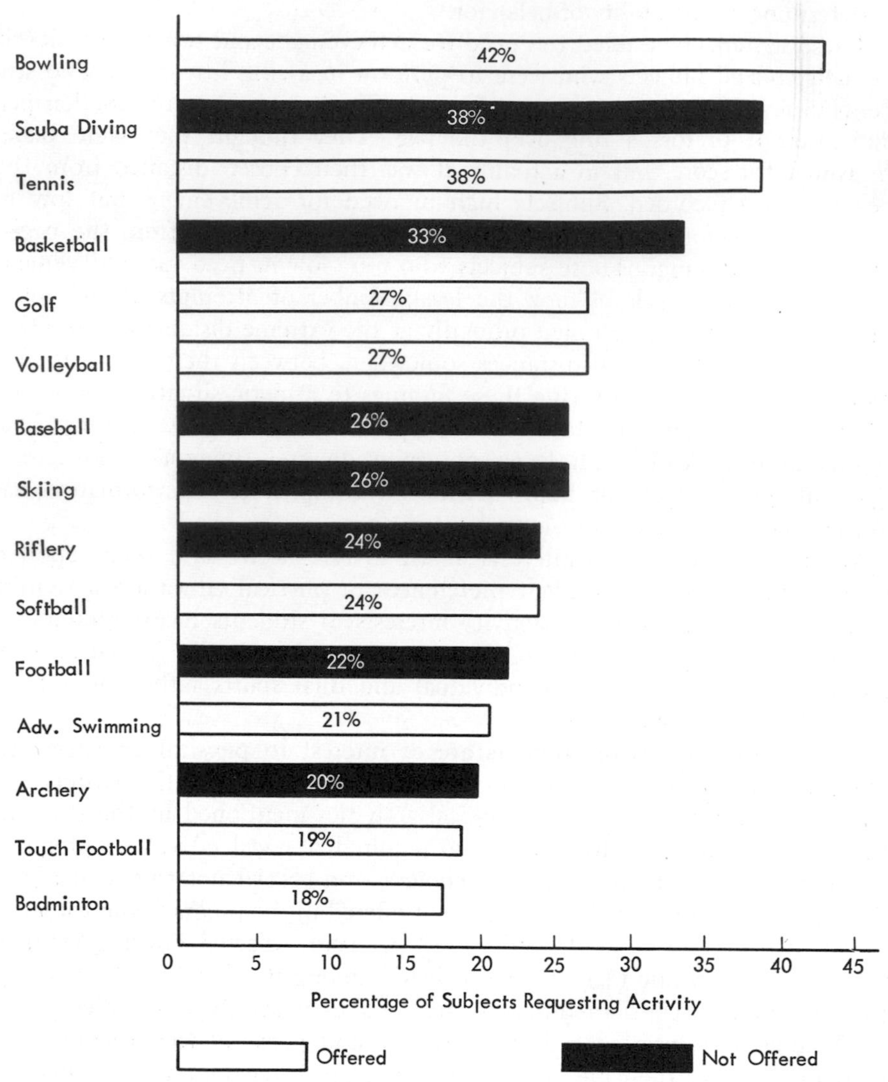

Figure 9–5. Activities most preferred by students: a comparison of the activities offered and not offered by the department. (From Singer, Robert N. Factors Influencing Male Students in Their Choice of an Activity in the Service Program, Unpublished Master's Thesis, The Pennsylvania State University, 1962.)

Summary

No treatment of the learning process would be complete without reference to the sociopsychological influences that uniquely distinguish individuals in their approach to and success in learning motor skills. A person's personality, composed of many traits, in varying strengths and degrees of interaction, determines the nature of his behavior.

Interest and success in particular physical activities will contribute to and affect personality development. There is a tendency to believe that personality traits act in such a manner as to encourage participation in certain activities. Although the personality of athletes has been distinguished from nonathletes, consistent personality patterns of groups of athletes have not been obtained. It does appear that superior athletes may be differentiated from lesser athletes on certain personality measures. Some of these measures are need to achieve, personal endurance, sensitivity, and ambition.

The effects of participation in programs of physical education and athletics may be favorable, detrimental, or unnoticeable on personality development. Without the benefit of longitudinal studies, it is difficult to ascertain the specific favorable effects of organized athletic activity. There is much suggestive evidence for the relationship of participation in sports, especially successful participation, to desirable personal and social traits. Social status is associated with an interest in varied sports activities as well as proficiency in them.

Attitudes set a frame of reference for perceiving that which we are to learn. If the learner has a favorable disposition toward learning, the learning process itself is facilitated and material is retained more effectively. Value systems, as displayed in such general qualities as sportsmanship, are probably affected by sports participation, but unfortunately, there is mounting evidence that athletic experience is associated with poorer sportsmanship attitudes. Also, these attitudes become progressively less desirable from childhood to adulthood.

Student needs and interests should be considered when prescribing activities or understanding activity selection. Although need to achieve is an important determiner of success, probability of success is greater when it interacts with low anxiety levels.

References

Atkinson, John W., and Litwin, George H. Achievement Motive and Test Anxiety Conceived as Motive to Approach Success and Motive to Avoid Failure, *J. Abnorm. Soc. Psychol.*, 60:52–63, 1960.

Biddulph, Lowell G. Athletic Achievement and the Personal and Social Adjustment of High School Boys, *Res. Quart.*, 25:1–7, 1954.

Booth, E. C., Jr. Personality Traits of Athletes as Measured by the MMPI, *Res. Quart.*, 29:127–138, 1958.

Bretsch, Howard S. Social Skills and Activities of Socially Accepted and Unaccepted Adolescents, *J. Educ. Psychol.*, 43:449–458, 1952.

Cassel, Russel, and Childers, Richard. A Study of Certain Attributes of

High School Varsity Football Team Members by Use of Psychological Test Scores, *J. Educ. Res.*, 57:64–67, 1963.

CATTELL, R. B. Some Psychological Correlates of Physical Fitness and Physique, in *Exercise and Fitness* (A Collection of Papers Presented at the Colloquium on Exercise and Fitness), Chicago: The Athletic Institute, 1960.

CLARKE, H. HARRISON, and GREEN, WALTER H. Relationships Between Personal-Social Measures Applied to 10-year-old Boys, *Res. Quart.*, 34:288–298, 1963.

FLANAGAN, LANCE. A Study of Some Personality Traits of Different Physical Activity Groups, *Res. Quart.*, 22:312–323, 1951.

GUILFORD, J. P. *Personality*, New York: McGraw-Hill Book Co., Inc., 1959.

HARLOW, ROBERT G. Masculine Inadequacy and Compensatory Development of Physique, *J. Pers.*, 19:312–323, 1951.

HAZELTON, HELEN, and PIPER, JUNEROSE. A Study of the Social Values of a Team and of Two Individual Sports as Judged by the Attitudes of Freshman College Women, *Res. Quart.*, 11:54–59, 1940.

HUSMAN, BURRIS F. Aggression in Boxers and Wrestlers as Measured by Projective Techniques, *Res. Quart.*, 26:421–425, 1955.

JOHNSON, WARREN R.; HUTTON, DANIEL C.; and JOHNSON, GRANVILLE B. Personality Traits of Some Champion Athletes as Measured by Two Projective Tests: The Rorschach and H-T-P., *Res. Quart.*, 25:484–485, 1954.

JOHNSON, WARREN R., and HUTTON, DANIEL C. Effect of a Combative Sport Upon Personality Dynamics as Measured by a Projective Test, *Res. Quart.*, 26:49–53, 1955.

KEOGH, JACK. Relationship of Motor Ability and Athletic Participation in Certain Standardized Personality Measures, *Res. Quart.*, 30:438–445, 1959.

KISTLER, JOY W. Attitudes Expressed About Behavior Demonstrated in Certain Specific Situations Occurring in Sports, *Coll. Phys. Educ. Assoc. Proc.*, 60:55–58, 1957.

KROLL, WALTER, and PETERSEN, KAY H. Study of Values Test and Collegiate Football Teams, *Res. Quart.*, 36:441–447, 1965.

LAKIE, WILLIAM L. Personality Characteristics of Certain Groups of Intercollegiate Athletes, *Res. Quart.*, 33:566–573, 1962.

LA PLACE, JOHN P. Personality and its Relationship to Success in Professional Baseball, *Res. Quart.*, 25:313–319, 1954.

LEVINE, J. M., and MURPHY, GARDNER. Learning and Forgetting of Controversial Material, *J. Abnorm. Soc. Psychol.*, 38:507–517, 1943.

MCAFEE, ROBERT A. Sportsmanship Attitudes of Sixth, Seventh, and Eighth Grade Boys, *Res. Quart.*, 26:120, 1955.

MCCRAW, L. W., and TOLBERT, J. W. Sociometric Status and Athletic Ability of Junior High School Boys, *Res. Quart.*, 24:72–80, 1953.

MEYERS, CARLTON R., and OHNMACHT, FRED W. Needs of Pupils in Relation to Athletic Competition at the Junior High School Level, *Res. Quart.*, 34:521–524, 1963.

MURRAY, H. A., et al. *Explorations in Personality*, New York: Oxford University Press, 1938.

OGILVIE, BRUCE, and TUTKO, THOMAS. Review of Research on Athletic Personality, paper presented at the North American Society for Psychology of Sports and Physical Activity Meeting, Las Vegas, Nevada, March, 1967.

RICHARDSON, DEANE. Ethical Conduct in Sport Situations, *Coll. Phys. Assoc. Proc.*, 66:98–103, 1962.
SCHENDEL, JACK. Psychological Differences Between Athletes and Nonparticipants in Athletics at Three Educational Levels, *Res. Quart.*, 36:52–67, 1965.
SEYMOUR, EMERY W. Comparative Study of Certain Behavior Characteristics of Participant and Non-Participant Boys in Little League Baseball, *Res. Quart.*, 27:338–346, 1956.
SKUBIC, ELVERA. Studies of Little League and Middle League Baseball, *Res. Quart.*, 27:97–110, 1956.
SLUSHER, HOWARD. Personality and Intelligence Characteristics of Selected High School Athletes and Non-Athletes, *Res. Quart.*, 35:539–545, 1964.
SPERLING, ABRAHAM P. The Relationship Between Personality Adjustment and Achievement in Physical Education Activities, *Res. Quart.*, 13:351–363, 1942.
STAGNER, ROSS. *Psychology of Personality*, New York: McGraw-Hill Book Co., Inc., 1961.
STEINHAUS, ARTHUR H. Fitness Beyond Muscle, *J. of Sports Medicine and Physical Fitness*, 6:191–197, 1966.
SYMONDS, PERCIVAL M. Education for the Development of Personality, *Teachers College Record*, 50:163–169, 1948.
THOMAS, ROBERT J. An Empirical Study of High School Drop-Outs in Regard to Ten Possibly Related Factors, *J. Educ. Sociol.*, 28:11–18, 1954.
THUNE, JOHN B. Personality of Weightlifters, *Res. Quart.*, 20:296–306, 1949.
VOLBERDING, ELEANOR. Characteristics of Successful and Unsuccessful Eleven-Year-Old Pupils, *Elementary School Journal*, 49:405–410, 1949.

Annotated Student References

ALLEN, ROBERT M. *Personality Assessment Procedures*, New York: Harper & Brothers, 1958.

A survey of the techniques and procedures used for evaluating personality.

ALLPORT, GORDON W. *Pattern and Growth in Personality*, New York: Holt, Rinehart and Winston, 1964.

A fine source for a student with little background in the psychology of personality.

BONNER, HUBERT. *Psychology of Personality*, New York: The Ronald Press Co., 1961.

A comprehensive description of personality, as viewed from varied approaches to the topic.

BROWN, ROGER. *Social Psychology*, New York: The Free Press, 1965.

Encompasses and examines many of the issues associated with the study of social psychology.

COWELL, CHARLES C. The Contributions of Physical Activity to Social Development, *Res. Quart.*, 31:286–306, Part II, 1960.

Surveys the literature on the effects of physical activity upon personal and social adjustment.

DUKES, WILLIAM F. Psychological Studies of Values, *Psychol. Bull.*, 52:24–50, 1955.

A comprehensive review of the nature and findings of the research related to values.

KOCH, SIGMUND (ed.). *Psychology: A Study of a Science*, Vol. III, New York: McGraw-Hill Book Co., Inc., 1959.

Distinguished contributions to the study of personality, social psychology, and related areas.

SCOTT, M. GLADYS. The Contributions of Physical Activity to Psychological Development, *Res. Quart.*, 31:307–320, Part II, 1960.

Reviews many articles pertaining to physical activity and psychological development.

10

An Overview: Learning Principles

It would be very convenient for the physical educator to be able to have a list of certain absolute truths or learning principles to follow. He could use these as handy guidelines in his particular teaching situation. Unfortunately, although we now know more about conditions that contribute to learning than ever before, very few conclusive statements can go unchallenged.

The reasons for this predicament are obvious. Learning is no simple matter. So many factors interact to influence the outcome of the learning situation that it is almost impossible to treat any aspect of the learning process without regard for all these factors. One of the greatest problems in writing a book of this nature is to provide some sort of order to the learning process out of a turmoil of apparently conflicting experimental and theoretical evidence. Furthermore, application of psychological research to the acquisition of motor skills usually associated with the physical educator's domain is a risky business. Small wonder, then, that learning principles, when they do appear in the literature are usually so conservative and general that they amount to nothing more than commonsense.

Nevertheless, the need for more specific learning principles, encompassing at least some of the many factors discussed in this book, should be heeded. Hopefully the writer's presumptuous attitude, that he is capable of such an endeavor, will aid him as he attempts this formulation, to make a list of these principles. The principles are based on the writer's interpretation of the research evidence and should by no means be taken to imply that they are founded on experimental findings that are in complete agreement. Also, no principles are final. They are meant as tentative operational guidelines, to be reinforced or modified by future research evidence.

For the sake of continuity, the principles are parallel to the major divisions of this book. Four categories of principles have been formed, which include

Basic Considerations in Learning; the Nature of the Learner; Environmental Conditions; and Sociopsychological Factors.

Basic Considerations in Learning

1. *Learning and performance* are not synonymous terms, for performance is a function of an individual's past experience (learning) as well as other variables, mainly motivation. There are many occasions that, for various reasons, performance levels do not reflect the true amount of learning that has occurred. Although performance scores are the best indicators of learning as of the present time, an evaluation of learning should not be based solely on task performance.

2. Motor learning and performance are handicapped if *physical qualities,* such as strength, speed, and endurance necessary for the skilled movement are not well developed. It is important that these qualities especially as they relate to the task at hand be developed to a reasonable degree.

3. *Human abilities* have been classified in different ways, but regardless of terminology these abilities as well as specific skills related to a given task must be present if proficiency is to be demonstrated.

4. Although a certain *body type* or *body build* contributes to success in specific motor activities, it is by no means a necessary factor. Classification and grouping by this method is unnecessary for the learning of most motor skills.

5. *Height and weight* factors appear to have little value in predicting achievement in the majority of motor skills. Thus, as with body builds, classification of students for activities by this method appears to be unwarranted.

6. Although *balancing ability* is important for athletic success, the performance of individuals in different tests of static and dynamic balance do not correlate highly. Selected sports probably require unique balancing abilities. Therefore, this ability must be developed specifically for each activity.

7. *Coordination* is required for many skills, ranging from positioning and precision laboratory tasks to the performance of athletic activities. It should not be expected that coordination is a unitary factor, allowing individuals to achieve successfully in a wide assortment of tasks. This ability, like balance, must be developed specifically for the task at hand.

8. *Reaction time, reflex time,* and *movement time* each refer to related but dissimiliar neuromuscular functions, and obtained correlations between them are not high. In other words, success in these acts, which work in various combinations in many motor skills, depends on different factors.
   a. Athletes, or people who practice reacting quickly, usually have faster reaction times and movement times than nonathletes. These factors are probably associated with successful accomplishment in a number of motor skills.
   b. A person can react more quickly to touch or sound stimuli than visual stimuli. If a faster reaction is desired, it would be best to consider the nature of the stimuli and those that will facilitate the process.
   c. Reaction times become longer if fatigue has set in, if the organism is reacting to complex stimuli, or if the subject is past or before the third decade of life. Performance in tasks dependent to a great extent on reactions decline when any one or combination of these situations are present.

9. There is no general *kinesthetic sense.* It is specific to the test and the part of the body involved in the skill. Kinesthesis, or proprioception, is apparently related to successful motor performance, and like balance, coordination, and other abilities, must be developed specifically for a particular task.

10. The *senses,* especially those involving equilibrium, vision, touch, and kinesthesis, play an important role in motor proficiency.
    a. The senses should not be restricted for a period of time before performance and should be kept in a state of alertness during performance, for it is necessary to have regular sensory stimulation in order to maintain sense acuity.
    b. Highly skilled performers selectively attend to the surrounding stimuli; irrelevant cues are disregarded. The amount of sensory information presented at any one time is more than one person can react to; therefore only the most important information must be selected. Guidance and experience can help the learner to become selectively attentive.

11. Stimulus patterns are always present in the environment, but it takes our *perceptual mechanism* to make sense of these stimuli, to organize and interpret them. In most cases, perceptual information promotes appropriate motor activity.

12. *Cognitive, structural,* and *motor factors* correlate most highly in early childhood and less highly with age. Past early childhood, there is little reason to expect any meaningful relationship between intellectual and motor abilities. Mentally retarded children are

poorer than normal children in performance measures. In fact, motor performances appear to be more evenly equated when comparing normal with retarded children by using their mental ages rather than their chronological ages. It appears that varied and extensive perceptual-motor experiences in the early years are extremely important for later academic achievement and athletic success.

13. *Emotional states* accompany motor learning and performance, some of which are inhibitive and others facilitative.
   a. Tension, anxiety, and stress are examples of different emotional states, each of which operates to promote or hinder performance, depending on the nature of the individual and the environment.
   b. People with high anxiety levels generally perform more poorly than those low in anxiety on complex motor tasks such as required in the more advanced stages of most sports.
   c. Stressful situations are more disruptive to the learning of complex tasks than simple tasks. Evidently, then, it would appear that greater sensitivity for the students on the part of the teacher is needed during the learning of more difficult motor skills.
14. The learner is *totally* involved in any learning experience, and skill attainment might very well be related to such personal factors as physical characteristics, motor abilities, acuity of senses, perceptual abilities, cognition, and emotional status. All these variables must be considered for every individual and for every task.

The Nature of the Learner

1. *Tests* have been designed to measure motor ability, motor fitness, motor capacity and motor educability. All have the best of intentions, but they have not been very successful in meeting their objectives.
   a. Motor tests measure different things and do not afford consistent results between tests. Tests of motor capacity and motor educability are limited in number as is research defending their validity. Motor-ability tests, of much greater popular acceptance, are also of limited value.
   b. It is doubtful if there is such a thing as a general motor ability but rather motor abilities. Motor abilities themselves are usually correlated but only slightly, e.g., the ability to balance does not mean an ability to react quickly or an ability to demonstrate great strength.
   c. Motor-ability tests would appear to have their best value in diagnosing extremes, either the highly or poorly coordinated

individuals. Beyond this function, these tests have questionable value.

d. The research that favors task specificity over a general motor factor would also serve to question the belief that there is such an individual as an "all-round athlete." The all-round athlete is an exception not a rule, and success in a few activities is no indication of similar status in other activities.

2. *Success* in many sport skills is determined by (1) experience and intensive practice in a wide range of motor skills, especially in childhood; (2) genetic factors; (3) continuous motivation; and (4) the relatedness of the skills to be learned to each other. Student and family history information in these areas may provide the teacher with some insight into the student's expected level of achievement in a given activity.

3. *Form* in performance is an individual matter. Good form based on the latest mechanical, anatomical, and kinesiological evidence is to be strived for in the beginning. Individual differences, especially in body structures and proportions, necessitate the allowance for many means of skill execution. Therefore, a learner should not be cast in a mold but, rather, allowed to express himself within the limitations of his structure.

4. The *level of aspiration* we set for ourselves in a given situation determines personal success or failure and is a result of past successes and failures in the situation.
   a. Higher levels of intended achievement, within reason, usually result in higher levels of performance.
   b. Success results in a rise of the aspiration level; failure, in a lowering of this level.
   c. Success is more influential than failure on the aspiration level.
   d. It may be surmised that the learner should experience a reasonable amount of successful trials if his motivation is to remain high and continue to rise.

5. There is reason to believe that if *fatigue* is not excessive, performance may suffer slightly whereas ultimate learning may not. The learning process should be controlled so the learner does not practice beyond a point where performance is detrimental to learning.

6. The performer's *level of skill* will require dissimilar learning considerations on the part of the instructor.
   a. Especially with the beginner, his attention should be directed to understanding purposes and goals associated with the activity.
   b. Physical activity should be emphasized and maximized in the

early stages of motor learning. This is especially true with younger children and complex skills.

c. For most beginners, shorter practice periods spaced more often are preferable to fewer extended practice sessions.
d. New skills should be taught in such a way that the learner performs in practice the way he is expected to in the actual situation.
e. Critical details of performance should be analyzed with the advanced learner rather than the beginner.
f. Advanced learners benefit more than beginners from extensive and intensive verbal instructions.
g. Advanced learners, because of their greater skill development and higher motivation levels, can concentrate for longer periods of time in practice than beginners.

7. Individuals progress in skill acquisition at varying rates of speed, but *early success* does not indicate later achievement. Some students are slow learners and others are fast learners of a particular task; a situation which requires the teacher to allow each individual the amount of time it takes for the learning of each task.

8. *Critical periods* refer to those optimal periods to acquire skills. Successful skill attainment at maturity is not dependent on the earliness of instruction, but rather its timeliness.
   a. Delay in experiences or a restriction of them may have detrimental effects on learning later in life.
   b. Although critical learning periods for certain behavior have been experimentally verified with animals, we can only advance the theoretical premise that an optimal learning period exists for the learning of anything as far as humans are concerned. As to the acquisition of basic skills, i.e., crawling, walking, and so on, their sequence is fairly predictable although the specific age each occurs varies from individual to individual.
   c. It does appear as if many athletic skills can be introduced at an earlier period of life than once was thought possible.

9. In early childhood, there is a *related development of motor patterns and intellectual skill*, and it appears that a child trained in basic motor movements does improve his intellectual achievement. Various personal characteristics may be expected to be highly correlated at this time of life.

10. From early childhood to maturity, human behavior becomes more individualistic rather than similar between organisms. The *interrelationship* of physical development factors and intellectual achievements are only slightly correlated with respect to school-aged children. There is some suggestion that those motor tasks that re-

quire greater perceptual and cognitive involvement, such as coordination and balance tasks may be used to predict accomplishments in the academic area.

11. There is great difficulty in ascertaining the *optimal age* for skill in motor performances, for a person today demonstrates superior skills at earlier and later ages than ever before. Data on outstanding Olympic and professional athletes indicates the middle twenties as the general period in life when most male athletes reach their peaks in performance. Nevertheless, once maturational readiness is present for a given activity, diligent and correct training can lead to a high proficiency in that activity.

12. *Sex differences* in motor performance become more apparent with increasing age after early childhood. Boys typically accelerate in motor performance during the adolescent years while girls level off and even demonstrate performance decrements. These differences in performance can be explained by reasons other than merely anatomical and physiological dissimilarities between sexes. With social approval and increased motivation, girls and women achieve much greater skill levels in a variety of sports.

13. *Genetic factors* limit potential performance, but there is quite a gap between the operational level of an individual and his theoretical limits.
    a. Most human behavior is learned, rather than influenced by hereditary factors. Therefore, the physical educator can influence behavior by providing students with directed desirable environmental experiences. Genetically imposed limitations can be overcome through individual learning programs.
    b. Environmental experiences actually determine the level of skill attainment; thus, motor skill is dependent on the interaction of both genetics and environment.
    c. Hereditary factors, to a certain extent, determine activity interests and athletic success. Knowledge of familial activity tendencies aids in predicting an individual's interest and proficiency in specific types of activities.

Environmental Conditions

1. *Practice* alone does not lead to perfect performance. Errors may be practiced and perpetuated, or boredom may set in from mere repetition. Practice is beneficial if a number of factors are operating.
    a. Attention to relevant cues does improve performance, and the learner should be directed with those cues whenever possible.
    b. Intent to improve leads to better performance.

c. If desirable factors are present, more practice will result in better immediate performance and certainly in later retention. Overlearning is more effective for ultimate retention than learning to a criterion.
d. Rather than artificially practiced activities, such as slowing down the responses demanded for the sake of concentrating on accuracy, practice should approximate ultimately desired movements as nearly as possible. Practice sessions should simulate contest situations.
e. Extended practice is of more value to those learners who demonstrate initial difficulty with the task. The relationship between initial and final status, although somewhat predictable with simple tasks, is not nearly as correlated with complex tasks.
f. There is an apparent change in the factor pattern with practice. Abilities important for early success in a given motor task are not necessarily the same as those contributing to later proficiency. The teacher might emphasize cues consistent with the abilities most contributing to success during the various stages of skill acquisition.
g. There are many means of measuring the effects of practice, and different techniques offer dissimilar results and interpretations of the data. Consistent measuring methods aid in obtaining a more reliable means of comparing practice effects over a wide range of skills and manipulated learning conditions.
h. Although there are about four basic types of learning curves to describe the acquisition of complex motor skills, the most frequently obtained one is the negatively accelerated curve. In this case, learning is rapid at first and improvements decrease with practice until there is an apparent leveling off. The relative complexity of the skill to the learner determines the nature of his learning curve.
i. A plateau, which is a leveling off in performance after rapid improvement and which precedes another improvement stage, has rarely been obtained in experimental studies although empirical evidence points to the existence of this phenomenon. There have been numerous reports of the incidence of plateaus during the acquisition of athletic skills. During this difficult period of task reorganization, patience and motivation must continue to prevail.

2. *Motivation* distinguishes performance from learning. If a person is unmotivated to perform the desired responses, he does not learn. Motivation is also a factor in explaining variable performances.
a. Higher motivation impedes progress in complex tasks. Highest performance is attained by individuals with intermediate motivation or drive, and as tasks increase in complexity, individuals with

less drive do better. Evidently, there is an optimal motivational level for each task.

b. Motivation may stem from an intrinsic or extrinsic source. Intrinsic refers to doing something for its own sake and extrinsic, to material gains. Both types of motivation can improve performance, but intrinsic motivation is preferable and supposedly a more effective, sustaining, type of motivation.

c. If a person already is performing under high drive, it is doubtful if various kinds of motivational techniques can improve his performance.

d. Better learned skills are less prone to be disrupted by manipulated environmental conditions; e.g., varying motivational conditions are more influential during the initial and unstable stages of learning.

e. Varying the amount of reward appears to result in a change of performance in favor of the reward with the greatest magnitude.

f. Each person responds to a motivational technique in a different manner; thus the appropriate one must be applied to his learning situation at the right time if most favorable results are to be observed.

g. Reinforcement is a form of reward and increases the probability of the desired act to occur. Random reinforcement is a more effective continual form of motivation than constant reinforcement.

h. Motivation does not automatically increase with success and decrease with failure, for much depends on the difficulty of the task and the anxiety level of the performer. There are many instances when failure, instead of discouraging the learner, heightens his motivation.

i. When learning a new task, learners should experience as much success as possible in the early stages, before failure.

j. Reward is a more stable and stronger influence for desired behavior than punishment. The learner is more apt to perform effectively when he is rewarded positively for correct responses.

k. Knowledge of results, or feedback, is a form of reinforcement and is extremely important to the learning process. There is always some knowledge of results (KR) available to the performer of motor skills. Higher levels of performance are reached when KR is specific and immediate.

3. *Administration of practice sessions* affects the learning, and more probably, performing of skills.

a. It appears that shorter practice periods with shorter rest periods extended over a longer period of time are most effective for the acquisition of a number of motor skills.

b. As to the learning of a skill in one given practice period, distributed practice exerts a more positive influence on performance than massed practice. This is evident because although immediate skill acquisition is favored under distributed practice, tests of later retention demonstrate little difference in performance between initially massed and distributed practice groups.

4. Gross motor skills are usually *retained* for a longer time duration than any other types of learning materials.
   a. Reminiscence, a performance increase after a rest interval, has been obtained in many studies investigating the occurrence of this phenomenon. It appears as if massed practice tends to lead to greater reminiscence effects.
   b. More meaningful material is retained better by the learner. Therefore, the teacher should insure that each newly introduced task is understood and has meaning to the student.
   c. Overlearning of a skill results in more effective retention.
   d. The learning and retaining of a particular response might very well be affected by what is learned, especially of a related nature, either before and after training on this response. Proactive inhibition and retroactive inhibition refer to the negative effects of these situations. Information on the student's activities prior to the learning of a given skill and afterwards might provide keener insight into performance expectancies on this skill.
   e. Forgetting probably is because of not merely the passage of time, but rather the intervening events between practice and recall. With fewer intervening events recall should be better.

5. There is no single *method of instruction* appropriate for all teachers, for all students, and for all skills.
   a. As to whole-versus-part methods of instruction, simple skills should be taught by the whole method whereas complex skills require some sort of breakdown.
   b. Generally speaking, because of their degree of complexity and organization, various skills might be favored under different learning conditions. With high task organization (interrelatedness of component tasks), however, the whole method appears to be preferable to the part method for skill acquisition.
   c. More intelligent subjects are likely to fare better under the whole method of instruction.

6. Motor skills can be learned without the benefit of *overt physical practice*.
   a. Mental or image practice, which is task rehearsal in the mind, yields better performance on a motor skill than no practice at all.
   b. Physical practice is more effective than mental practice, and the combination of mental-physical practice is slightly inferior or

equal to physical practice alone. Although active participation is necessary to promote learning, evidently a certain amount of practice time can be spent in mental rehearsal without a loss in proficiency.

7. With most *serially-learned* material, that which is learned first is retained best, the last learned is mastered second best, whereas the middle is last to be recalled. However, gross motor skills are generally retained very well, and the order in which they are learned appears to make little difference as to retention effectiveness.
8. Although *drill* is satisfactorily used as a means for strengthening certain acts, a *problem-solving approach* may have much potential for the learning situation, especially in reaching objectives unattainable under the drill method. Particular learning situations warrant one or the other. As an example, drill is effective for skills performed in stable environments, whereas greater flexibility in thought and movement, or problem solving, is associated with skills performed in changing, unpredictable environments.
9. Although *teaching machines* and *programmed learning* have been successfully employed in industry and education, their potential has yet to be realized in physical education. Nevertheless, teaching machines can be used for the learning of content material associated with an activity, e.g., rules, strategy, mechanical and physiological principles, and history. The principles behind programmed learning can be applied to the teaching of motor skills.
10. The introduction of teaching *cues* and *aids* facilitates learning where traditional methods fail. They serve the purpose of changing routine teaching methodology, thus acting as motivators.
    a. The ability to learn and perform motor skills may very well be related to being able to apply external (instructor-provided) words and internal words (verbal mediation) to these acts. In order to perform effectively the learner must be able to associate certain movement patterns with certain verbal cues.
    b. Although it is logical to assume that an understanding of mechanical principles as applied to motor acts should benefit the performer, this premise is not always true. The best that can be said at this time is that some individuals prosper more, some less, when time is devoted to the learning of mechanical principles. It must be remembered that time spent learning mechanical principles takes away from time spent in participation. Principles may transfer, but not necessarily.
    c. Cues and abilities should be emphasized relevant to the learner's stage of proficiency. Visual cues, especially in the initial stages of learning, appear to be the most important sense cues in the learning of many motor skills. Kinesthetic cues and abilities are important at higher levels of skill proficiency.

d. Visual cues, whether of the natural type or man constructed, have usually been of great service to individuals learning motor skills. With certain specifications, visual cues can become more effective as a teaching aid. Specific, precise, and nearer visual cues are easier to attend to than general, vague, and more removed cues.

e. Visual aids, in such forms as motion pictures, slides, and force-time graphs, are somewhat valuable, but research does not indicate their conclusive worth as teaching aids. However, they probably serve to provide supplementary information, enliven teacher routines, and motivate students.

f. Although music has served as a stimulator, motivator, or relaxer on behavior in some other areas, the influence of musical sounds and tempi on motor performance has yet to be scientifically verified. Therefore, the use of music to promote more effective performance is a questionable practice.

g. Kinesthetic feedback plays a vital role in motor performance. There are times when it is more beneficial to concentrate on the movement instead of visual stimuli which at times may serve as distractions.

h. Many training devices have been developed to supplement teacher instruction, and research, although sparse, on the various types of equipment indicates the value of some over and beyond usual teaching procedures. Ball machines, special nets, simulated golf courses, and the like, provide the learner with the means of practicing under more game-like conditions. They also may help to eliminate errors and hasten the learning process.

11. *Transfer*, which is the influence of a learned task on one to be learned, underlies almost all of learning. It is rarely, if ever, that one learns something completely new to him. New tasks require a different patterning of movements usually already found in the performer's repertoire of learned movements.

a. Behavior and performance is influenced by previous experiences; and in a given situation, positive, negative, or zero transfer may occur from prior to present learnings. The present learning situation and the student's past learning experiences must be analyzed in order to understand better how he will perform.

b. If transfer is to occur successfully, desirability of the transfer must be taught. Transfer will more probably occur when relationships, resemblances, and concepts between two learning situations are explained and demonstrated for the learner.

c. Greater resemblance between task elements, between their respective stimuli and responses, results in a greater amount of positive transfer. When the new learning situation contains stimuli similar to the old situation but requires a new response, negative transfer occurs.

d. Transfer is influenced by such factors as amount of practice on prior task, motivation to transfer skill, method of training, and intent of transfer.

e. Learning how to learn, which involves learning the technique of attacking a particular kind of problem, is another aspect of transfer which leads to improvement from merely learning materials similar in nature.

f. The effect of initial-learned-task difficulty on other to-be-learned tasks is uncertain. When concerned only with the nature of the response, the degree of transfer from a difficult to an easy task is greater than from an easy task to a difficult task. Possibly, learning should progress from the simpler to the more complex conditions if an appropriate response is required to a continually changing and unpredictable pattern of stimuli.

12. Motor performance that occurs in a *social context;* in competition, in cooperation, or in front of people, may be improved, worsened, or remain the same. Generally speaking, these social influences serve to have a positive effect on achievement.
    a. Competition and cooperation ventures lead to more successful performance than sole performance. Whenever possible then, it is desirable to involve several people in a task than to have them perform individually and alone.
    b. Since group performance is not dependent on individual scores, people should not be paired on the basis of individual achievement. For this reason, it is more desirable to train potential team members in a team context rather than individually.
    c. Excluding such factors as skill complexity, degree of skill attainment, and anxiety level, the mere presence of others is usually found to have a positive effect on performance.
    d. If a skill is in the initial stages of being learned, the presence of others may have a variable effect on performance. Observers serve to distract or motivate the novice performer. With increased skill, these observers have less of an impact on an individual's performance.

Sociopsychological Factors

1. Man's behavior in a given situation is more complex than simple conditioning processes in operation. His responses are affected by many *sociopsychological* factors, namely, his attitudes, values, and personality in general.

2. Activity interest and participation is based on numerous variables, one of which is the interaction of the individual's *personality traits.*
   a. Athletes may be distinguished by sport on personality measuring instruments, although for various reasons inconsistent results have been obtained. With better personality assessment tools, better experimental methodology, and more longitudinal studies, we may be able to classify persons in sports by personality traits.
   b. The effects of participation in varsity athletics and programs of physical education may be favorable, detrimental, or unnoticeable to personality development. However, athletes, as a group, are usually found to have different personality profiles from non-athletes.
   c. It appears that superior athletes may be distinguished from lesser athletes on certain personality measures. It is questionable whether these differences are because of heredity or caused by personal experiences. When individuals possess a high need to achieve, psychological endurance tolerance, and other desirable personality traits, along with skilled and conditioned bodies, their potential for outstanding achievement is enhanced.

3. *Social status* and acceptance is usually positively related to athletic interests and success. The young athlete is given social prestige and demonstrates leadership qualities.

4. *Attitudes* set a frame of reference for perception of that which is to be learned. If the learner has a favorable disposition and is receptive, the learning process is facilitated and material is retained more effectively.

5. *Value systems,* as displayed in a general quality such as sportsmanship, are probably affected by sports participation. Unfortunately, there is mounting evidence that athletic experience and success is associated with poorer sportsmanship values. Either it is unrealistic to expect athletic success to occur with high values, or physical educators, coaches, teachers, and families are negligent in guiding the formulation of such ideals.

6. *Need to achieve,* when coupled with a low-test anxiety level, results in realistically high levels of aspiration and superior performance on complex tasks.

The Application of Learning Principles

The compilation of this list of learning principles, or perhaps any inventory, is incomplete and subject to criticism. A statement is difficult to make without qualification. However, the list of generalizations, although subject to change and certainly not definitive or completely true, represents an attempt to skeletonize the large body of knowledge relevant to learning, more specifically, the learning of motor skills.

The list of learning principles, if it may be called that, casts aside the camouflage and psychological jargon in an attempt to present isolated, and in many instances, unrelated statements. It is meant to serve as a guideline for the physical educator and not to be quoted out of context. It would be best in many cases to explore the principle of interest at greater depth before applying it to a given situation. The list itself represents the gleaning of information from countless journals and books. These publications are coming off the presses at such a tremendous rate that it is an almost impossible feat to keep up with the latest findings and views in related learning areas.

Learning principles, constructed from the research evidence, should serve as the framework for any learning theory. The value and validity of any theory lies in its ability to incorporate all these more or less accepted statements and apply them to explaining and predicting human behavior.

The physical educator is responsible for knowing and utilizing learning principles if he is to be a more effective teacher. He benefits from the efforts of researchers and theorists. His goal should be to apply learning principles that have the greatest probability of being successful in the situations he faces. The mere consideration of all the possible factors that might interact to affect the performance of a group implies a greater understanding of and sensitivity to the learning process. Once he considers individual differences, he has come that much further.

Perhaps one of the greatest difficulties in teaching consistently with learning principles is the impracticality of distinguishing individuals from a group. Although certain principles generally apply to groups at large, individuals do learn at different speeds with different incentives, attitudes, and interests and with varying degrees of developed abilities. Nevertheless, methodologies have been advanced in this book to try to overcome this problem. Much depends on the desired objective: group standards or individual achievement and satisfaction.

Another concern is the usage of principles mainly derived from controlled laboratory experiments, isolated novel tasks, and with a limited amount of random and representative subjects. Numbers of the newly formulated principles, arising from such experiments, conflict with commonly accepted practices. How many of us wish to teach in a manner that contradicts our own commonsense? Unfortunately, it is this situation precisely that hampers progress, for one will never know if something works until he attempts to put it into practice.

Teaching and learning efficiency accompanies practice that is consistent with scientific evidence. It is hoped that the list of learning principles as well as the content of this book will be of value to the physical educator, coach, or anyone else interested in and dedicated to improving human learning and performance in motor skills.

Annotated Student References

Learning and Performance in General

Berelson, Bernard, and Steiner, Gary A. *Human Behavior: An Inventory of Scientific Findings*, New York: Harcourt, Brace and World, Inc., 1964.

Generalized findings pertaining to the behavioral sciences are condensed and organized from the vast supply of available literature.

Berlin, Pearl (ed.). A Symposium on Motor Learning, *Quest*, Monograph VI, 1966.

This edition is dedicated to attacking aspects of motor learning with contributions from leading physical educators.

Bilodeau, Edward A. (ed.). *Acquisition of Skill*, New York: Academic Press, 1966.

Chapters are contributed by prominent investigators in experimental psychology on the various topics related to motor skill acquisition and performance.

Cratty, Bryant J. *Movement Behavior and Motor Learning*, Philadelphia: Lea & Febiger, 1964.

Provides excellent resource material related to human movement and learning.

Cronbach, Lee J. *Essentials of Psychological Testing*, New York: Harper & Row, Publishers, 1960.

Describes methods of testing of interest to industrial, clinical, educational, and military psychologists.

Gagné, Robert M., and Fleishman, Edwin A. *Psychology and Human Performance*, New York: Henry Holt and Co., 1959.

An introductory book in the area, dealing with the more practical aspects of human behavior and performance.

Hilgard, Ernest R. *Theories of Learning*, New York: Appleton-Century-Crofts, Inc., 1956.

Well-written, interesting presentation of the works of the leading learning theorists during this century.

Knapp, Barbara. *Skill in Sport: The Attainment of Proficiency*, London: Routledge & Kegan Paul, 1964.

A book on motor learning written expressly for physical educators.

Kurtz, Kenneth H. *Foundations of Psychological Research*, Boston: Allyn and Bacon, 1965.

Contains methodologies of psychological research as well as experimental findings on human behavior.

MEDNICK, SARNOFF A. *Learning,* Englewood Cliffs, N.J.: Prentice-Hall, Inc., 1964.

Simply written, designed for the beginning student in learning.

MELTON, ARTHUR W. (ed.). *Categories of Human Learning,* New York: Academic Press, 1964.

An attempt at formulating a new taxonomy of human learning, with discussions on the problems relevant to the seven categories representing the various types of research.

SIDOWSKI, JOSEPH B. (ed.). *Experimental Methods and Instrumentation in Psychology,* New York: McGraw-Hill Book Co., 1966.

Designed for the advanced student of learning, this comprehensive book describes experimental methods and instrumentation used in the major areas of psychology.

STEVENS, S. S. (ed.). *Handbook of Experimental Psychology,* New York: John Wiley & Sons, Inc., 1951.

Although not of recent vintage, this book still contains a wealth of knowledge on everything related to learning, with articles contributed by thirty-six leading psychologists.

TRAVERS, ROBERT M. *Essentials of Learning,* New York: The Macmillan Co., 1963.

Analyzes the results of research on learning, with special implications for students in education.

Author Index

Subject Index